SOCIAL SPECULATIONS:
VISIONS FOR OUR TIME

Books by RICHARD KOSTELANETZ

AS AUTHOR
The Theatre of Mixed Means
Master Minds
Metamorphosis in the Arts

AS CO-AUTHOR AND EDITOR
The New American Arts

AS EDITOR
On Contemporary Literature
Twelve from the Sixties
The Young American Writers
Beyond Left and Right
Imaged Words & Worded Images
Possibilities of Poetry
John Cage
Moholy-Nagy
Social Speculations

Social
Speculations

Visions for Our Time

Edited and with an Introduction by
RICHARD KOSTELANETZ

WILLIAM MORROW AND COMPANY, INC.

NEW YORK

1971

For Donald Cohen,
Friend and teacher,
Who showed the way

Copyright © 1971 by Richard Kostelanetz

Printed in the United States of America

Library of Congress Catalog Card Number 74-123150

If history teaches anything with complete clarity, it is that a society which fails to act and plan for the future is already doomed.

—MARCUS GOODALL,
Science and the Politician (1965)

The need . . . seems to me to be for an attitude toward change, an attitude which views change as something not to be opposed, and not just to be met, but to be seized upon with enthusiasm, an attitude which views change as the essential quality of growth, which thinks of growth as the essential meaning of life, and which thinks that the future is a good idea, which I do.

—W. WILLARD WIRTZ,
"The Challenge of Automation" (1963)

One of the most gripping historical dilemmas facing mankind at the moment is that at a time when one generation has accumulated a vast battery of intellectual and instrumental power whereby it can reshape the global environment almost at whim, its successor is adamantly rejecting the principles of living upon which that accumulation is based.

—RICHARD KEAN,
Education Through Dialogue (1967)

PREFACE

There is in the world today an "invisible college" of people in many different countries and many different cultures who have this vision of the nature of the transition through which we are passing and who are determined to devote their lives to contributing toward its successful fulfillment.

—KENNETH E. BOULDING,
The Meaning of the Twentieth Century (1964).

"Change is the metaphysic of our age," opened my preface to *Beyond Left and Right* (1968), to which this collection is a sequel; and the world of, say, 1950, if we came upon it today, would seem a quaint exhibit in a museum or perhaps even a flea market. Indeed, life when that preface was written, early in 1968 —the time of flower power, and the Eugene McCarthy campaign, when students were uprising in Paris and at Columbia and Robert Kennedy was still alive—already *feels* a long, long time ago. And so this collection differs from its predecessor, which as an anthology subtitled "Radical Thought for Our Times" emphasizes alternative ways of considering contemporary problems, particularly "how we think about radical change." *Social Speculations* takes a step beyond to present images of human possibility, envisioning the future that is, with increasing speed, coming into sight as the present. Thus, intellectually as well as chronologically, this anthology represents an appropriate successor to the earlier book.

Some of the speculations outlined here are more feasible than others—some indeed are a step, or even a half-step, away from realization; but even the most fantastic seem informed by that increasingly common recognition that practically anything conceivable to man may well be ultimately possible. Moreover, what is true for man's increasing power over physical things may parallel his mastery over social life as well. The basic truth is that despite our increasing awareness of social deficiencies, life is more congenial, for more people around the world, than ever before; for the decline in starvation and premature death, as well as the absence of pervasive wars, join such factors as the more effective distribution of abundance in creating a minimally satisfactory situation for a greater percentage of the world's peoples. Indicatively, even within America our standards of "the good life" have risen so high that most native "poverty" seems affluent by world standards.

Nonetheless, with the growing rapidity of change comes the demand for further transformations and, thus, the urgent need for visions of what might happen, the more thoroughly fleshed and detailed the better. Images of such alternatives depend not only upon intellectual comprehension of current realities, such as the pace and impact of technological development, but also upon imaginative projections that are closer in quality to "fiction" than social analysis. The following speculations are as far beyond "left" and/or "right," as they are historically or even currently conceived, as was the material in the earlier book; for if we are to use dichotomies, it now seems more valid to divide thinkers into backward-lookers and forward-lookers—respectively, those who regard present life as similar to the past (and thus amenable to classic palliatives) and those who see today as radically different and, thus, requiring unprecedented forms of characterization and solution.

Nearly all of the following social speculations were published recently; most, indeed, were written in the latter half of the past decade. Most come from freely ranging, fertile minds who mix comments upon diverse areas of experience into adjacent sentences; so that the categories into which the following essays are grouped—"History," "Knowledge," "Planning," etc.—establish more of a rough guide to the book's terrain than definitive divisions. Most of the speculations broach intellectual territory so virgin that there are no extant guidelines and sometimes one alternative seems as likely or as attractive as another; but out of the evaluation of such possibilities should come policies meriting action, not only within established governments but also in private organizations and one's own life. Most speculative thinking dismisses as irrelevant such criticisms as the conventional "it can't be done," and as worse than irrelevant such pessimism, if not fatalism, as would let each man abdicate his responsibility to control, and rechannel the drift of contemporary change. Finally, almost everything discussed in this book is universally relevant— as valid to old as young, to Americans as Europeans, to black as white; for the presupposition of this book, as well as *Beyond Left and Right,* is that "as all of us ride this space ship called 'Earth' together, pernicious ideas of irreconcilable racial and/or religious and/or geographic differences are false to our common humanity."

This book's introduction deals with the importance of speculations in social change today, and sketches the intellectual biases and background that hopefully unify the examples filling the body of the book. Certain selections have been abridged, or extracted from longer essays; and footnotes were generally deleted. Since speculations know no restriction or limit, there is in the back a bibliography of other relevant literature, intended also to supplement the list in the earlier volume. If *Beyond Left and Right* reflected, to quote the earlier preface, the "coming of intellectual age in the sixties," then this book and its introduction reflect an increasingly persuasive sense of the seventies as a time when, a backward Presidential administration notwithstanding, social dreams of all kinds could well come true.

I am grateful to all the authors and/or their publishers for granting me permission to reprint the essays included here. Every effort has been made to trace the ownership of all copyrighted material and to make full acknowledgment of its use. If any error or omission has occurred, it will be corrected in subsequent editions, provided that notification is submitted in writing to the publisher. My gratitude also goes to my two loyal editors at William Morrow—William McPherson, whose support of *Beyond Left and Right* extended to the commissioning of its sequel, and James Landis, who supervised everything after that. My old friend to whom this book is dedicated, Donald Cohen, introduced me to this kind of thinking, which jibed with my earlier analysis of contemporary thought and art; and both he and his wife Rosalind deserve my thanks for their continuing hospitality toward both the author and his works.

Richard Kostelanetz

New York, New York
14 May, 1970

CONTENTS

III. *ENVIRONMENTS*

IV. *CITIES*

INTRODUCTION
THE POLITICS OF SPECULATION

If "Be yourself" is nature's first injunction to
man, "Transform yourself" was her second—even
as "Transcend yourself" seems, at least up to now,
to be her final imperative.

—LEWIS MUMFORD,
Transformations of Man (1955)

The crucial question confronting us now is not whether we can
change the world but what kind of world we want, as well as how
to turn our choices into realities; for nearly everything even
slightly credible is becoming possible, in both man and society,
once we decide what and why it should be. As metamorphosis de-
fines the character and drift of the times, the problem for those
desiring a better life, for mankind and for themselves, becomes
channeling and molding these increasingly rapid forces of change.
"All the trend curves we may examine," writes Buckminster Fuller, "show rates of acceleration which underline the unprecedented nature of things to come." As autonomous as most of this
change is, only man can impose degrees of direction and value
upon history—create a willed, rather than a fated, future. Therefore, as persuasive as most "radical" criticism of present inequity
may be, a social thought truly relevant to our times must turn
from negative carping, no matter how perceptive, into offering
visions of what can, and ought, to be done. The ineffectuality of
what is known today as "radical thought" points up the need for
a revolution in how we think about fundamental social change,
and one strain of speculative thinking contributes to such an intellectual transformation.

If the function of "the intellectual" is supposedly dissent, to
the visionary mind goes responsibility for generating leaps be-

yond conventional thinking, ideally in an endless procession of imaginative ideas and inspiring blueprints (e.g., R. Buckminster Fuller, John Cage, Paul Goodman, Herman Kahn). Knowledge is power, the saying goes; and a resonant vision can become the most powerful stimulus behind comprehensive transformations. Need one take an example more fundamental than heterosexual relations, which have changed drastically in the past decade because certain people once had a vision of an oral contraceptive and set about to realize one (overcoming, needless to say, taboos and obstacles within the scientific community); and not only are the currently decreasing birthrates indebted finally to their vision, but so is the recent revolution in sexual parity and desire. Because women need no longer fear they might become pregnant without their assent, they can make themselves more available and inviting in fact and in fashion. Therefore, the radical modern ideal of "sexual freedom" has become more practicable through technology. In short, the metaphor for change draws less upon organic metamorphosis than scientific revolution, which is to say a leap ahead from one way of doing things to another, rather than a gradual evolution. Furthermore, answers to the question of how different the future can or will be conclusively separate today's conservatives from the genuine revolutionaries.

Social speculations are, essentially, articulated options, options which *may* be realized by people both inside politics and out; for a vision both comprehensive and detailed helps make human choices more considered and purposeful. As knowledge is power, so foreknowledge can be even greater power; and speculations, at their most relevant, propose alternatives that most of us would not be likely to consider on our own. "Roughly," I suggested in *Beyond Left and Right* (1968), "the fundamental processes of social change today start with dreams (whose mother may well be necessity), for the desire for something impossible is the first step toward a vision of its realization." For that reason, generating a feasible vision is the most essential type of significant social action; because without the envisioned goal, nothing gets invented and/or change progresses uncontrolled. "The forecasting of invention is not separate from invention itself," writes Donald A. Schon. "The principal step is the conceptual one. When you predict the electric car, you have made the adventure. We are not standing outside the process of change but participating in it." As speculations come in various forms, they can be realized in diverse ways—the need for an invention, the recognition of a new invention's possible uses, a plan for reorganizing one's environment or oneself; new ways to exploit existing materials, and so forth; but an ethic conducive to innovation assumes that every realm in society susceptible to change can respond to visionary ideas. Social speculations exist in the collective mind as a reservoir of alternatives that individuals and groups can appropriate to their needs, while a related repertoire includes scenarios of likely, but less attractive, futures. For both these reasons, "impracticality" is simply not a valid objection to creating, considering, or remembering a serious social speculation.

The most feasible visions match human desire to the current forces encouraging innovation. The greatest of these forces, of course, is technology, which in no previous age has wielded such a pervasively determining role. As both the source and the disruption of progress, its influence includes the steadily increasing pace of both technological development and its dissemination, which is to say not only the number of new machines and growing command over generating the subtle processes of invention, but also the decreasing lag between an average invention's birth and its maturity of general availability and use. The enlightened industrial institutions of America, if not the entire world, are currently committed to continuous invention and rapid distribution, not just as fad replacing fad but on behalf of an actual improvement in the quality and usefulness of things; and research departments of some of the wisest industrial endeavors have organized extensive considerations of the future.

Need one say that even the most ethereal Americans would sense their lives seriously impoverished without the electric light, the radio, the telephone, the television, and the automobile; and new technologies continually offer man more comprehensive command of his environment. Not only does the future promise greater control over the weather, but we can also build increasingly large environmental structures, such as Buckminster Fuller's proposed geodesic dome over midtown Manhattan, and technology also offers the most persuasive solutions to the current universal need for more abundant and humane inexpensive mass housing. For these reasons, nothing today is more pernicious than dialectical historical thinking, for the general human condition need not get worse before it gets better. Despite all of its perceptive criticism of industrial malaise, what is most lacking in classic Marxism is a rich and convincing vision of the future; so that "revolution" is advocated in the name of a class (and by an elite) and certain economic values, rather than ecumenical social speculations. Nonetheless, as clear as the current major drifts are, the details of any particular new conception are likely to remain unclear, subject first to unexpected developments and then to the power of human choice.

Man has always been highly adaptable; and though dependent upon machines, he has become less enslaved to "the human condition," which is to say he is now more free to reject dimensions of current life and willfully create something else. Technology functions to extend not only human body and desire, but also man's continuing adaptation to his environment. Broadly considered, "technology" includes both the development of new machines and the creation of new techniques, to do old tasks more quickly and more effectively. Indeed, a true social innovation has as multiple an impact upon diverse dimensions of society as a new machine. With the automation of industrial manufacture, for instance, comes the disappearance of much back-breaking effort, to the particular pleasure of those who do the work (but sometimes the despair of "humanists" who complain of "dehumanization"). "I don't do nothing but press these two buttons," a veteran employee at Ford once gratefully remarked. "Sometimes I use my thumbs, sometimes I use my wrists and sometimes I lay my whole arm across. The only time I sweat on the job is when the sun is a hundred and something outside." Just as the major solutions to the so-called "threats of automation" lie in more automation, so the further elimination of labor informs some of the more immediately applicable speculations— a robot to help around the house, automatic guidance of individual transport (cars, trucks, etc.), distribution of messages by facsimile printing, etc.—as well as the next set of speculations, which deal with what people could do with their increased leisure.

With technological advances comes not the abolition of labor
—something always needs to be done—but the possible abolition
of laborious work.

Major social transformations of all kinds can be traced directly
to the impact of technology; and no matter who makes or markets
the machines, intrinsic in their autonomous development and
dissemination are certain ecumenical and egalitarian social biases.
"Growing exponentially, Western technology has now led to the
globalizing of human experience and the smashing of the physical
barriers between peoples," writes the historian Lynn White, Jr.
"This is the prerequisite to breaking through the other barriers
between them. Whatever the incidental problems, it is a prime
spiritual achievement." For one thing, a child coming of age today
possesses sensory receptors so extended that he is instantaneously
"tuned in" to the entire world, since events in one place, as seen
on the television screen, feel as close as those in any other—
Prague is as immediate as Chicago, language differences notwithstanding—and as millions of minds receive the same message
simultaneously via the media, they undergo a common, indubitably ecumenical experience. This unprecedented psychological
situation, indebted largely to the communications machines, puts
a new shape upon the maturing political sensibility of the young.
The unprecedented truth is that technology, rather than competing with nature, has become a second nature, so to speak—a
complementary environmental system—whose impact upon the
maturing individual is now as decisive as is primary nature; and
this new *reality* is continually redefining man's relationship to his
planet. "An important result of more travel is the rapid and widespread exchange of cultural, economic, political and technological
ideas," writes James R. Bright. "No longer is geography (or sheer
distance) such a critical barrier, hindrance, or help to war or
trade." And Buckminster Fuller's own experience of the earth's
geography inspires this radical remark: "I travel between Southern and Northern hemispheres and around the world so frequently
that I no longer have any so-called normal winter and summer,
or normal night and day."

Among the prime purposes of speculative thinking should be, as
noted before, the consideration of what to do with new and
probable inventions; for truly relevant social thinking must

assimilate as well as inspire technological change. So much of the lag between recent major inventions and their transfer to general use—think of the transistor (originally invented back in 1948) or scotch tape (invented merely to repair paper)—can be blamed upon sheer lethargy in imagining possible applications. The present demands richly detailed and conceptually feasible speculations—conceived with a leap beyond the obvious—of what can be done with computers, transportation vehicles, microcircuits, atomic energy, chemotherapy, preventive medicines, and so forth; for without such intellectual effort and the resultant discoveries, technological potentials will remain invisible and wasted. In fact, the availability of a certain innovative machine creates new needs and opportunities; so that the mere existence of the computer, for instance, has already increased drastically the sheer number of computations made in society. A related objective is the technological exploitation of unused natural resources, particularly the oceans, which are abundant in both food and materials, or the energy of the sun.

The negative side of the same process requires the continual gauging of possible secondary reactions to primary developments. As Fred Warshofsky notes, no one "in 1903, could have foreseen that in America the automobile would kill fifty thousand people a year, that it would affect our foreign policy vis-à-vis the Middle Eastern oil producers, that it would change our sexual mores, . . . or that it would pollute the air in almost every city in America." Speculative thought must also deal with the truly knotty issues of morally ambiguous technologies, such as the likelihood of non-lethal but devastating weapons, more comprehensive spying and record-keeping, and electrical and chemical self-stimulation to satisfy one's emotional needs—one pill there for energy, one shock here for sexual pleasure, etc.—for these questions ultimately cannot be evaded. (The most facile palliative, if not the great liberal evasion, is establishing a commission of establishmentarians to report on the problem.) For better and worse, America is the prototype of advanced industrial civilizations; and so it is here that such issues must be confronted now.

One of the major achievements intrinsic in technological advance is the doing of more with less (and sometimes much, much less)—ephemeralization is Fuller's word for this process.

Just as computers today are several times smaller than their less powerful predecessors, and new materials like polymers offer greater strength in smaller volume, so within the economy this principle means more money, goods, and goodies for less effort, making abundance of several kinds increasingly pervasive in advanced economies. Not only has technological advance given people in general more wealth than before and more genuine energy at their personal command—and there are more truly wealthy people—but, as in America, our standards of "poverty" have risen to such unprecedented heights that more than three-quarters of the remaining world could be classified as poor. The problem for social institutions—corporations as well as governments—is then how best to increase this surplus and redistribute it more equitably to the needy and disadvantaged; and from this should follow not only consideration of direct subsidies to the poor (solely because they are poor, not just because they are Negroes, aged, or students) as well as a substantial Guaranteed Annual Wage and, beyond that, the possible abolition of "money" as a medium of economic exchange. After all, the young find lucre so much less lucrative than their elders that this old medium of work-incentive is losing its social efficiency. Affluence also makes obsolete those economic ideas that regard people as competing for a fixed amount of cake, because the current moment requires visions of how best to recirculate the increasingly burgeoning frosting.

The swifter pace of historical change reveals the temporariness of most current artifacts, aspirations, and behavior patterns, in addition to producing visibly growing gaps between the generations; for since most people carry into old age those attitudes and values they gained while young, the general differences in sensibility displayed by people born and growing up only a generation apart becomes increasingly more noticeable. "Today," a Yugoslav economist recently observed of a discrepancy with parallels around the world, "a militant Catholic over forty and a militant Communist over forty have much more in common than two militant Catholics, one over forty and the other twenty, or two Communists of like ages." Life in the Western world today is riddled with tokens of pervasive generational difference—outlandish clothes, long hair, marijuana, public nudity, unrestrained sexuality, and rock music played at thunderous volumes—and young people today are generally more sophisticated than their parents were at like ages. Discrepancies of this kind largely account for why most youth around the Western world would find themselves alienated from self-made, sex-negative, "light classical," patriotic, industrious presidents and chancellors, who came of age in the 1930s; but with the inevitable accession to power of these young, not only in government but elsewhere in society, will doubtless come radical changes in the dominant attitudes, as well as, given the drift of history, further generations of alienated young. The construction of a "new world" is continually in progress.

America, standing on the edge of the Westernizing world, has a culturally commanding position, so all that happens in this most "advanced" of nations is likely to occur everywhere else in the world—whether the pervasive use of television or transistorized radios, or the popularity of motion pictures or rock music. Thus it is important that enlightened Americans create exemplary machines, blue prints, and arts of life worthy of export; for what is created here is liable to go abroad, whether we like it or not—astronauts and movie stars become symbols of universalized faith, etc., although national cultures remain distinctly individual. Moreover, there is more real interdependence among countries today; so that an invention or policy-change in a major power is likely to have repercussions around the world. Particularly in America, therefore, social thought requires a broader synthesis which treats all significant problems in terms of the entire world, encompassing all nations, races and sexes; for thought with anything less than the consideration of all mankind in mind serves to perpetuate archaic divisions in society.

Much change is indebted to new ideas, not only as they inspire new machines but also as they inspire new techniques; and these new ideas and technologies are also changing appreciably the traditional processes of education, partially to foster minds more predisposed to visionary thinking. "If knowledge is power," writes Walter J. Ong, "then knowledge of how to generate knowledge is power over power." Not only the more extensive and extended education of the young, but the more frequent reeducation of the old (many of whom were once "well educated") creates the need for more open-ended conceptions of learning. As an increasingly greater percentage of a country's population is involved in either teaching or learning—in the United States the rate is rising from one-fourth to one-third—education becomes a culture's most serious business. Indeed, the unending generation of new knowledge inspires the ideal of continuous learning, both in schools and out; and the modern principle of more-for-less allows more free time for continuing education. As a result, one could pursue a succession of careers, each field perhaps requiring an extended period of education; and thanks also to all the education channeled through the communications media, some advanced nations are fulfilling the old ideal of a universally somewhat-knowledgeable society. (And another possibility, indebted to educational television, is the abolition of needlessly expensive schoolhouses.) Moreover, in response to the times, much "new" education successfully speeds up the comprehension of old materials, such as mathematics and language, as well as incorporating a concern with dimensions of experience not considered before, such as physiological perception, ecology (the reciprocal relation of diverse forms of life) and the possibilities of superhuman intelligence and physical performance. Beyond that is new truth—that making the previously invisible visible is among the primary means of determining what is most truly important, and most demanding of change. Indeed, much contemporary change is perceptually invisible; for as Buckminster Fuller points out, "99.9 percent of the accelerating accelerations of the physical environment change affecting all humanity's evolution are transpiring in the realms of the electromagnetic spectrum realities which are undetectable directly by the human senses."

Furthermore, the development of information technology accelerates the evolution of thinking itself, in addition to demanding not the teaching of data but instead, the intellectual means of organizing and retrieving needed information. "Interdisciplinary" education, for instance, serves both to inculcate a variety of intellectual structures and to encourage that kind of comprehensive overview characteristic of visions; and educational authorities at all levels should sponsor procedures and incentives designed to "free" the learning mind of constricting habit and cliché. Beyond that, as Robert Theobald notes, "It is the task of education to make the impossible appear relevant," for the major deficiencies in current social thinking are less philosophical than imaginative. That general lack of relevance mentioned before can be blamed less upon a lack of rigor or knowledge than upon a fundamental paucity of both visions and conceptual structure; for truly successful planning, as well as "systemic" and "synergistic" thinking, depends upon the most adequate forecasting possible. The hard fact is that without minds to take the requisite leaps, there will be fewer of the necessary changes; and without the appropriate education of imaginative capacities, there will be no visionary minds.

The major historical changes of recent years are largely indebted to developments occurring outside official "politics"—new technologies, affluence, population increase, generational change, social fashions, etc. Politics instead deals with what governments should do, or what who should do with governments; and for this reason, politics has nothing to do with initiating or popularizing the telephone, television, the automobile, the airplane, the birth-control pill. Not only have governments had little actual impact upon the resulting social changes, but many of them have yet to acknowledge the new realities shaped by many of these technologies. "While governments exercised their traditional prerogatives," writes John Brockman, "the process continued unnoticed. Who ever voted for the telephone?" Nor did or could legislators initiate automation, invention, abundance, social speculations, or so much else important to recent beneficence, for even the most enlightened politics functions in today's world not to foster change but merely to keep the laws abreast of history, decide who holds public office and, inevitably, put the brakes on social development.

The politician, as well as the lawyer, tends to approach new issues with the tools of precedent; but current problems, if not the times, demand thinking that transcends previous experience. "Paradoxical as it sounds," notes Herman Kahn, "reality has left experience far behind; and central as 'common sense' is, it is not enough." No national administration in the world today, not even Pierre Trudeau's, can be regarded as instinctively innovative; and neither is any major local administration particularly more progressive. The tragic modern truth is that even the "best" government can never contribute much to, as Lynn White puts it, "the slow progress of unshackling us from our past," and the politicians themselves are, almost without exception, too deferential to the conventional discussion to espouse truly visionary programs. (When once I showed a sketch of Fuller's Manhattan dome to the research director of a New York City Congressional campaign, she curtly replied, "It won't go with either [the candidate] or the voters.")

For those who would truly want to transform the world, politics offers a trap less concerned with genuine leadership than with standing on the stage and supervising a cumbersome bureaucracy; so that a visionary disappointed by the conservatism of politics, no matter what his rationalizations, is really too innocent to realize his prophetic mission. "Being by design a protective institution," writes Peter F. Drucker, "[government] is not good at innovation. It cannot really abandon anything." And so it is that many extant governmental agencies were founded to cope with problems long gone, such as agricultural underproduction; for the bureaucratic machinery and its occupants did not disappear with the death of the problem. (In fact, business is generally more successful than government at the contemporary necessity of phasing out what is no longer relevant.) Were a speculative innovator to run for political office, his real success would come not from victory (which would probably be detrimental to his well-being), but from publicizing his ideas before audiences not otherwise open to him. This kind of strategy also demonstrates that persuasive speculations are ultimately more powerful than conventional politics; and translating new ideas into realities, at all levels of life, is the most crucial and genuine "management" of our time. The demand is for that kind of thinking and procedures called "engineering," now applied to nonmechanical problems; and in principle nothing need be considered exempt from change.

Since the present moment knows no historical precedent, and also stands so far beyond the recent past, the times demand that we think profoundly about what has not been pondered before—revolution and change, in thought as well as life, are continuing obligations. A further truth holds that much in the future will be unexpected—the paradox emphasized by Herman Kahn's classic remark that the greatest surprise would be the absence of great surprises. Since everything important is likely to change appreciably within our own lifetimes, perhaps the best measure of a particular speculation's visionary quality would judge how conceivable such ideas were only a few years ago; and then the most valuable speculative thinking in this unending process would be that which inspires further speculations. "While the necessity for such traditional virtues as common decency, humane consideration, and liberal tolerance remains a historical constant, the prerequisite for a relevant radical thought today is a profound sense of our historical uniqueness," I wrote two years ago. "Only thinking that transcends the old pieties and categories—that is clearly beyond both 'right' and 'left'—can discover the new sources of malaise and formulate ideas that will nourish the roots of our future common experience."

Changes transform the form of thought about transformations; so that unlike the utopians of past ages, current visionaries think less about static worlds than about possibilities, usually in only one area of activity at a time; for not only are such dynamic images of possible change, unlike utopian schemes, subject to endless modification and respeculation, but no dynamic problem admits of a single definitive solution. Most previous predictions of the future seem indubitably modest today, and they invariably fail to pinpoint the diversely revolutionary effects that certain crucial changes are bound to instigate. Just as there is no end to history, so there can be no limit on possible transformation, or end to speculative planning.

A world in great change needs, in Fuller's phrase, "the periodic replacement of old forms by new forms," regardless of whether these fundamental transformations be called "evolutionary" or "revolutionary"; and without such changes there can be no future —only archaic hangovers from the past. The keys that turn today into a more attractive tomorrow are well-considered social speculations, which at once recognize, instill, and exploit the major drifts in society—technology, affluence, greater population, generational difference; for visionary ideas, as the primary cause of change, should inform planning that ushers the desirable future into the present. For the same reasons that such ideas have never been so necessary as now, social speculations will become increasingly more important in the future.

I

History

The future cannot be predicted, but futures can be invented. It was man's ability to invent which has made human society what it is. The mental processes of invention are still mysterious. They are rational, but not logical, that is to say deductive. The first step of the technological or social inventor is to visualize by an act of imagination a thing or state of things which does not yet exist and which appears to him in some way desirable. He can then start rationally arguing backwards from the invention and forward from the means at his disposal, until a way is found from one to the other.

—DENNIS GABOR,
Inventing the Future (1963)

OUR SPACESHIP EARTH

by R. BUCKMINSTER FULLER

I HAVE often heard people say, "I wonder what it would be like to be on board a spaceship," and the answer is very simple. What *does* it feel like? That is all you have ever experienced. You are all astronauts. I am sure you do not immediately agree and say "Yes, that's right, I am an astronaut." I am sure that you do not really sense yourself to be aboard a fantastically real spaceship—our spherical Spaceship Earth.

Of our little sphere you have seen only small portions. However, you have seen more than did any historical man, for he saw only one-millionth of the Earth's surface. You have seen a lot more, but not enough to see and feel Earth to be a sphere unless you happen to be a Cape Kennedy capsuler.

Our little spaceship Earth is only eight thousand miles in diameter, which is almost a negligible dimension in the great vastness of space. Our nearest star—our energy-supplying mothership—the Sun, is ninety-two million miles away and the next nearest is one hundred thousand times further away. It takes two and a half years for light to get to us from the next nearest star. That is the kind of space distance we are flying. Our little spaceship Earth right now is traveling at sixty thousand miles an hour around the sun and is also spinning axially, which at the latitude of Washington, D.C., adds approximately one thousand miles per hour to our motion. Each minute we spin at one hundred miles and zip in orbit one thousand miles—quite a spin and zip. When we launch our rocketed space capsules at fifteen thousand miles an hour, that additional acceleration speed which we give the rocket to attain its own orbit around our speeding spaceship Earth is only one-fourth greater than the speed of our big spaceship.

Reprinted in excerpt from William Ewald, ed., *Environment and Change*. Copyright © 1968 by Indiana University Press. By permission of the publisher.

Spaceship Earth is so extraordinarily well invented and designed that to our knowledge humans have been on it for two million years, not even knowing that they were on board a "ship." And our spaceship is so superbly designed as to be able to keep life regenerating on board despite the phenomenon entropy, by which all local physical systems lose energy. So we have to receive our biological life-regenerating energy from another spaceship, the sun.

Our sun is flying in company with us at just the right distance to give us enough radiation to keep us alive, yet not close enough to burn us up. And the whole scheme of spaceship Earth and its live passengers is so superbly designed that the Van Allen belts, which we did not even know we had until yesterday, filter the sun and other star radiation impinging upon our spherical ramparts in such concentration that if you went naked outside the Van Allen belts it would kill you.

Our spaceship Earth's designed diffusion of that radiant energy of the stars is put to work in such a way that you and I can carry on safely. We can go out and take a sunbath but are unable to take in enough energy through our skin to keep alive. So part of the invention of the spaceship Earth and its biological life sustenance is the capacity of the vegetation on the land and the algae in the sea, employing photosynthesis, to impound the life-regenerating energy for us in adequate amount. But we cannot eat all the vegetation; in fact, we can eat very little of it. We cannot eat the bark or wood of the trees nor the grasses. But insects can eat these and there are many other animals and creatures that can. We get the energy relayed to us by taking the milk and meat from the animals. The animals can eat the vegetation and we can eat a few of the fruits and tender vegetation petals and seeds. We have learned to cultivate more of those edibles by genetical inbreeding.

That we are endowed with such capabilities as that of discovering the genes, and RNA and DNA, and other fundamental principles governing the fundamental design controls of life systems is part of the extraordinary design of the spaceship Earth, its equipment, passengers, and internal support systems. It is therefore paradoxical but explicable, as we shall see, that up to now we have been misusing, abusing, and polluting this extraordinary chemical energy-interchanging system for successfully regenerating all life.

One of the interesting things to me about our spaceship is that it is a machine just as is an automobile. If you own an automobile, you realize that you must put oil and gas into it and you must put water in the radiator and take care of the car as a whole. You begin to develop quite a little thermodynamic sense. You know that you are either going to have to keep the machine in good order or it is going to fail to function. We have not been seeing our spaceship Earth as a beautifully designed machine that must be comprehended and taken care of in toto. There is one outstandingly important fact regarding spaceship Earth, and that is that no instruction book came with it. I think it is very significant that there is *no instruction book* for successfully operating our ship. In view of the infinite attention to all other details displayed by our ship, it must be taken as deliberate and purposeful that an instruction book was omitted. Lack of instruction and resultant education has forced us to find that there are two kinds of berries—a red berry that will kill and a red berry that will nourish us. And we had to find out ways of telling which was which red berry before we ate it or we would have died. Because of the lack of an instruction book, we were forced to use our intellect, which is our supreme faculty, to devise scientific experimental procedures and to effectively interpret the significance of the experimental findings. Thus, because the instruction manual was missing, we are learning how we can safely anticipate the consequences of an increasing number of alternative ways of extending our satisfactory survival and growth—both physical and metaphysical.

Quite clearly all of life as designed and born is utterly helpless at the moment of birth. The human child stays helpless longer than does the young of any other species. Apparently it is part of the invention "man" that he is meant to be utterly helpless through certain anthropological phases and then begins to be able to get on a little better—begins to discover some of the physical leverage-multiplying capabilities and the many nonobvious resources around him which will further compoundingly multiply those life- and knowledge-regenerating advantages.

I would say that designed into this spaceship Earth's total

wealth was a big safety factory which allowed man to be ignorant for a long time until he had amassed enough experiences from which to extract progressively the system of generalized principles governing the increase of energy-managing advantage over environment.

The *designed omission* of the instruction book on how to operate and maintain spaceship Earth and its complex life-supporting and -regenerating systems has forced man to discover just what his most important capabilities are. *His intellect had to discover itself.* Intellect in turn had to compound the facts of his experience. Comprehensive reviews of the compounded facts of experiences by intellect brought forth awareness of the generalized principles underlying all special and only superficially sensed experiences. Objective employment of these generalized principles in rearranging the physical resources of environment seems to be leading to humanity's, eventually to total, success and readiness to cope with far vaster problems of universe.

SUMMING UP

---

by NIGEL CALDER

What follows is my attempt to summarize as concisely as possible the main predictions and problems for the next twenty years that arise from the contributions to the 1984 series in *New Scientist*. In interpreting the picture that emerges, we should bear in mind the limitations in the method of collecting the contributions. Expert contributors were asked to forecast conditions in 1984 on the basis of known possibilities and trends, rather than to speculate freely. The series was planned

Reprinted from *The World in 1984*, Vol. II, edited by Nigel Calder, by permission of Penguin Books. First published in 1965.

with some preconceptions of what subjects were important and what the experts might say about them. Accordingly, the discussion has not been entirely "open-ended." There are some obvious gaps, both in topics and in national representation. Some topics (for example, *weapons, business, law,* and *religion*) were deliberately excluded. Others were not obtained in time for inclusion: these were *Europe* and *U.S.S.R.* as main topics, and *earth sciences, pipelines,* and *buildings* as subsidiary topics.

Great efforts were made to make the series as international as possible, but in the outcome there has been great reliance on British, American, and French contributions. Some of the thirteen Russians approached at first agreed to take part but, late in the day, they all withdrew at once. It seemed like a political ruling.

It is not possible here to convey the nuances such as "almost certainly" or "can reasonably expect" with which many of the authors qualify their statements. Where there is explicit disagreement or implicit controversy on important points, I have posed them as questions.

TABLE A   MAJOR TECHNICAL REVOLUTIONS

Character of change	Technical aspects	Possibilities arising
1. Revolution in information: vast increases in computing and telecommunications capacity, and wide use of electronic storage and retrieval of information.	Computers a good deal faster and easier to "converse" with. Computers linked in nation-wide and world-wide networks. Messages by computer network (in digital code). Big increase in communications using millimeter radio, laser beams or communications satellites.	Television-telephones. "Dialing" for news, books, etc. Worldwide weather and disaster warning services using satellites.
2. Revolutionary consequences of biology.	Understanding of living systems, including the human brains. Manipulation of genetic structure. Development of "bio-engineering." Understanding of aging process.	"Biochemical machines" for food production, energy transformation, chemical manufacture, and information storage. Alteration of cell heredity. New Engineering controls modeled on biological systems. Transplantation of organs and wide use of artificial limbs and organs. Modification of the developing brain. Conquest of viruses, heart disease, and cancer?
3. The beginning of the exploitation of the oceans.	Fish-rearing and transplanting. Fish concentrators. Midwater trawls. Working on the seabed at 600 fathoms. Obtaining minerals from seawater and the seabed.	Use of "new" protein sources (squid, red fish, Antarctic krill). Control of weather and climate by warming or cooling seawater?
4. New forms of energy.	Big increase in generating efficiency (including "MHD" methods). Wide use of fuel cells as small power units and for energy storage. Growth in nuclear (fission) power. Demonstration of power generation by controlled fusion.	"Footloose" industries. Large-scale desalting of water.

Effects on the individual	Social aspects	Global aspects
Ready access to information (a data store in the home?). Close surveillance by government computers? Use of television links instead of business travel.	"Abolition" of libraries, paper work and typists. Wide use of computers in every field of activity. Increase in local broadcasting. No more newspapers as we know them?	Worldwide instantaneous reporting. Language translation. Big investment in communications (but increasing nationalism in these services?)
Longer life. Better treatment of mental disease. Inhibition of aging or "medicated survival"? Loss of individuality by surgical implantation?	Better understanding of human behavior. Need for moral criteria in biological manipulations. Danger of a racket in transplantable organs. Danger of "mind control."	Understanding of complexity of living systems. Opportunities for enlarging food production.
New way of life for some. Better coastal resorts and seaports.		UN ownership of ocean floor? UN surveillance of climate-control experiments?
Fuel-cell generators in the home. Fuel-cell batteries for cars.	Decentralization of power generation? Quieter road transport.	Shift of populations to regions where water and conventional energy sources are scarce.

TABLE B EVOLUTIONARY CHANGES

Pattern of change	*Some factors*	*Some consequences*
1. A continuing race between food and population.	50–60 percent increase in world population. Conquest of some major diseases leading to 50 percent increase in expectation of life of children in poorer countries. Food production unlikely to keep pace in poorer countries of Asia. Less land will be required for producing materials that can be synthesized. Farming becoming a "science-based" industry in the richer countries.	Agrarian reform required in many of the poorer countries. Increase in food exports from richer to poorer nations. People will have to eat unaccustomed foods. Huge investment in water supplies required.
2. General industrial progress, including automation.	Extensive use of numerical control in high-speed automatic workshops. Greater use of automatic aids in aircraft, ships, trains, and cars. Use of "designed" materials in engineering, including very strong steels and biological-like composite materials. Energy use more than doubled. Three- to fourfold increase in air travel(?) and a big jump in air freight. Fivefold increase in petrochemical production.	Prosperity linked with investment in automation. More "scientific" management and closer links between science and industry. Opportunities for decentralization with small-scale automated plant. Fewer workers on the land and in factories; more in service, marketing, and research activities. Growth in the middle class. Glorification of "work" cannot endure.
3. Growth in knowledge.	Mathematical theories of complex systems. More plausible theories of the universe and the fundamental particles. Possible surprises from landings on the moon and from biological exploration of Mars. Understanding of the dynamical processes of the earth's and the sun's weather. Knowledge of the earth's upper mantle. Emergence of the social sciences. Growth in biological knowledge as in Table A (2).	

TABLE B EVOLUTIONARY CHANGES *(Cont.)*

Pattern of change	Some factors	Some consequences
4. Life even more oriented toward the family and the home.	New materials and labor-saving devices. Domestic robots. "Ideal climate" in the home. Almost limitless access to information from the living room. Growth in automatic merchandising.	Higher status of women.
5. A great advancement of education.	Recognition of the economic importance of education. Wide use of teaching machines, programmed instruction, radio, and television. Development of better methods of teaching. Growth in adult education and re-training. Emphasis on science and technology in the poorer countries.	Wider literacy (90 percent of the world's children at school compared with 50 percent today). Teaching better suited to the individual student. Broader-minded education and more humanistic teaching of science. Reassessment of the role of the teacher.

TABLE C CONFLICTS AND CHOICES

Points at issue	Relevant scientific factors	Social and political factors
1. World development: is it going to happen fast enough to make the poor richer?	Technical knowledge could have spectacular effects (e.g. in health and agriculture) if the resources were available to apply it.	Will the gap between rich and poor countries widen or narrow? "Furious crusade" against poverty needed? Better conditions of trade for poorer nations? Trading groups among poorer countries (federation?). Social revolution needed, e.g. in Latin America?
2. International relations: war, cold war, coexistence or cooperation?	Thermonuclear war would be disastrous. Spread of "independent nuclear deterrents"? Bigger international scientific effort—in laboratories, weather centers, space exploration, etc. Development of "peace research."	Numerous small conflicts. Racial conflict. Rich versus poor nations conflicts? Increasing nationalism and isolationism? Increasing trade. International commercial enterprises. "Middle path" for less-developed countries? Scientists as peacemakers?
3. Government: will it be more or less democratic, more or less rational?	State power increased by big computers. Danger of "mind control." Computer simulation and operational research in policy-making. Possibility of "instant" polls of the whole population on current issues. Increased scientific advice for government.	More farsighted and "logistic" outlook in government. Increased knowledge of facts narrowing the range of choice. More "professional" politicians; more critical electors. New political theories?

TABLE C   CONFLICTS AND CHOICES (*Cont.*)

Points at issue	Relevant scientific factors	Social and political factors
4. Ecological attitudes: what will become of the natural environment?	Continuing pollution? Wildlife doomed except in reserves? Better knowledge of soils and biological interactions.	Wiser planning of land-use and landscapes? More use of land for recreation.
5. Cities: squeeze or sprawl?	Urban studies advancing. Better means of transport or restrictions on traffic? Very cheap buildings leading to impermanence?	Vast growth in cities (Calcutta 30 million?). Turmoil in and around many cities. Cities centered on universities? Or airports?
6. The individual in 1984: will he enjoy life?	Increase in neuroses. More use of behavior-influencing drugs. Malnutrition from eating the wrong foods? Invention of new gambling games.	Not *much* shorter working week, but longer holidays. More crime? More generous provision for the old and the sick. Disenchantment about economic growth? Need for a secular morality? Need for "the humanities" to question ends and means.

OUR WORLD IN REVOLUTION

by OLIVER L. REISER

Many of you have heard the story of the French nobleman who, when asked what he did during the French Revolution, replied: *I survived*. For him that was enough—a man-sized job. Today we can say, *that's nothing!* We are living through at least ten revolutions, all going on simultaneously.

There are not a few persons today who have lived through two world wars and the great depression in between. Now all of us, young and old alike, are face-to-face with new threats to our civilization: the possibility of thermonuclear war, automation in industry, the computer revolution, and whatever else may come. But like it or not, no modern Joshua can stop the clock of history.

I am not reporting something you do not already know when I state that a considerable part of the jittery condition of the world is due to apprehensions about what is happening to our time-honored values. In all this turmoil, men wonder about the fate of what are called the ethical and spiritual values of mankind. This, indeed, is the core of what we are concerned with in the present discussion.

In order to give these philosophical reflections some contact with realities—and that means to get as close as possible to actual social situations—let me list what seem to me to be the ten major revolutions already under way in our society. By a revolution we mean, of course, a rather complete overthrow of some existing order of things.

Of the revolutions already under way or sufficiently close in time for study, the last, the tenth revolution, is just looming on the horizon. It may be that this coming revolution will in its total impact and influence overshadow the other revolutions, and it may help to resolve the disharmonies created by its predeces-

Reprinted from *Challenge*, 24, by permission of Oliver L. Reiser and Leland Stewart. First published in 1967.

sors. In any case, here is my description of the revolutions (or revolutionary trends) already in process.

1) *The revolution in international relations.* This includes the emergence of so-called "backward" nations and the upsetting of the "balance of power"—such as it is—that has preserved a measure of international stability. This includes also the political explosions in various parts of the world, especially in Africa, Asia, and South America. The breakdown of colonialism, the collapse of the British, French, Dutch, and other empires, has resulted in the creation of many new, usually smaller, nations. These new nations frequently lack the knowledge and experience in self-government essential to viable democracies, and so military dictatorships often result.

2) *The revolution in race relations.* The colored peoples in all parts of the world, but especially the members of the black race in the United States, are rebelling against the domination by the white or Caucasian race. The protests against the "master-slave" relations and the revolt against "second-class citizenship" have created tensions and conflicts in areas where there is resistance to change. If this conflict between the old and the new combines with the emerging nationalism just mentioned, this aggravates the emotionally tense situation. There is even a revival of talk about an incipient "yellow menace" growing out of the alleged increasing power and influence of Chinese communism.

3) *The sex revolution.* This rebellion against the older puritanical codes and patterns takes many forms. The traditional virtues of chastity and faithfulness to marriage vows are widely disregarded. Birth-control pills and contraceptive devices are undermining the fact and the value of virginity. "Wife-trading" and "husband-swapping" are becoming a kind of fad, it is said. Divorce and broken homes are symptomatic of our disintegrating social institutions. Homosexuality is on the increase. Today, some assert, a third sex is emerging—symbolized in popular trends by the fact that boys are beginning to look like girls and girls like boys.

4) *The revolution in attitude toward crime, delinquency, and work.* The denigration of honest toil goes along with the resort to

extralegal ways of making the "fast buck," and the new maxim, "only saps work." The right to chisel; padded expense accounts; cheating the government on income tax returns—these are only less obvious forms of the practice of robbing a bank.

The increase in crime rate and the acceleration in juvenile delinquency rate are especially noticeable. The "teen-age problem" is a phase of the "sick urbanism" of large cities, but suburbia is also familiar with it. Not only is the crime rate going up faster, but our attitude toward crime is undergoing a change. It has even been suggested that if American tolerance of crime increases to the point where we accept crime as "normal," we may be forced eventually to make a choice between a criminal state and a police state.

5) *The psychopharmacological revolution.* This, too, has many forms. It refers to the increased use of alcohol, tranquilizers, narcotics, "pep" pills, and other avenues of escape from the anxieties of an increasingly complex and difficult world. The cocktail party is the social expression of a frenzied world of neurotic personalities. The use of other forms of mind-controlling drugs, such as LSD and other psychedelics, is on the increase. These "consciousness-expanding" drugs, it is said, serve the needs of those who desire what is called "total experience."

6) *The revolution in transportation.* This is best symbolized by the vastly increased air travel and transportation (now becoming supersonic), and the creation of a new social class, the "jet set." "The god of America is acceleration," said one observer.

Further examples and consequences of this revolution will appear in the next section. Meantime, it needs to be noted that the large cities desperately need a "mass transit revolution" to speed up the movement of vehicles to and from urban centers—else our cities will choke and die in their own traffic snarls and auto exhaust fumes.

7) *The revolution in communication.* This refers not only to the "mass media" of radio, television, and newspapers, all of which make it easy to be entertained and hypnotized by visual stimuli, but also to new developments such as one David Sarnoff predicted regarding home TV's receiving programs and films from

all over the world. True, we are more informed than ever; but "informed" by the news media which slant the news in ways required by the narrow gauge institutions of our fragmented world.

The combination of the "transportation revolution" and the "communication revolution" will surely produce a progeny of awesome developments. At this point you may suspect that I am speaking as a science fiction reporter and have therefore allowed my imagination to run wild. But that this is not the case is confirmed by a glance at the report and studies from the RAND Corporation. In glancing over a large list of possible developments, one finds the following projects listed as conceivable undertakings:

Manned lunar landings; permanent bases on the moon and manned landings on Mars; multi-generation missions to other solar systems; extra-terrestrial farming; operational lasers for space-communication; lunar-based laser beams for space-vehicle propulsion; development capabilities for destruction of space-satellites; intergalactic communications; and so on.

In this list of development one is dismayed to observe what great ingenuity our research workers demonstrate in designing the engines of war for possible global conflicts of the future, and how few new ideas are generated for the prevention of wars and the perfection of the arts and sciences of peace.

8) *The revolution in education.* This revolution is one that is long overdue, but when it comes it may not be of the sort that the new world circumstances will require—for one thing, because the people and forces which are in control of education are not likely to have the required vision and know-how.

Of course, we are already acquainted with closed-circuit television, "teaching machines," "talking typewriters," and similar mechanical aids which are being utilized. These tools are the forerunners of the "automated classrooms," as they are called. It looks as though the old-fashioned school teacher with the human touch is on the way out, soon to be as extinct as the dinosaur.

Our universities and research institutions will become "think factories," wherein the "knowledge industry" will be automated and computerized, and everything will be "optimized"—except perhaps the dignity of the human individual.

9) The next revolution may be called *the psychosocial revolution*. This could take various forms, including the new religion of naturalistic or evolutionary humanism as set forth by Sir Julian Huxley. In any case, this revolution will be accompanied by a growing interest in Oriental religions and philosophies. The old-fashioned religions of the organized and authoritarian churches and faiths will become passé, and some new religious viewpoints and attitudes will emerge. This could be a forerunner of our tenth revolution.

10) For want of a better term, this may be called the *psychogenetic revolution*. It will be observed that so many diagnoses of society's ills, and the proposed remedies, take human nature *as we now find it* as the basis for judgments about future developments. Present human nature is taken as the focus and authority for value preferences, and moral judgments are then rendered in terms of conformity with (or the rejection of) present alternatives and standards.

But looming on the horizon of human evolution is the vision of a "new being" (to misuse Paul Tillich's term); this would be a psychosocial revolution such as Sir Julian Huxley might have envisaged. *Man-made humans*—this is the next step in man's control of nature. Instead of taking man's present biological and psychological make-up as something "given"—final even if far from perfect—science soon will face the awesome and reverent task of remaking man. This would be a psycho-biological revolution which Sir Julian Huxley has not allowed for, though his brother Aldous had some incompletely formed ideas along these lines.

Perhaps it may be possible to open up new vistas of human experience, *new dimensions of consciousness,* through a biological and psychological alchemy (sometimes wrongly termed "genetic surgery") by way of the control of the DNA-RNA basis of gene replication and mutations. Directed control and guidance of these mutations (a kind of orthogenesis) could produce the "new humanity." The experimental utilization of psychedelic drugs indicates that something novel in human experience *is* possible, perhaps along the lines of the mystical experience as described by William James in his book, *The Varieties of Religious Experience,* and dealt with by Maurice Bucke in his study, *Cosmic Consciousness.* This would be a psychic revolution which would demonstrate that the inner life of man's consciousness can be far richer and more intense than any previously known in past and present societies. Mutant personalities gifted with an emergent psychic illumination could transcend current environmental impoverishments and limitations.

One hope for the creation of a better world seems to lie in the harmonious integration of aspects of personality which are now frequently at odds with each other. If reason and emotion, intellect and feeling, the head and the heart and the hand, could be brought into synergic relations, we might unify personality and bring about what I have sometimes called cortico-thalamic integration. At present such characteristics as courage, imagination, love, and understanding are infrequent traits in exceptional individuals. These traits need to be integrated and universalized. We need to invent "mass production" techniques for evoking talents that are latent in mankind. This is a matter of taking rare qualities like sensitivity, love, and insight and universalizing these characteristics. The task of an evolutionary humanism would indeed be most difficult if we had to begin all over again; our hope for the future lies in the fact that there is no human being living who does not have some of these qualities to some degree. To that extent every indivdual is potentially a member of the new humanity.

As one might anticipate, the full impact of the previous nine revolutions may well be disastrous to the human spirit—unless some new resources of human nature are opened up and perfected. The idea that men can find a new freedom in another dimension of human experience may seem like a form of "escapism" to some psychiatrists. Such a characterization surely would be sophistry. Especially is this so if it is true, as some students insist, that the real path of self-development will come through voluntary disciplines such as concentration, fasting, meditation and yoga exercises.

The striving for self-perfection should not be confined to the boundaries of a mountain hermitage or the enclave of a desert anchorite. The key to the more enduring satisfactions and maximum human values lies in the processes of cooperation and sharing. This means that we cannot realize the *World Brain* of H. G. Wells, or the *Noosphere* of Teilhard de Chardin, or my own conception of a *World Sensorium,* if each group insists on its particular point of view to the exclusion of alternatives. We can, however, make progress toward social synthesis by way of the integration of human knowledge, if we expand our cooperative efforts beyond the boundaries of institutions and face up to the problems of building a "planetary democracy."

At the present time we do not know a great deal about the role of social contexts and controls in the development and frustration of the psyche. On the one hand, there are studies on the perceptions of time and space, and objects in space, among socially deprived persons. Jules Henry (*Trans-Action,* March 1965) reports that the extremely poor, because of their preoccupation with sheer existence, actually fail to perceive time relations as other people do. Children from deprived homes have to be taught to differentiate among objects before they can begin a normal course of instruction at school.

On the other hand, when a mature individual is detached from his society, from his sense of obligation to follow its ways of thinking—as with the solitary who renounces the world, or someone whose inhibitions have been relaxed by chemical means—he may "see visions," and experience reality in a new way.

In general it would seem that men see the world in terms of their needs to adjust to it. Apparently most animals do not respond to the whole world but only those parts of it to which they are predisposed to react in order to stay alive. Similarly, human beings are limited first of all by physical necessities, then they are controlled by the requirements of society. Finally, one may secure leisure and freedom for a contemplative relation to the world.

The cumulative effect of these studies is to strengthen the conclusion that the very structure of consciousness shifts with the mode of society, and conversely, especially in relation to the means of comunication. This latter idea has been developed by Marshall McLuhan, who claims that the type of consciousness engendered by typography (the isolation of visual experience from other bodily experiences), i.e., space as occupied by repeatable units, made possible the development of mass-production, grid-cities, and other forms of atomism. If we could combine visual, auditory, and tactile experiences again, we might recapture the sense of the unique as against the repeatable, and this might even show up in morality, where individual conscience would decide each situation on the basis of its unique character.

The moral of all this is that the well-integrated individual needs both the wholesome social environment and the leisure and privacy of the life of contemplation. Man at present is an intermediate form in the evolutionary scheme of life. Psychologically man is in a state of becoming; he is a bridge. Heredity has given man the past and the present as ingrained in his genes and chromosomes, and mutations of these will show him the possible paths to the future. Man has a tremendous memory bank from past forms of biological evolution and his own cultural achievements, and from these he must next induce the selective changes in psychobiological constitution which are necessary to create the new humanity. Within man there is the potentiality of bringing these things into being, and man has only to learn how to set himself free in new dimensions.

THE NEXT 100 YEARS

---

by ISAAC ASIMOV

T HE WORLD's population is increasing quickly, and each year the World Almanac will be presenting its population statistics with a sharper sense of urgency. But population will level off. By 2000, when the world's population will have

Reprinted from *The World Almanac* (1968) by permission of the editor.

reached six billion, scientists expect that birth control will be well-established over most of the world. A plateau will have been reached and the main talk of the Twenty-first Century will be to keep it from being exceeded.

By 2068, a major effort will be in progress to increase the quality of the human population. Gene-analysis will be the technique used. Each child as born will have its gene content checked as routinely as its footprints are taken. This gene-analysis will be an essential part of the medical records, since it will give information as to possible physical and mental weak points. The attempt will be to encourage only the birth of those children who may be expected to have a gene pattern that predisposes them toward excellence.

Increasingly, there will be a tendency to control not only the number of births but the right to parenthood. Perhaps the greatest social controversy of 2068 will be between those who favor an absolute right on the part of society to dictate who may or may not have children, and those who dispute man's understanding of what constitutes "excellence" and who advocate the "right-to-have-children."

Each side in the dispute may have to take into account the rapid development of "ectogenesis"; that is, the development of fetuses outside the human body. This will have several advantages. Women will be freed of the biological task of actual child-bearing. Embryos can be nurtured under optimum conditions, something not always available in the natural womb. Genic analysis can be carried through before birth, thus allowing a more liberal policy on conception, since checks would be possible afterward. The techniques involved in ectogenesis will be delicate and space-consuming, and even in 2068 the process will not be common. It will have become important enough, however, so that the World Almanac of the time may well list numbers of births in two columns: "natural" and "ectogenetic."

The goal of controlling quantity and quality of population would be quite impossible without some international agency making full use of computerized equipment. In fact, the computer, as it develops steadily over the next century, will make the present division of the planet obsolete. The necessary controls that will keep six billion human beings alive and comfortable in 2068 can only be planet-wide in scope.

We will still be a world of nations in 2068, for tradition and self-esteem will keep us "national" in feeling. But the computers that alone will be able to guide the world economy and make the necessary decisions will transcend the nations, which will, in real importance, be at about the level of our county governments of today. Since computers are designed to solve problems on a rational basis, the computerization of the world will be its rationalization as well. Decisions, for instance, will be directed that will alter conditions that give rise to social friction, thus minimizing the danger of national wars or internal rioting. This will be done not because wars or riots are immoral, but because they are irrational. And society will, by and large, obey the decisions of computers because to avoid doing so will bring disaster.

By 2068, the active desire to raise human intuition above the complex computer-driven calculations will be gone. There will still be "intuitionist" parties and societies in various parts of the globe that will refuse to use computers and will carry on anti-computer activities, but they will have no influence. In fact, the computer will be an integral part of the domestic scene by 2068. The home computer that keeps tabs on bills, makes out checks, organizes shopping and menus, turns on appliances, keeps tabs on the family pet, and controls the cooking, will solve the servant problem.

There will even be a tendency to use self-contained mobile computers (or "robots") as a kind of literal servant-substitute. These, however, will still be a luxury in 2068. The tendency in that year will be in the other direction, instead; toward consolidation. More and more households will be tied in to a large community computer for the sake of greater efficiency. And, of course, the Central Planetary Computer will keep track of all statistics, down to the minutest, for instant recall. The statistical contents of a reference book like the World Almanac will be largely computer-prepared and computer-checked, though it will still require the active and agile intelligence of the human personnel to decide *which* statistics and *how* the whole is to be organized.

Energy will not be a problem in 2068. The key breakthrough into the practical use of fusion power will have been made at least a half-century before. The oceans will then offer a supply of deuterium as an energy fuel that will last in copious quantity for millions of years. By 2068, man will have gone beyond that. There will be space stations circling Earth that will be capable of absorbing and transmitting solar energy to Earth, a source that will last for billions of years. The world of 2068 will be one of infinite energy, and therefore one in which we can control the environment easily. For instance, the difficulty today in obtaining fresh water from the sea or metals from low-content slag, or in removing pollutants from air and water, is not any lack in understanding but is a matter of expense only. In 2068, with infinite energy at our disposal and very advanced techniques, expense will be no factor, and the world's resources can be mobilized with ease and efficiency to support six billion in far greater affluence than we can now support three billion, and without the accumulation of waste or pollution.

Food supply will be crucial, of course. The last decades of the twentieth century will see a greater and more intelligent use of the ocean as a food source. In the twenty-first century, the great age of ocean-farming and ocean-herding will begin. Plants will be grown underwater and sea-life will be "domesticated"; that is, bred and cared for, so that the annual increase may be exploited without danger of overuse.

But the great trend in 2068 will be the use of microorganisms as food for mankind. Yeasts and algae can be grown far more rapidly and efficiently than the higher forms of life can. They can be flavored to suit and eventually can be prepared in varieties of forms, textures and tastes that will outshine more common classes of foods. They will also be carefully designed to supply optimal nutritional needs. Food will become the product of gigantic laboratories and the percentage of space on land and sea which must be devoted to food will be decreasing in 2068. More and more of the Earth's surface can be turned into amusement resorts, parkland and wildlife refuges.

Even Earth's surface load of cities will be declining in 2068. The twenty-first century will see man burrowing underground. The process will only be underway in 2068; the majority of mankind will still be living aboveground; but the future will be clear. Every city will already have its underground portion; many newer suburbs will be entirely underground.

The underground city will have as its chief advantage an utter freedom from weather vicissitudes or day-night change. Tem-

perature will be equable the year round and there will be neither
wind nor rain nor snow. Well-lit and well-ventilated, the underground cities will be computer-designed from the start for ra-
tionality and comfort. With the day-night cycle gone, the entire
planet can eventually be put on a single "planet-time."

Nor will the underground dweller be deprived of the touch of
nature. Quite the contrary. Where the modern city dweller may
have to travel twenty miles to get out "in the country," the underground dweller will merely have to rise a few hundred feet
in an elevator, for once a city is completely underground, the
area above can be made into parkland.

With abundant energy and advanced computers lifting from
the shoulders of mankind all forms of routinized and unrewarding
labor, there will be room and scope for fun and creation. In this
endeavor, human beings will compete freely and with an increasing feeling of social equality. As the planet becomes a computer-
guided community, the sense of "foreigner" will diminish. Ghettos
and slums will disappear as copious energy makes affluence possible for all and as computerized decisions modify conditions
that would otherwise be brought about by irrational feelings of
bigotry. Some people may still choose to be selective in their social and intimate associations, but there will be no great gaps in
living standards or opportunity between one loose association
and another; no economic barriers between them; and therefore
no burning fears or hatreds.

With the declining birth-rate, the rise in ectogenesis, the disappearance of routine housework, and the conversion of all work
into a low-muscle, high-brain endeavor that can be performed
by either sex, it is clear that the woman of 2068 will be completely equal to man economically and socially. The family will
no longer be an essential economic unit and sex will no longer
be tied to child-birth. Sexual associations will be looser in 2068
and more casual. The sorrows of unrequited love and of jealousy
will not disappear, but perhaps they can more easily be recovered
from in the casual atmosphere of the time.

In 2068's world of leisure and comfort, the greatest industry
will be that of supplying what may be called "amusement."
Sports and shows of all sorts will still be popular, but there will
be entirely new outlets. One-man reaction motors can place individuals in the air, so that the sensation of scuba-diving can

become air-borne. Trips to the Moon may be common and large space-stations may be established in orbit about the Earth for the chief purpose of supplying vacationers with no-gravity fun. The casual life will allow greater individual tastes in style and manner of behavior. There probably will be chemicals to supply a world of inner illusion without adverse side-effects, and large sections of the population may choose to withdraw into themselves.

Matching the emphasis on amusement will be that on education. By 2068, a substantial percentage of the human race will be seriously devoting the major portion of their lives to a continuing program of education in a variety of fields. Education will be quite comfortable and amusing in 2068. Closed-circuit television and microfilms will offer dramatic ways of transferring information. Computers will design courses in any subject to match the capacity and temperament of the individual. The central library of the planet will be open to everybody and anything in it available on demand through a computerized copying service.

Those who choose education as their goal will have a chance to develop what creativity they possess and to participate in the important work of the world of 2068, the further increase and refinement of knowledge. Those groups who, in 2068, will be pushing hard for controlling the quality of births will undoubtedly have as their goal the increase in the percentage of those who would be so constituted, temperamentally, as to choose continuing education over passive amusement.

Space will still offer an outstanding technological adventure in progress in 2068. A successful, self-supporting colony on the Moon will be celebrating more than half a century of existence. It will be a sizable community, increasing quickly in numbers and drawing a large immigration from Earth. Also the development of rational underground towns on the Moon and the discoveries by the Lunar colonists of techniques for the proper utilization of microorganisms for food will have stimulated similar changes on Earth. Nor will the Moon serve merely as a human residential community. The greatest astronomical observatory will be established on its far side and huge research complexes will be working on chemical and physical techniques that utilize hard vacuums. A Lunar-based computer will analyze data from probes that circle the Sun at closer-than-Mercury distances and from satellites that circle the Earth, watching its atmospheric changes. Weather-forecasting on Earth will become a science and so will another kind of weather-forecasting: that of predicting changes in the Solar wind, necessary, if space travel is to be safe.

By 2068, there will also be a small colony on Mars and manned probes will have swept across the neighborhood of Venus and Mercury. Temporary landings will have been made on Ceres, the largest of the asteroids. But the outer planets will still remain to be explored. In 2068, the news headlines will feature the preparation for manned flights to the moons of Jupiter. (These headlines, by the way, can be on television screens, called for at will, with any news item or feature reproduced on paper for your records, as desired, at the push of a button. Many, however, will wish to obtain printed newspapers, complete with comics and feature columns, for leisure reading and for absorption in depth— and that will be available, too.) Unmanned probes will have preceded the flight, both to the neighborhood of Jupiter and to the planets beyond. It will be clear that by 2100 man will have explored to the limits of the Solar system.

Are there any great unsolved problems that will face the world of 2068? In the fields of science and technology, two overriding ones will remain.

In the first place, the gap between the Solar system and other planets circling other stars will still be unbridgeable in 2068. Is the gap permanently unbridgeable, or can there exist techniques undreamed of, even in 2068, by which the distance can be crossed, without unbearable expenditure of energy and of time? The importance of reaching the stars is that somewhere out there are other life forms and even, in all likelihood, other intelligences. To study other forms of life or to make contact with other intelligences would represent a chance at a monumental advance of knowledge.

Second, the thorough understanding of the human brain will still be an unattained goal in 2068. The biochemistry of other tissues will be solved in considerable detail by then and it will be possible to "create life" in the test-tube—that is, to synthesize nucleic acid molecules capable of reproducing themselves. But the big problem will remain; the intricate interrelationships of the human brain will still be out of sight. A major push in this direction will be in progress in 2068. After all, a true understanding of what makes us tick will make it possible for mankind to guide itself all the better in a further rational advance that will, by 2168, make the world of 2068 seem, by comparison, nothing more than a collection of cavemen huddled about a brushfire.

TOWARD THE YEAR 2000

by KARL W. DEUTSCH

As an exercise, I have tried to imagine that a group of intellectuals had met in 1765 and had tried to predict the year 1800, or in 1865 and had tried to predict the problems of 1900. In jotting down, with the vision of hindsight, some of the problems in the first period, 1765 to 1800, certain extremes became apparent. A major energy source—steam power—was harnessed; a major scientific breakthrough occurred in quantitative chemistry; major political revolutions occurred in America and in France; there were major cultural renaissances; political equality became a major issue; and a major transformation of warfare occurred through the rise of mass armies. A certain number of evils, such as torture as part of normal juridical processes, began to disappear, and slavery came under attack, but new evils appeared with the rise of industrial distress and child labor. Between 1865 and 1900 we get another new energy source—electricity—and the combustion engine, the peak of the railroad age, and the full triumph of industrialization; labor unions and socialist parties, unheard of in 1865, appear; social equality and welfare, rather than political equality, became the new issues;

Reprinted in excerpt from *Daedalus,* Journal of the American Academy of Arts and Sciences, Boston, Massachusetts, Volume 96, Number 3. First published in 1967.

imperialism and colonialism have their heydey in these thirty-five years; chattel slavery disappears and is even suppressed in Central Africa; serfdom goes out; industrial distress, tuberculosis, and suicide become some of the major evils of the time as then discussed.

If I try to project this and make a guess for the period between 1965 and 2000, I find that we can state our problems under five headings. The first: *The Technological Changes.* We will have major new energy sources, presumably nuclear, but perhaps also something as unexpected as electricity was in 1865. Automation and information technology will be fully implemented. We will see the triumph of the computer comparable only to the triumph of the railroad in the past century, or the triumph of the automobile in the first half of this century. We will probably see the beginning of interplanetary transportation, and a stream of scientific information coming from laboratories in outer space. This will give us knowledge comparable to what the microscope supplied at the end of the nineteenth century.

The second is *Psychological and Sociological Problems.* In the advanced and rich countries we will see a preoccupation with quality of life and leisure, and in the poor countries a demand for more food, machinery, medicine, and freedom from poverty. The gap between the two could tear the world apart in a deadly conflict. We will have to hand over economic growth itself to automatic machinery in order to develop automatic factories to make more factories. If we can automate not just production but economic growth, mankind can have its goods and also worry about leisure. If we do not do that, somebody will have to produce the capital goods that a world population of six billion people will need at the turn of the century. We will in any case also have by the end of the century severe maintenance problems; as we get more and more capital equipment, we will need more and more people to service and maintain them, and we are not getting these people.

The main problem in this second group, a sociological and psychological one, will be the socialization of adolescence. In the eighteenth century, grade-school education was thought of for the first time and introduced; from 1865 to 1900 grade-school education triumphed, and high-school education began to spread. In the period before us, college education will probably become standard in advanced countries, and high-school education standard in the developing countries.

The third group is the *Political Problems*. The advanced countries will become overwhelmingly urban. Through reapportionment people will become much more equally represented, and this will also come about through the decline in educational differences. The difference between illiterate and literate is qualitatively greater than the difference between senior college and junior college, or even between senior college and high school. It will, therefore, be much harder to maintain gross inequalities in political representation. Moreover, if the content of people's heads becomes more valuable, governments will find it more expedient to treat them with some respect and some consideration. This is likely to make people less expendable than they used to be.

We may get a permeation of criminal jurisprudence with the concepts and techniques of mental health. Since mental health is receiving huge amounts of research money, we will get from the resultant psychopharmacological findings all kinds of other methods—a technological development—which by that time will begin to merge with our criminal jurisprudence system.

We may also get a growth of the public sector of the economy in non-Communist countries from the present level of roughly 30 percent in advanced countries to anywhere between 40 and 50 percent. This does not mean that the government will keep it all, but the government may distribute half of the national income. If there is anything to the law of declining marginal utility, we may find that people fight much less severely for marginal units of income when all of them are getting richer. Labor conflicts in advanced countries will become even less violent than they are now; resistance to high income taxes will become less and less desperate because people do not really mind giving up marginal proportions of their income if their income is high enough. This may mean a decline in resistance against an international income tax to be collected in the advanced countries in a way comparable to that by which Massachusetts and Connecticut are now being taxed for the benefit of New Mexico and Mississippi.

We may get, therefore, an international transfer payment problem.

This brings me to the fourth problem: *Economy and Demography*. We will have six billion people in the world. With recent annual growth rates of 4 percent in the total income of the world, we may easily have a quadrupling of world income from 1,800 billion dollars for the more than three billion people living now to 7,200 billion dollars for the six billion population that may be expected in 2000 A.D. (and remember how misleading an average is here), from the present figure of $600 per capita to $1,200 per capita by the end of the century. The present range of per-capita national products, however, is from less than $100 to $3,000. If the transfer payments do not get anywhere, by the end of the century the range may be from $200 in the very poor countries to $6,000 in the very rich. I expect that the tendency toward declining marginal utility, however, may make the rich countries quite contented with $5,000 per capita, and it may, therefore, be possible to make available very major amounts of capital for the developing countries.

This leads finally to the fifth heading: *The International Question*. We may find a greater willingness on the part of the advanced countries to use as much as 5 percent and conceivably even 10 percent of their income for the economic development of the backward countries—perhaps 5 percent about halfway through the period and 10 percent by the end of the century. At the moment advanced countries are employing less than 2 percent of their income for economic development elsewhere.

Just as evils such as chattel slavery and child labor disappeared in earlier periods, we may see the disappearance of organized preparations for all-out war, although this does not mean that we will not have all sorts of limited troubles. If we cut the arms burdens of the world by the end of the century from roughly 8 to 10 percent of world income, which they are today, to 4 or 5 percent, it might be possible to transfer that much to capital formation; this would in turn add another percent to the growth rate of world income, given even a fairly conservative estimate of a capital output ratio.

We may have new evils—in the socialization of adolescence, in finding meaningful occupations, in the problems of a society suffering from information overload. Labor might be so expensive that maintenance will be deferred and equipment, neighborhoods, and houses neglected. This may then be combatted by automated maintenance procedures and a cultural emphasis on caring for things or for people. The English responded to the ugliness of the incipient industrial age and the "dark satanic mills" by a nationwide effort to keep the brass and silver polished, by stressing the appearance of care, of maintenance, of concern, of solicitousness. A response similar to the British reaction to the severe onslaught of early industrialization may become worldwide.

ALTERNATIVE FUTURE WORLDS

by HERMAN KAHN

WE LIST BELOW twenty-one themes which suggest where important aspects of the next decade or two might lie. The ordering is for convenience of exposition and has no other significance, nor does the number twenty-one have any special significance. It seems to be a convenient number to use, being large enough to allow much specificity in the categories and yet small enough to be reasonably manageable.

Classical Themes:
  1. Containment and Confrontation (Chi – χ)
  2. Communism on the March (Kappa – κ)
  3. Other Manifestations of Soviet Power (Sigma – σ)
  4. Mostly Peaceful and Prosperous Grand Design (Gamma – γ)

Reprinted from *New Approaches in International Relations,* edited by Morton A. Kaplan, Copyright © 1968 by St. Martin's Press. By permission of St. Martin's Press.

   5. Détente—Many Structural Stresses (Delta – δ)
   6. Extensive Multipolarity (Mu – μ)

A New and Old Theme:
   7. Challenges from Europe (Eta – η)

New Political Themes:
   8. Challenges from Japan (Iota – ι)
   9. Challenges from China (Psi – ψ)
   10. Challenges from Latin America (Lambda – λ)
   11. Challenges from other Underdeveloped Nations (Omega – ω)
   12. New Super Powers (Upsilon – υ)
   13. Major Realignments (Rho – ρ)
   14. Erosion or Resurgence of the West (Epsilon – ε)
   15. Typical Phases or Patterns (Phi – φ)

New Technological Themes:
   16. Technological Challenges and Opportunities (Tau – τ)

Medium and Long-Run Prospects:
   17. Gallois-Millis-Khrushchev Non-war (Nu – ν)
   18. Other Relatively Successful "Arms Control" (Alpha – α)
   19. Post-Nuclear-Use International Systems (Pi – π)
   20. Other Basic Change in International System (Beta – β)
   21. Other Themes (Omicron – o)

The themes are grouped in five categories for convenient discussion. We will, however, only make some preliminary comments on each theme in this report.

Each theme is identified with a Greek letter since, rather than refer to "Containment and Confrontation Worlds," it is often more convenient to speak of "Chi Worlds." Thus when discussing various forms of "Containment and Confrontation Worlds," they may be labeled Chi-1, Chi-2, and Chi-3. And various subclassifications can also be labeled (such as Chi-1.1, Chi-1.2). While this system may be a slight burden for the reader (and tend at times to a certain deadliness in the discussion), it seems to provide useful increase in the ability to systematize discussion, especially since one use of this report is as a "text" for Hudson Institute Seminar-Courses. We hope the reader will not only tolerate this terminology but even come to find it useful. However, we will use it so little in this paper that even the allergic reader should not be too alienated—at least not for this cause alone.

There is clearly an implicit framework and emphasis built into the selection of the twenty-one themes, a framework and emphasis which we judge appropriate to the plausible problems of international relations from 1965 to 1975 and perhaps beyond. On the other hand, this framework and emphasis is not so restrictive that it forecloses discussion of any particular issue of importance. Thus while other researchers might impart a different view of the current international situation and its likely developments, they could still use the suggested framework for much or all of their discussion without doing violence to it (although possibly adding overlooked themes).

The twenty-one themes that will be described below are a first step toward the construction of a systematic group of Alternative World Futures (AWFs). Any particular world future is likely to have several specific elaborations of the themes synthesized into some coherent picture of the relevant aspects of the world as a whole—or the themes can be studied in isolation. Not only is it possible to meld consistent themes together, it often also is possible to meld inconsistent ones in a way that creates "worlds" with tensions, or with plausible internal conflicts or contradictions. We will, in what follows, usually discuss the themes separately (leaving to a later report on contexts and examples the discussion of the packages), thus losing in this report much of the richness of "reality" but eliminating also the arbitrariness and specialization associated with any particular correlation of specific themes. Some of the most interesting work which the Institute hopes to do will involve such systematic exploration of combinations of themes and of how such combinations may change considerations.

We have labeled the first six themes "classical AWFs"—classical in the sense that much of the discussion of the last twenty years has been preoccupied with these themes. Thus almost all policy-makers and decision-makers are familiar, to some degree, with the possibilities listed. One of our major arguments is that the next ten to twenty years are likely to see the introduction of relatively new themes. While we think of the world in the next decade or so as having a reasonable probability of relative calm, its calmness in part will be the calmness of gestation and preliminary evolution for new structures and tendencies. To some great degree, then, the last fifteen themes are likely to be at least as interesting as the first six—indeed for our purposes more interesting.

1. Chi (Containment and Confrontation) Themes

These are cold and near-hot cold wars. They are likely to consist substantially in retrogression to the conditions of 1948, 1950, or 1953. Thus they usually assume relatively tight alliance structures, and usually a bipolar world with both sides pressed against each other, perhaps in "eyeball-to-eyeball" confrontations.

2. Kappa (Communism on the March) Themes

The nightmare of the late forties and early fifties. The unity and morale of the Communist bloc are restored. The Communists are strong, aggressive, rapidly increasing in power, while the Western bloc is disunited, weak, demoralized, and everywhere on the defensive or in retreat.

3. Sigma (Other Soviet) Themes

Even if the Soviets were no longer leaders of a worldwide revolutionary movement or of a major bloc of Communist states, they would still be one of the great world powers and we would be much concerned with their military and foreign policies. In Sigma Worlds we study: (a) a decline of Soviet power which could include internal disunity and weakness in the Soviet Union or simply a relative withdrawal of the Soviets from international affairs and influence, either because of a Russian "neo-isolationism" or because of an inability of the Soviet to project effectively their internal power externally. In any case, the Soviets of this projection lose their morale and vigor, experience disintegration, or otherwise tend to slide back or turn inwards; (b) a nationalistic Soviet Union which exploits Communist ideology when convenient but is essentially an assertive power with nationalist motivations. Such a U.S.S.R. might have territorial ambitions, or pan-Slav tendencies in policy, or follow economically or politically aggressive policies without conventional territorial ambitions but in order to limit or destroy the power of competitive nations; (c) etc.

4. Gamma (Mostly Peaceful and Prosperous Grand Design) Themes

These, in effect, are worlds in which the major constructive and positive international objectives of the U.S. government have been achieved. They ordinarily are worlds in which conflict among nations is channeled by legal and open means, much as is economic competition in an orderly but free marketplace. Such conflict provides useful social functions, stimulating and directing various kinds of changes and "natural" developments, but without violence. This world contains no "enemies"—at most only opponents or competitors. The threat of war or of escalation to violent levels of conflict has either disappeared or is under firm control.

5. Delta (Détente—Many Structural Stresses) Themes

Something between a relatively "violent" Gamma World and an unusually "serene" Chi-Mu (see below) combination, often with much sound but little fury. Conflict may be nascent and potential—i.e., many inter- and intra-bloc crises and strains may exist which could escalate, but they seem to be under practical and effective control, even if this control is not always explicitly recognized in the public rhetoric. Thus, in contrast with the entente Gamma Worlds or hostile Chi Worlds, these are détente worlds. Conflicts still exist but there is a large measure of agreement on what to disagree about and how to handle conflicts. There is tacit acknowledgment of various nations' vital and traditional areas of interest, and implicit agreement on behavior in the low-level escalations which inevitably occur (or are caused). Because rules or conventions have been established, there is a widespread expectation that conflicts, at least in the foreseeable future, will not escalate to large-scale warfare. There may also be some effort to develop the entente conditions of the Gamma Worlds.

6. Mu (*Extensive Multipolarity*) Themes

This kind of world could involve the restoration of something like the old-fashioned Great Power nation-state system, possibly with an extensive diffusion of nuclear weapons. In all Mu Worlds there is at least a partial erosion or breakdown of bipolarity as the dominating form of the international structure, either because of the increasing strength, vigor and assertiveness of powers other than the Soviet Union and the United States, or because of an inability of the Soviet Union and the United States to utilize the strength they possess. Such conditions are usually, but not necessarily, at least initially associated with Delta Worlds.

7. Eta (*Challenges from Europe*) Themes

For more than 500 years Europe has been the great center of the modern world's civilization. For some 300 years Europe actually dominated the world. There are those who believe that after World War II Europe went into the same kind of irreversible decline as did the Egyptians, Assyrians, Persians, Classical Greeks, Romans, various Chinese dynasties, and even the Renaissance Italians, sixteenth-century Spanish and Portuguese, seventeenth-century Dutch, and eighteenth-century and nineteenth-century British. All eventually declined in power; so, it is assumed, has Europe as a whole declined—there is ample precedent for such decline. But even if this estimate were accurate, Europe could still be the breeding ground—an occasion and cause—of important international crises and other developments. But there is another possibility; particularly and most obviously because there has been a sustained and spectacular economic growth rate in Europe in the last decade, and an increasing political and military assertiveness, but for other reasons as well, Europeans are occupying more and more the center of the international stage, and as creators and major actors rather than as puppets or pawns. The belief of so many that the mantle of Europe was about to be inherited by the Soviets, the Americans, or the "new nations" is no longer so widely held—and thus many new (and old) issues are raised.

8. Iota (Challenges from Japan) Themes

We turn now to the new political themes. Japan plays a very special role in our consideration of such future possibilities. It is possibly the most achievement-oriented of all modern societies; it is cohesive; it is technologically adept; it is in many ways the natural leader of Asia and the "nonwhite" peoples—though for various reasons, most rising out of its aggressive and provocative history in the second quarter of the twentieth century, it has not achieved this leadership. But it may turn out that Japan will become, as the last two Japanese Premiers have been fond of claiming, one of the three pillars of the modern democratic world— the other two, of course, being Europe and the United States. Or it may be that Japan will find a more assertive and independent role to play—either within or outside the framework of world affairs that exists today. In any case, any serious study of future possibilities must pay attention to the various roles which Japan can undertake.

9. Psi (Challenges from China) Themes

China, of course, is the great contemporary bugaboo. It has replaced Genghis Khan and the Mongols, Tamerlane, the Turks, the yellow (Japanese) peril, even the Soviet menace, in much popular literature and thinking. The degree to which this is justified, the various ways these forebodings could materialize, obviously are important elements in any study of future possibilities. But the range is very wide and the full range should be considered.

10. Lambda (Challenges from Latin America) Themes

For the last two centuries, Latin America has been culturally isolated from modern Europe, a world backwater—indeed, sometimes referred to as "a backwater of a backwater" (the Iberian Peninsula). But soon it, too, seems likely to claim a certain share of the center of the international stage both as a creator and an actor, as well as providing occasions for conflicts and competitions by others. Indeed, Latin America could, by the end of the twentieth century, prove to be one of the great new forces. By the year 2000 it is expected to have a population surpassing that of North America by perhaps two to one, and a GNP which, while not comparable with that of North America in the year 2000, could be comparable to the U.S. GNP of today.

11. Omega (Challenges from Other Underdeveloped Nations) Themes

The important major areas here, of course, are Black Africa, the Arab League, the "Southern Tier" bordering the Soviet Union (Turkey, Iran, Afghanistan, Pakistan), India, Southeast Asia (including Indonesia and the Philippines), and perhaps Eastern Europe (including Yugoslavia and Greece) and the economically backward areas of Western Europe (Spain, Portugal, southern Italy and Ireland). All of these areas are either undergoing rapid change or experiencing serious frustration because they are not changing. All have their typical instabilities; all can present their typical challenges to the world.

Many will feel that we display a lack of focus and judgment in placing all these areas together in the single class of Omega themes, but we would judge, though experience may prove us wrong, that the emphasis is about right (i.e., from our point of view China and Latin America seem worth special attention; all of the other underdeveloped areas together are about equally important to these two).

12. Upsilon (New Super Powers) Themes

Hardest of all the possible worlds for an American or Russian to consider undoubtedly is one in which America and Russia are succeeded in world preeminence by another great power or by several new great powers. There are no obvious candidates for this new role or roles, nor (in the short run) is the transitional process easy to imagine. Yet it would perhaps have been no easier for a nineteenth-century Englishman to imagine the decline of British world power, though in Russia and America there were plausible candidates for succession. Consider, though, a West European or all-European union which mobilized the material and intellectual resources of the continent to an aggressive political and military mission. Consider, too, that this kind of challenge might come at a time when the United States and the Soviet Union were undergoing a failure of nerve, or a disillusionment in their political ambitions, or an emotional withdrawal from world involvement, or even internal crises or failures that undermined their ability to carry on great power international policies. Or consider the possibility of a major part of Asia's finding inspired leadership and challenging the existing world powers by means of a political or revolutionary strategy that undercut their technological superiority. Even though this Upsilon World is the least easy to imagine, it is, in the long run, the most certain: Soviet and American primacy in the world is, on the evidence of history, certain to be transitory, and the interesting questions are really how long the primacy will endure and the process by which it will be ended.

13. Rho (Major Realignments) Themes

One of the startling things about the twenty postwar years is the degree to which alliance relationships have been stable. However, the kind of flexible, rapid, and even bewildering changes of partners that characterized the diplomacy of Europe and the world generally in the five centuries before World War I may in the future be to some degree restored. While it is unlikely that alliance policies will be as flexible as during the Concert of Europe era, some important changes may occur in the current structure. Thus Rho Worlds envisage situations in which there not only has been a change in the classical bipolar structure, but actual realignment of the broken components or the new actors. Such realignments can be important and dramatic, and despite recent trends are common in history.

14. Epsilon (Erosion or Resurgence of the West) Themes

The world today presents a rather perplexing and paradoxical aspect. Everywhere many of the central ideals and concepts (dignity of individual man, progress, consent of the governed, technology, science, etc.) associated with Western Europe are more or less accepted, or paid lip service to (and from this point of view, Marxism and other current socialisms are all Western heresies, belonging, in large degree, to the Western tradition). In addition the physical prosperity of that part of the world made up of Western Europe and its direct progeny is at a peak, both relatively and absolutely (and it is interesting to note that most of the countries which are now modernizing most rapidly and successfully are the ones that tend to be closest in culture to Western Europe, i.e., Eastern Europe, Greece, southern Italy, Spain, Portugal, Ireland, and Latin America).

Yet Western Europe and even to some degree Western civilization is in a state of retreat or at least withdrawal. Much of this withdrawal is clearly voluntary and in part reflects a change in the concept of the national interest, the internal morale of the countries concerned—both colonizer and colony—and/or a change in moral or other standards. In part it is clearly a retreat forced by the development of forces that were themselves initially created, at least in part, by Western European precept and example and in part by a disillusionment with Western European ideals (resulting from the excesses of World Wars I and II even more than the excesses of colonialism). Nevertheless it is clear that the balance of physical power, technology, science, and probably even morale lies with Western Europe and the United States. (And to some degree the other areas of the world are likely to accept the Western nations at their own evaluation—thus, if these nations, as a group, achieve high morale the third world is likely to grant them great respect; when they have a low morale the third world, and others, will indeed be contemptuous of them.) It is not in the least inconceivable that the West may experience a renaissance of political assertiveness as well as of internal morale.

It is also quite possible that despite its material vigor the retreat of the West will continue, that there will be a further erosion of morale which may be followed by a decline in strength and dynamism. For example, if the Nazis had taken over Europe there would have been an abrupt repudiation of some important (but not all) Western ideals and values, even though physically

Western Europe might have experienced an enormous increase in power. More likely than a revival of totalitarianism in its Hitlerian form seem developments along the line suggested by such authors as Spengler, Orwell, Huxley, Sorokin, and others. Or such a decline would take the form, which many see as common in history, of a weakening of the moral fiber of a society as a result of its very success. This might mean that these societies would no longer be capable of the kind of efforts necessary to compete with vigorous, enterprising, and dynamic "new" societies.

15. Phi (Typical Phases or Patterns) Themes

There are, of course, many cyclical theories or semi-cyclical theories of history. In our own country the names of Toynbee, Quigley, Sorokin and Spengler are usually associated with such ideas, though earlier centuries also had their theorists of rise and fall. Some of these, such as Toynbee's hypothesis of social "Challenge and Response," seem at least partially valid, describing a typical pattern of events even if failing to give a completely plausible explanation of this pattern. Many such theories can be used to supply a useful language, such as Sorokin's "Idealistic, Ideational, and Sensate Cultures," without the use of this language necessarily implying any acceptance of the theoretical implications of Sorokin's analysis. One must also consider such patterns as are provided by variations in business cycles or in the recovery of nations which have been temporarily submerged as a result of defeats in war, etc.

16. Tau (Technological Opportunities and Challenges) Themes

To some degree these opportunities and challenges can be studied in isolation, but eventually our major interest will be studying how technology can affect the various worlds and be affected by these contexts.

17. Nu (Gallois-Millis-Khrushchev Non-war) Themes

These describe a particular type of arms control world in which the possibility of eruption to all-out wars or the large-scale use of thermonuclear weapons against a major power simply is not plausible—either actually or potentially—yet the world remains basically multipolar and mostly unorganized by any international sovereignty or explicit international institution, though these institutions may have important roles in certain Nu Worlds.

18. Alpha (Other Successful "Arms Control") Themes

In addition to the world described above there are other ways in which the use and control of nuclear threats and force could be more or less successfully controlled. Included is some greater legal ordering of the current relative disorder and anarchy of the world—the many different kinds of developments in the area of explicit international law and international legal arrangements generally as well as the implicit customs and expectations of a nation. We will also consider the newer aspects of arms control— ways by which access to, and the use of, violence might be controlled by agreement, conventions, and widely shared expectations. (These areas are also included, to some degree, in the Beta Worlds discussed below.) Finally, arms control practices and institutions might be built up on variations of the *lex talionis* rule.

19. Pi (Post-Nuclear-Use International Systems) Themes

If there is a third use of nuclear weapons (the first two having been at Hiroshima and Nagasaki) it is likely to be an important turning point of history. There is, first of all, the prospect of a new world system emerging from a war which destroys the old system—possibly a new system of one or several dictatorships, autocracies or technocracies established by the surviving nations; possibly a supranational authority established by the surviving political authorities or institutions (not necessarily nation-states) or by the participants in the war themselves; possibly a system closer to feudalism, a multiplicity of those regional powers or "city-states" which survive the destruction or discrediting of national governments; possibly, if the war had been really severe and extensive, something approaching world anarchy—a world of robber barons and isolated communities.

There is also the possibility of a less momentous use of nuclear weapons, but one in which the psychological impact and the expectations and images that are created have a profound effect on international relations. Some argue that this is one of the most important types of world to be considered, since if thermonuclear war (or some lesser use of nuclear weapons) really is likely or even a serious possibility, the shock of such war or use would plausibly make new political beginnings or radical international reforms a real possibility; it might prove important to have made some intellectual preparations that might provide useful guidance in such a crisis.

20. Beta (*Other Basic Changes in International System*) Themes

Other kinds of changes that could be associated with, or be independent of, the Alpha and Nu Worlds could also occur—in particular there could be some basic change in the nation-state system that has dominated international relations for the past three or four hundred years. While many consider our nation-state system to be the natural and inevitable way of organizing the existing world, during most of recorded history it would have been thought of as an unlikely and transitory system, and this judgment may yet turn out to be correct before the twentieth century is over. Such changes need not take the simple form of a constitutional or confederal world state. Many other structures are possible.

21. Omicron (*Other*) Themes

This is clearly a catchall category which includes some international themes that could arise from internal changes in the United States or Europe other than those that have already been suggested in other categories. For example, one might imagine the United States developing by the end of the century into a high-consumption, leisure-oriented society, in which the European tradition of the gentleman of leisure would be to some extent reestablished—that is, individuals would emphasize acquiring and using different kinds of skills, few of which were related to their normal vocations. (Thus if one asked somebody in this situation what he was or did, he would be likely to reply that he was a skier, a diver, an artist or a poet rather than a manager, lawyer or computer programmer.) Such a U.S. is compatible with a "smug, self-satisfied" neo-isolationism, a crusading interventionism, an attitude of objective observer and/or active participant in the international scene, or with a frightened, or blasé, selfish nationalism jealously guarding or aggrandizing U.S. wealth—but all with overtones which reflect the emphasis on high consumption and leisure.

There are other possibilities, too. For example, we have considered elsewhere the rise of a near-"Orwellian" 1984 state through the continued heavy involvement of the United States in a large number of foreign areas and the consequent effects on people of this kind of medium-level but dramatic and "institutionalized" war. Such a situation might also lead to a revival of what might be thought of as the "Roman virtues," or to a kind of garrison state. Another scenario suggests a neo-isolationist withdrawal by the United States from international affairs, perhaps followed by an abrupt and dangerous return. All these and many other possibilities need consideration.

ELEMENTS OF GLOBAL MORPHOLOGY

by DANE RUDHYAR

Let us look at the earth-globe. We should have learned to see it as a globe pivoting around the polar axis; its continental masses of land and oceans dotted with islands, big and small, spreading over its surface in characteristic shapes. Here mankind lives. Within this global field men produce and strive to

Reprinted from *Modern Man's Conflicts* (1948) by permission of Philosophical Library.

reach harmony within themselves and with one another—strive, alas, so far most unsuccessfully as a rule. How can they hope to reach harmony as men, if they do not understand the harmony that chords all lands and seas as a dynamic whole, as an integral field of operation? The earth-surface is a whole, and it is dynamic in as much as it is constantly in motion and in a state of morphological change. The earth whirls in space in a complex combination of motions which constantly modify the "geomorphic" and geostatic equilibrium of its lands, seas and air-currents. Mountains and continents rise and fall. Ice ages come in waves. There may be even greater changes in the polarization and axial inclination of our globe as a whole, whence vast cataclysms that imprint deep-seated remembrances in the collective unconscious of all civilizations.

The earth may not be strictly speaking "alive"; but it is the matrix—or matrical "field"—from which all living organisms emerge and within which they operate in unity or diversity, as material organisms and as participants in a cosmic-planetary drama of evolution. Most living organisms remain unconscious of this participation, live and die in a, to them, meaningless sequence. A few human beings at all times reach full and direct consciousness of this great evolution; give to their less aware comrades visions and symbols to foreshadow what the latter in turn may come to experience; and, passing on, remain as indivisible units of consciousness and power within the great oneness of Man.

From the thin layers of this earth-surface, all life springs forth. Surely, if we can only visualize and understand our global world as a whole of organically (or quasi-organically) interrelated parts and functions, we may end by sensing and perhaps clearly understanding what each of these continental and oceanic parts represents in the economy of the whole. What we need is a sense of *gestalt*—that is, of integral form—and of symbolic values; to which the records of history (and even of persistent worldwide tradition) should add much meaning, if they too are understood in terms of "wholes of time," i.e. of cycles. We need a new approach to geography and to the geographical basis of history and civilization; we need, both, an integrative approach and an engineer's approach—thus we need branches of knowledge which we have called respectively "geomorphics" and "geotechnics."

Our planet is a whole; human civilization is a whole. In the Age of plenitude, creative fulfillment can only come to man as these wholes are taken as foundations for living, feeling and thinking. The now obsolete European geopolitics was not based on such a goal of total human fulfillment and productivity. It was only a realistic foundation for the "struggle for power" which is the essence of politics, a broad and intelligent foundation for the effective domination by one or more nations and classes of the energies available on this globe. American Technocracy, while less obvious in its purpose, ultimately would reach toward a similar goal under a Howard Scott type of engineer-controller. Geopolitics deals with states, with the conquering urges of nations which "must be educated up from smaller to larger space conceptions," or decay as the "result of a declining space conception" (Frederich Ratzel).

In the Age of global plenitude which we envision *politics would be superseded by management*. States would become managerial organizations concerned only with the planning and maintaining of full production. The old legalistic structure of the state, which is the legacy of the Roman world and which has only the value of an expedient, would operate in terms of management of energy. *There is no meaning in "law" except in the realm of management of power; every other field of human activity should operate under the principle of "harmony in mutuality."*

We italicized the above statements because they are fundamental. What we call "geotechnics" is the science of management of the total resources of the earth as an all-inclusive field of operation. And by "geomorphics" we mean the understanding of the structure of this field, not primarily in terms of the amount of materials, energy and human beings available for production on each and all lands or seas, but rather in terms of the geomorphic structure and shape of continents and oceans. These global structures, after all, condition climates and population, migrations and the course of civilization. They are as significant to anyone attempting to understand the past, present and future of humanity as a whole, as the study of the shape of a person's body and features is to the endocrinologist and psychologist (or even criminologist) whose business it is to understand the temperament, character and behavior of men. We might thus speak of geomorphics as a kind of "geognomy" similar in intent to physiognomy; a modern and "scientific" version of the latter having been provided by Dr. Sheldon's studies in *The Varieties of Human Physique* (Harper, 1940) and his classification of human bodies and temperaments into viscerotonic, somatotonic, and cerebrotonic.

We can only briefly suggest here the possibilities of this new field of geomorphic study, but a typical instance can be pointed out which will lead us to the main point of this chapter. This instance is the remarkable morphologic similarity between Asia and Europe. Both Asia and Europe have three southward peninsulas. Indo-China, India and Arabia match respectively Greece, Italy and Spain. Ceylon is the structural equivalent of Sicily; Indonesia, of Crete and the Greek archipelago down to Rhodes (which is, in a very general sense, a miniature Australia).

If we look at the continental mainland, we find Tibet (and the adjacent mountain ranges of China) matching Switzerland and Bohemia. The Mongolian and Siberian plains correspond to Germany and Poland. China in the East is like European Russia; while in the West, central France stands for Persia, with Brittany shaped much like Asia Minor, and the French Atlantic coast below Brittany, like Syria and Palestine—the Gironde and Dordogne valleys with their prehistoric cultures paralleling that of the Tigris and Euphrates.

Such correspondences might seem mere chance figurations were it not that there is a startling parallelism between the characteristics of the cultures which have developed in these corresponding geographical structures. Indo-China with her highly developed art and music, and Java with her rich culture, remind one forcibly of Greece and the earlier Cretan civilizations. India has been the center of religious doctrines for Asia, just as Italy has been for Europe. The ancient city of Nasik, sacred to Rama, stands (near Bombay) where Rome is in Italy; Benares, where Florence grew. Curiously enough the Arabs settled in Spain (Arabia's structural equivalent in Europe), and both Arabia and Spain are rugged lands, angular shaped, with fanatic, intense, proud populations. As significant are the historical-cultural correspondences between the nations which grew respectively in Persia and in France (Zoroastrian civilization matching the old Celtic culture), in Mongolia and in Germany (military and mystical peoples avid for space-conquest in an inorganic sense), in China and Russia (lands of the "good earth" and of robust peasantry long controlled by a small aristocracy).

The general picture presented by the relationship of Europe to Asia is that of miniature to full-sized original. Europe is not unlike the budding protuberance on a navel orange, which is a small replica of the orange itself. It appears thus as a specialized reproduction of the vast Motherland for a particular evolutionary purpose. In another sense, of real historical-cultural validity, we might say that Europe is to Asia as the conscious and intellectual part of man's total psyche is to the vast collective unconscious. The conscious is a differentiated organ of the unconscious, in the sense that the brain and the cerebrospinal nervous system constitute differentiated organs of the total human organism. Religion is the progeny of the collective unconscious (Asia); science, that of the rational conscious (Europe).

In such a parallelism differences are as significant as similarities. We spoke of Italy and India, Switzerland and Tibet as occupying similar places in the two geomorphic structures. But we should notice at once the fact that the Alps describe a convex arc of mountains above the Northern Italian plains, while the Himalayas describe a concave arc over the plains of Northern India. If we consider the two mountainous masses of Switzerland and Tibet as the "geo-spiritual" centers of their respective continents, we get the idea of the European center radiating outward, while the Asiatic center is focused inward; and we see how well this describes the difference between European and Asiatic types of spirituality.

Another way of looking at the Eurasian land-mass is to see it as one shape extending from 10° longitude west (West Ireland) to 170° longitude west (Eastern tip of Siberia). Dividing into two this span of 200 degrees of longitude, we find longitude 90° east as the pivotal meridian; and it passes through Calcutta, Tibet, near Lhassa and near the highest mountain of the globe, just west of the Gobi Desert and the Mongolian People's Republic, through a most important part of Siberia (Sibirsk region) and along the great Ienisei river which may become a great trade-route in the future. Around the pivot of this 90° east meridian we might see soon the total population of the Eurasian world almost evenly divided; even now the combined population of India, Persia and the U.S.S.R. balance approximately that of China, Japan, Indo-China and Indonesia. And there is a general similarity of position between the Scandinavian peninsula and Kamchatka, the British Isles and Japan—the correlation between the last two island-groups being particularly significant in terms of world-history and racial background.

The main point we wish to make here, however, is the polar relationship between, on one hand, the big land-mass constituted by Europe, Asia and Africa (or "Eurasiafrica"), and on the other, the Americas. This relationship provides the logical foundation for the future global society. It establishes the great geomorphic dualism of human civilization. Just as the North and South Polar regions are complementary in that the former is an apparently empty circle of water, while the latter is a quasi-circular land-mass; so the two basic continental structures of the earth, America and Eurasiafrica, have shapes whose characteristics complement and polarize each other.

The Americas can be reduced in shape to two southward pointing triangles—a symbol of "descent" of spirit and "masculine" activity—while Eurasiafrica is a sprawling "feminine" shape, with Europe as a highly differentiated miniature form of the great mother of races and religions, Asia. Some geologists have claimed that at one time the two continental masses were united, then broke away very slowly (over many tens of thousands of years)—the line of fission being now the Atlantic ocean. The western contour of Europe-Africa and the eastern shores of the Americas suggest broadly such a possibility—if the western bulge of Africa is made to fit into the depression of the Gulf of Mexico and the southern coast of the United States.

We are inclined to believe that the mythical Atlantis might have been, rather than a now sunken continent, this whole continental mass *before it broke in two;* in other words, the earth's continents in a condition of undivided unity—whereas now they constitute essentially two polarized masses. This would be significant—if it could be proven true—in that it would correlate with the mythological reference to an Atlantean humanity, at first pure and sinless, *then dividing into two camps* as a result of the abuse and misuse of sexual powers.

However this may be, the fact is that today man's global field of operation is typically bipolar. At the center of the two land-masses we find, in Eurasiafrica, the Mediterranean Sea and, in the Americas, the Gulf of Mexico. The former has been a focal point for Eurasiafrican culture; the latter has also been, and presumably will even more become, a focus for the Pan-American culture which, after a number of centuries (and perhaps even millennia) will gradually be established, we may well presume, as an entirely new human expression. Today "American" civilization, North and South, is fundamentally an outgrowth of European impulses and ideologies; and we believe it is merely a matrix into which new spiritual seeds have been and are being sown, which will take a very long time to mature, through many crises and probable obscurations. It seems likely that the first typical developments in truly American culture will come from the lands surrounding the Gulf of Mexico—Mexico itself being a probable focus, as it also was in the time of the Mayans, and perhaps long before.

All of which may be called "speculations," and must remain so until a new understanding of planetary cycles of geological and anthropological development is reached. What is factual and very concrete, however, is the relationship (historical, political and economic as well as geomorphic) between the Americas and Eurasiafrica—and particularly today, while human civilization is still predominantly "north-hemispheric," between North America (including what is unfortunately called Central America) and Eurasia. *Global harmony and international peace depend almost entirely upon the type of relationship and interchange established between these two complementary masses of land and of humanity;* and most of the problems we face today are due to the fact that, in 1919–20, the American Senate and the American people at large refused to assume the responsibility of such a permanent relationship, while supporting and helping a long-winded attempt to crush Soviet Russia and thwart her evident historical and geographical destiny in any integral and globally organized humanity.

We are not referring here to the communist ideology or the political methods of the Soviets. We are speaking of concrete and realistic facts of geography and history, and of nothing else.

Basically, it is these facts which determine, if not political systems and cultural ideals in themselves, at least their failure or success in establishing themselves on a particular soil. Likewise, the supremacy of England in world-politics was founded upon the fact that she, as an insular outpost of Europe to the west, was in position to use preeminently and to capitalize upon the gold and cotton of America, and to merchandise and transport across the seas much of America's wealth, especially after Spain's downfall. Now, however, that the Americas are becoming definitely established as one of the poles of a global economy, and that Soviet Russia has aroused to productive activity the central regions of Eurasia, the role of England is becoming unnecessary in terms of geotechnics—even if it can be still considered very important in the realm of spiritual values and world-civilization; provided the English people can focus their creative energy there.

The role of French culture can be similarly understood in terms of the fact that France links the Northern seas, the Atlantic and the Mediterranean, and is the westernmost outlet of Eurasia —more so than Spain, whose geotechnical significance resides in her position as the western point of contact between Africa and Europe, this fact having predestined her to be the seat of the great Mozarabic culture and thus a most important link between the Near East and France at a crucial time of European history (around 900 A.D.). France is, by her position, a natural outpost for the Russian hinterland of Europe, being the point of convergence of Northern, Central and Mediterranean Europe—and as well of North Africa; and inasmuch as a passively polarized Africa responds to an active and positive Europe, France's control over West North Africa—from Tunisia to the Congo, with Dakar as a center—was an inevitable geotechnical result. For the same reason, Russia is bound, sooner or later, to expand her influence over Egypt and the Arab world, England's hegemony there being a transitional factor which must lose its basic importance as a global polarization becomes fully established between the U.S.S.R. and the U.S.A. The connection between India and the whole of South Africa is also a matter of geotechnical inevitability, and Gandhi's life is a symbol of this fact.

LIFE IN A.D. 2500

by BURNHAM PUTNAM BECKWITH

In the year 2500 the entire world will be governed by a single, stable world government. The leaders and middle executives of this government will be professionally trained social scientists and public administrators responsible only to their superiors or to their own professional association. Elections will have been completely replaced by public-opinion polls, and public opinion will be molded by education, publications, and broadcasts planned by the government to promote sound scientific thinking about all current socio-political problems.

The world government will be highly centralized. It will have about a dozen major regional administrative subdivisions, of which North America will be one. Each major industry—transportation, retailing, local public utilities, etc.—will be organized as a single publicly owned worldwide monopoly. The production of nearly all tangible goods will be guided by marginal profits and losses, not by economic plans. Most services—education, research, health care, child care, etc.—will be provided free of charge. Their total cost will exceed half the world GNP, and their outputs (but not their methods of operation) will be controlled by economic plans. Military defense, which now costs 8 percent of world income, will cost less than 0.1 percent, because nearly all military forces will have been disbanded.

Free trade will be universal, and the entire world output of many small goods will be produced in a single plant or local complex of plants. Specialization among factories and farms will have vastly increased. As a result the average tangible good will move several times as far as in 1960 to reach its consumer, in spite of the elimination of all cross-hauling of like goods.

Reprinted from *The Next 500 Years* by Burnham P. Beckwith (Exposition, New York, 1967). By permission of Exposition Press.

Less than 5 percent of the world's labor force will be engaged in agriculture, and nearly all of them will live in towns which offer most of the advantages of city life. Over 80 percent of the world's population will live in planned garden cities having more than a hundred thousand, but fewer than a million, inhabitants.

The world of A.D. 2500 will have a single near-universal culture. The vast majority of people in each occupation will speak the same language, read the same books, attend similar schools, and listen to the same TV and radio broadcasts. They will eat similar food, wear similar clothes, and drink the same drinks in all countries with similar climates. They will live in similar housing built in communities and cities planned by the same international architectural organization. They will work in similar factories, offices, and farms and travel on similar ships, planes, and buses. Their incomes will all be determined in the same way, largely according to a single world wage policy. They will all use the same methods of birth control and eugenics and have the same average number of children per family. Remaining cultural differences will be largely interoccupational, not international.

The great majority of the world's adults will be non-religious and amoral (without religious or moral beliefs). No church will receive any government financial support or tax exemption. Less than 20 percent of the world population will attend religious ceremonies or pray at home. No religious oaths will be required of witnesses or government officials. No country will have a religious sect which includes more than 10 percent of its population. And no laws or court decisions will be based upon natural rights or unverifiable moral principles. All governments and courts will strive to increase measurable welfare rather than to promote religion, justice, or morality.

In the year 2500 the typical American family will consist of two working adults and two children. They will have a real family income (including free goods and compulsory saving) well over twenty times the United States 1960 average and over twice the world average in 2500. They will live in a spacious six- to ten-room apartment in a large tall building with fine views from most rooms. The apartment building will be part of a carefully planned satellite community, built as a single construction project, in a region with a superior climate. Each apartment will be equipped with numerous labor-saving and recreational conveniences—built-in color television sets, air-conditioning and air-sterilization systems, dust precipitators, dumbwaiters or delivery tubes, built-in vacuum cleaner pipes in each room, television telephones, etc. It will also contain a library of over ten thousand microfilmed books, musical tapes, and movie films, which will occupy less than twenty cubic feet.

Most retail buying of convenience goods—drugs, groceries, standardized clothing, etc.—will be done by dialing catalogue numbers on a home retail-order taker, and purchases will be delivered to most homes by an automatic package-delivery system. All shopping goods will be displayed and sold in a single department store in each satellite city. Every home will have a set of catalogues which describe and picture in color all retail goods. The variety of United States retail goods will be much smaller than in 1960, due to simplification and standardization.

Color television sets will be built into one or more rooms of all homes. They will receive throughout the day and evening over one hundred different channels, no two of which will offer the same program at the same time. All TV programs in each region will be planned and coordinated by a single office so as to assure an optimum variety of programs at every hour of the day and night. All new plays, concerts, operas, major sporting events, and other popular entertainments will be broadcast repeatedly by television. And a wide variety of fine educational lectures, laboratory experiments, travel pictures, and historical films will also be constantly on the air. There will be no advertising before or during any TV broadcast, except during those few which consist entirely of informational commercials.

Both adults will work full time (three to four hours a day for about 200 days a year) and together they will earn far more than $200,000 (1960 dollars) a year. Taxes will take over half of this gross income and will pay for free medical, dental, psychiatric, and hospital care; child care and education for all children under twenty; scientific research (which will consume over 10 percent of world income), TV and radio broadcasting, etc.

Both children will live in public boarding nurseries, kindergartens, or schools for sixteen to twenty-two hours a day. All school systems will offer at least five separate educational channels, with different teachers, texts, and courses for each channel. Students in the highest channel will learn to read by age four or five and will obtain the equivalent of a good 1960 university degree by age sixteen; those in the next highest, by age eighteen. Both graduates and drop-outs will be assured a wide choice of jobs on leaving school and will always be able to find suitable employment, usually near home. As a result of this and other reforms, crime rates will be 80 percent below the 1960 American level. Alcoholism, tobacco use, narcotic addiction, and gambling for high stakes will be equally reduced.

Adults will spend two to ten hours a week in formal education throughout their lives. Physical recreational facilities will be relatively twenty to fifty times as abundant as they now are in the United States, and most adults will devote at least an hour each day, from age twenty to age eighty, to participation in some active physical sport.

By 2500 eugenic and education reforms will have raised the average American I.Q. above 140 (measured by 1960 tests). Males with an I.Q. below 130 will be subject to compulsory sterilization, before they have any children. The great majority of children will be the product of artificial insemination with sperm from superior men. The average strength, health, beauty, grace, and I.Q. of the United States population in 2500 will be superior to those of the best 0.1 percent in 1960.

Personal incomes will differ little. The richest American family of four will have an income less than double that of the poorest similar family. Most families will have incomes less than 20 percent above or below the average for similar families. Hence my description of the life of the average American family will apply to nearly all such families in 2500.

Average personal income will be almost the same in every occupation. The chief remaining income differences will be due to measurable differences in individual output, not to differences in education. Bonuses will be paid for doing unpopular work and for working in unpleasant climates.

Daily life in American cities will be far less complicated in 2500 than it is today. No one will have to make any effort to find a suitable job. This will be as easy as finding a retail store today. Few families will own private cars or homes and have to worry about the purchase, insurance, maintenance, repair, and resale of such property. The trusts which own and rent housing and pleasure cars will handle all such chores. Personal shopping will be largely replaced by mail and phone buying. And when people plan retail purchases, they will have full and honest information on all goods. They will not need to worry about deceptive advertising, shoddy merchandise, overselling, overcharging, etc.

Insurance against all risks will be provided all citizens without any effort or request on their part. No separate insurance premiums will be charged. All monthly bills will be deducted from personal bank accounts and reported on monthly bank statements, so no individual will have to make any effort to pay his bills. Personal loans will be freely granted to all persons with legitimate needs, without any special credit investigation, and loan collection will be as simple and effortless as the collection of other bills.

All housing will be in communities carefully planned so that nearly all residents live near shopping centers and their places of employment. To reach these places, they will walk, or ride slow quiet buses, along streets free of private cars and fast noisy commercial vehicles. As a result of these and other reforms street-accident rates will be more than 90 percent below 1960 United States levels.

The comprehensive simplification and tranquilization of urban life predicted above will help to reduce mental illness. Eugenic advances and the provision of ever more free psychiatric care will have the same effect. By the year 2500, United States mental illness rates will be more than 90 percent below 1960 levels.

It may be objected that urban life with so few remaining pressures and problems will be dull. However, elimination of job-finding, housekeeping, child-tending, and property-management chores will free men and women for more important and more stimulating problems and activities—adult education, travel, child training, social activities, wholesome sports, hobbies, reading. Instead of worrying about trivial problems and serious but unnecessary risks, people will worry about significant problems and necessary risks.

The language spoken by Americans and by most other people

in 2500 will be a new artificial language designed by linguistic scientists to help men learn, think, speak, and write more rapidly and clearly. Its use will enable children to learn more easily and rapidly how to read, write, and reason correctly and will reduce by over 50 percent the size of old books translated into the new language.

Each major province of the world government will contain one or more libraries with copies of all extant manuscripts and publications. These libraries will provide free or very cheap microfilm copies of any such item to any person upon request, usually within twenty-four hours. All private studies and homes will have microfilm projectors.

Most Americans will be employed in performing professional services in nurseries, schools, universities, research laboratories, design institutes, experimental stations, museums, medical clinics, hospitals, theaters, government offices, etc. Less than 10 percent will be employed in producing tangible farm or factory products. Nearly all factories will be highly automated and will operate continuously 365 days a year.

When stated in this summary form, my predictions of American life in the year 2500 may seem utopian. But nearly all have been based upon trends in American thought and behavior already obvious and well established in 1960. I am convinced that they are realistic, that future history will roughly verify the great majority of them. The results will be utopian. But, then, a medieval European peasant would look upon a modern American town as a utopia.

I have been describing how the typical American family will live in A.D. 2500. The life of people in other countries will be less luxurious but otherwise little different. After five hundred more years of steady cultural homogenization, all the people of the world will live similar lives. Average family income in backward countries will still be much less than half that in America, but the difference in style of life between a family with $50,000 annual income and one with $200,000 is minor now and will be minor then. The big cultural differences today are between families with a $400 annual income (China and India) and those with $12,000 (the United States), or between the very rich and the very poor within any country.

ARTIFICIAL INTELLIGENCE AND GALACTIC CIVILIZATIONS

by I. S. SHKLOVSKII and CARL SAGAN *

W E SHALL consider several questions, some of a philosophical nature. The discussion will be speculative in intent.

▽ We have mentioned several times the possibility that the lifetime of a technical civilization is not indefinitely long. △ It has been suggested that the thesis of a finite lifetime of technical civilizations is a sermon on pessimistic materialism. However, I believe that the combination of the words "pessimistic" and "materialism" is a contradiction in terms. Materialism is an objective analysis of the material world outside of and independent of our own consciousnesses. It is an attempt at an objective coping with the complexities of the universe. It is meaningless to label any particular law of nature as either pessimistic or optimistic. Even an attempt to comprehend the language of nature is a reason for genuine optimism; but ignorance and apathy go hand in hand with pessimism and obscurantism.

The acceptance of our individual mortality is no cause for pessimism. Why should it be any more pessimistic to assume that even societies of intelligent beings do not live forever? Just as the death of one individual does not obstruct the progress of society, the death of civilization on one small planet does not imply the end of intelligent life in the universe. Just as the activity of each individual can introduce a definite, although small, contribution to society, a given planetary civilization may make a contribution to the general development of intelligent life in the

---

* Sagan, an American astronomer, amended an earlier text by the Russian astronomer Shklovskii, whom he had never met, so that Sagan's contributions are surrounded by the symbols ▽ △ and collective pronouns signify common sentiments.

Reprinted from *Intelligent Life in the Universe* by I. S. Shklovskii and Carl Sagan. By permission of Holden-Day, Inc. First published in 1966.

universe. And finally, just as the participation of the individual in society would be impossible without some sort of communication, the contribution of one planet to the development of intelligent life in the universe as a whole cannot take place without interstellar communications.

▽ Perhaps many young technical societies, like young men, are unmindful of the end of life because it seems so distant in time, and because there is so much yet to do. But when men are older, the thought of death is not so fearsome, and the unfinished tasks are somehow fewer. We live in a time when the thought of violent and accidental death of our civilization is a legitimate cause for anxiety. But perhaps an elder civilization, long past the problems of infantile societies, will willingly embrace the Elysian dreams of the lotus-eaters, and sink into an eternal sleep. △

In the *Dialectics of Nature,* Frederick Engels concluded, in the last century, that the lifetime for intelligent life on any particular planet is finite, and that this is an inevitable consequence of the development of the universe. He wrote:

It is an eternal cycle in which matter moves, a cycle that certainly only completes its orbit in periods of time for which our terrestrial year is no adequate measure, a cycle in which the time of highest development, the time of organic life and still more, that of the life of beings conscious of nature and of themselves, is just as narrowly restricted as the space in which life and self-consciousness came into operation; a cycle in which every finite mode of existence of matter, whether it be sun or nebular vapor, single animal or genus of animals, chemical combination or dissociation, is equally transient, and where nothing is eternal but eternally changing, eternally moving matter and the laws, according to which it moves and changes. But however often and however relentlessly this cycle is completed in time and space, however many millions of suns and earths may arise and pass away, however long it may take before the conditions of organic life arise, however innumerable the organic beings that have to arise and to pass away before animals with a brain capable of thought are developed from their midst, and for a short span of time find conditions suitable for life only to be exterminated later without mercy, we have the certainty that matter remains eternally the same in all its transformations, that none of its attributes can ever be lost, and therefore also that with the same iron necessity that it will extermi-

nate on the earth its higher creation the thinking mind, it must somewhere else and at another time again produce it.

If the lifetime of a technical civilization is limited only by
astronomical factors, then civilizations might continue for several
billions of years—a period which we might be tempted to describe
as "eternal"—and the probability would be high that intelligent
life is almost ubiquitous. But the lifetimes of technical civilizations may well be limited. The majority of investigators believe
that this timescale may be very short ▽ compared with the age
of the Galaxy. △ However, we believe that this question must be
reevaluated in the light of recent advances in cybernetics and in
molecular biology.

Elsewhere, we have repeatedly used the words "intelligent life,"
taking it for granted that a definition of this term was self-
evident. But what in fact do we mean by "intelligent life"? Is a
being intelligent if it possesses the ability to think? If so, what
do we mean by "thinking"?

Human thought has been considered, ▽ until very recently,
△ the only form of creative thinking known to mankind. Thus,
any definition of "thinking" and "intelligence" inevitably leads
to a description of the activities of men, or of the specific functions of the human brain.

But the Soviet physicist A. N. Kolmogorov has emphasized that
such a definition is unsatisfactory in the light of current knowledge for two reasons: As astronomical and space exploratory in-
vestigations progress, there is the distinct possibility that we shall
encounter on other planets entities which have all the essential
attributes of life and thought but which are nonetheless essentially different from terrestrial forms of life. Second, there is now
the possibility of the duplication of any complex material system,
▽ and in particular, the artificial construction of a thinking
machine. △ There is, accordingly, a great need for a functional
definition of the term "thought" which is not confined to our
preconceived notions about the physical nature of this process.

A systematic approach to such a functional view of life and
thought leads us to a startling conclusion which, in our opinion,
is of substantial significance to the problem of intelligent life in
the universe. Kolmogorov writes:

. . . A model of the operational processes and organization of a material system must be constructed of other material elements in a new system which possesses the same essential characteristics of organization as the system which is being modeled. Therefore, a sufficiently complete model of a living being, in all fairness, must be called a living being, and a model of a thinking being must be called a thinking being. . . . The following questions are of general interest:

Could machines reproduce themselves? And in the course of such reproduction, could progressive evolutionary changes occur which would lead to the production of new machines which are progressively more perfect ∇ [that is, better adapted to their environment] △ than their predecessors?

Could these machines experience emotions? Would they feel desires; would they be capable of solving original problems which their creators did not build into them?

Negative answers to questions of this nature are frequently the result of the following misconceptions: (a) a too-limited definition of the concept of "machine"; (b) an idealistic interpretation of the concept "thought," by which it is easy to prove that not only machines, but also human beings could not think.

. . . However, it is important to understand that within the framework of materialist ideology there are no well-founded arguments against a positive answer to our questions. Such a positive answer is in accord with contemporary views on the origin of life, and on the physical basis of consciousness. . . .

The possibility that complete living beings can be constructed out of discrete units capable of information processing and control does not contradict the principles of dialectic materialism.

Kolmogorov cautions against oversimplified specifications of the basic requirements for the synthesis of artificial intelligent beings. At present, we understand but a small portion of man's conscious activity. Only the mechanisms of conditioned reflex and of formal logic are understood to any degree. Much further work remains to be done on an objective definition in terms of information theory of the intricacies of the creative activity of man and other aspects of his highly developed nervous system.

Kolmogorov continues:

. . . A serious objective study of the higher neural activity of man is a necessary link in the development of such mathematical humanism. As science has developed, the illusions of mankind have been progressively eroded. At the stage of half-truths and half-knowledge, these so-called "destructive conclusions" often become arguments against science itself, in favor of irrationalism and idealism. Thus, Darwin's insights into the origins of species, and Pavlov's studies of the higher nervous system have been described as degrading the higher capacities of man, debasing his ability to create moral and aesthetic ideals. Analogously in our time, fear that man is no better than a "cold-hearted" machine has produced a psychological argument for vitalism and irrationalism.

Artificial mechanical beings—robots—are a favorite subject of science fiction writers. They are usually pictured as an assemblage of nuts and bolts with the external shape of a man, but powered by electron tubes. In his play *R.U.R.*, the remarkable Czechoslovakian writer Karel Čapek coined the word "robot" to describe an artificial, manlike being, made of organic molecules. ▽ In Western science fiction, the word "robot" has evolved into an inorganic, usually metallic artificial being, while the word "android" has been used for an organic simulacrum of a human being. Actually, Čapek's original conception of the robot and the contemporary idea of an android have both been anticipated by the golem, an artificial human being which, according to Jewish folk legend, was created by the Rabbi of Prague to perform labors on the Sabbath from which Jews were forbidden by Biblical law. △ It is probable that after mankind has knowledge and control of the synthetic pathways for the production of proteins, under the guidance of the nucleic acids, artificial living organisms will have a natural external appearance. But it is premature to predict just how such artificial beings will look. We reemphasize that contemporary terrestrial science and technology cannot yet synthesize even the simplest living beings.

▽ We can estimate that the number of possible combinations of the approximately 4×10^9 nucleotide pairs in human chromosomes was $4^{4 \times 10^9}$. This corresponds to approximately 10^{10} bits of information contained in the genetic code, and required for the construction of a human being. We can show that the information content of the human brain is probably even greater than the information content of the genetic material. There are something like 10^{10} neurons in the brain, each of which has probably more than 100 connections (dendrites) with other neurons. It is believed that the information content of the brain is at least in part stored through the intermediation of such neurons, although additional nonelectrical information repositories—for example, proteins, or RNA, or even the configuration of membranes of cells in the brain—may be more significant. The number of possible arrangements of 10^{10} neurons, each with 100 dendrites, is $10^{2 \times 10^{10}}$, corresponding to an information content of some 10^{13} bits. Even if the great majority of the neurons in the brain are redundant or inactive, the information content of the human brain is far in excess of the information content of the genetic material. This is another way of saying that we are not born with all we know, and that the great bulk of our knowledge is acquired during our lifetimes.

▽ The characteristic mass of a human brain is $\sim$1300 grams. We may consider a typical neuron to be cylindrical in shape, with a radius of a few microns, and a length of perhaps 1 mm. The volume of a typical neuron is therefore about $\pi(3 \times 10^{-4} \text{ cm})^2(10^{-1} \text{ cm}) \simeq 3 \times 10^{-8} \text{ cm}^3$. Since neurons, like other biological material, have a density of about 1 gm cm^{-3}, each neuron has a mass of about 3×10^{-8} gm. 10^{10} neurons have, therefore, a mass of about 300 gm, and we see that a major fraction of the total mass of the brain is composed of neurons.

▽ The transistors which, in modern computing machines, are the analogues of the neurons in our brains, have masses considerably larger than 3×10^{-8} gm. Therefore, a computing machine with the same number of connecting units as the human brain would have to be much more massive. For example, if each transistor had a mass of $\frac{1}{100}$ of a gram, the total mass of an equivalent computing machine would be 10^8 grams, or 100 tons. We see that the human brain is marvelously microminiaturized.

▽ Many scientists believe that the complexities of human thinking are simply the consequence of the complexities of the interactions among 10^{10} units. Among organisms on Earth, there is a general, although by no means complete, correspondence between brain mass and intelligence; an even more striking correlation exists between intelligence and the ratio of brain mass to total body mass. It is in this context that the large mass of the dolphin brain—comparable to the mass of the human brain—is notable. If the information content of intelligent beings on other planets is stored in units of mass comparable to our neurons, then it is clear that they must be approximately as massive as we, or even larger. There is no general tendency for neurons to be of smaller mass in what we like to think of as the more advanced species on the planet Earth.

▽ But we can imagine other possibilities. Suppose, for example, that information is coded not on the level of neurons, but on the molecular level, and that provisions are made for the long-term stability of these information-carrying molecules. In the genetic material, such molecular information stores are of course used, and we have already mentioned that there is some evidence that molecules such as RNA are involved as a molecular basis of memory in animals and perhaps in human beings. We can imagine a crystal lattice, in which the information is stored by atoms in terms of the position they occupy within the lattice. If there are 10 possible atoms for each position, we require about 2×10^{10} total atoms to reproduce the information content of the human brain. A cube containing 2×10^{10} atoms has about $(2 \times 10^{10})^{1/3} = 5000$ atoms on a side. The atoms in a crystal are usually a few Å apart. Therefore, such a cubical crystal could be 10^{-4} cm, or about 1 micron on a side. Some examples of coding miniaturization in contemporary technology—not yet up to the efficiency of our cube—have been produced.

▽ This example of the cube, due to Philip M. Morrison, is probably the extreme in the compression of information. It would be very difficult to extract information contained within the crystal without disrupting the information contained in the exterior atoms of the crystal. But such examples do illustrate that organisms can conceivably be considerably smaller than we and yet contain a vastly greater quantity of information. If our intelligence is characterized by an information storage capability of, say, 10^{13} bits, what will we have to say to a member of an advanced civilization with a storage capability of 10^{20} bits?

▽ These considerations suggest not only that beings may exist elsewhere in the universe with intelligence substantially beyond our own, but also that we may be able to construct such a being ourselves. △ Of course, many difficulties would have to be overcome before an artificial intelligent being could be constructed. The greatest difficulty is not the storage of information, but the development of the very complex program that represents the actual operation of the brain and associated nervous system, which in turn represents thought. It is possible in principle to build a complex machine which would solve problems through the use of smaller, ancillary machines, into which simpler problems could be introduced. However, such cascaded machines appear to be cumbersome and slow. At present, it is not clear just how these difficulties will be overcome.

▽ Great progress has already been made in the construction of machines sufficiently complex to learn by experience and to show signs of creative thinking. Computing machines today can perform in a few seconds mathematical problems which previously would have taken a team of mathematicians decades. There is every reason to believe that artificial intelligence will be increasingly pervasive in the future development of our civilization. △ Cybernetics, molecular biology, and neurophysiology together will some day very likely be able to create artificial intelligent beings which hardly differ from men, except for being significantly more advanced. Such beings would be capable of self-improvement, and probably would be much longer-lived than conventional human beings.

One proposed cause for the aging process of organisms is the gradual accumulation of imperfections in the genetic code over the lifetime of the individual. ▽ As time progresses, more and more nonsense information is transmitted to the cytoplasm, and the proper functioning of the cell is impaired. But the information repositories and coding procedures of artificial organisms could be much more durable and stable than those of contemporary organisms. △

The division of intelligent life into two categories—natural and artificial—may eventually prove to be meaningless. We may anticipate the synthesis of body parts. For example, we all know that some artificial body parts, such as teeth, are widely used today. ▽ Partial substitutes for the lenses of our eyes have been common for some centuries, and today we are witnessing the very rapid development of artificial hearts, lungs, kidneys, and other organs. △ The intelligent beings of the future may be made largely of artificial organs. ▽ Is it therefore out of the question that the brains of our descendants may also be artificial, so that vast quantities of information may be made accessible without a tortuous learning process? Perhaps in the future we shall be able to plug in modular units containing the entire body of knowledge of specialized areas, which we may then unplug and return to our library when no longer of immediate use. △ In principle, we can anticipate the construction of highly organized, intelligent, self-improving, and non-anthropomorphic forms of life.

We have mentioned the possibility that the artificial intelligent beings of the future may be very long-lived. ▽ Their civilizations might be vastly longer-lived than civilizations like our own. △ Such long lifetimes could be very advantageous for interstellar contact among advanced communities. The sluggishness of two-way radio communication over interstellar distances tends to make such contact unsatisfactory for beings with lifetimes measured in decades. But for very long-lived beings, such communication would be much more interesting. Further, such beings would be able to undertake interstellar flights over vast distances at subrelativistic velocities ▽ without the use of metabolic inhibitors. △ Perhaps highly specialized beings could be constructed specifically for such flights of long duration. These beings would be capable of enduring the hardships of the flight, and of implementing the tasks awaiting them at the end of the journey. It would be impossible to draw a clear distinction between such specialized automatic machines, artificial intelligent living beings ▽ and natural advanced organisms of an exotic type. △

It is possible for intelligent life in the universe to make fundamental qualitative transformations of itself. ▽ Major improvements in the lifetimes of advanced technical civilizations and of the organisms which compose them, and qualitatively different advances in their intelligence, make the prospect of successful interstellar contact much larger. △

▽ Let us now consider the possibilities more in consonance with the discussion of the beginning of this chapter. Perhaps technical civilizations are nowhere able to construct long-lived artificial beings of vast intelligence; or perhaps, while they are capable, the lifetimes of the initial technical civilizations are so short that a society of intelligent artificial beings is never able to develop. △ Under these circumstances, could an advanced civilization create a large artificial satellite containing electronic equipment capable of transacting interstellar radio communications for periods of millions of years or longer? Such a satellite, launched into circular orbit high above the planet of origin, could have a life span of hundreds of millions of years. It is possible that we have an example of such a moon in our own solar system; and in fact, when I first developed the hypothesis that the moons of Mars may be of artificial origin, I had such a function in mind. The energy source for the equipment aboard the satellite could be either the radiation flux of the local sun or controlled thermonuclear fusion. The radio transmitters aboard the satellite would transmit modulated signals according to a pre-programmed plan; answers to these signals could be recorded, ∇ and appropriate responses automatically devised, according to program. △ In this way, two-way automatic radio contact among Galactic civilizations could be established.

There are, of course, formidable technical problems which must be solved before such a satellite would be feasible. The automatic equipment must function stably and be protected against meteors over immense periods of time.

There are three primary advantages for interstellar contact that an artificial satellite has over a station on a planetary surface. ∇ First, the satellite is capable of transmission at frequencies which are absorbed by the planetary atmosphere or ionosphere. △ Second, the lifetime of the satellite could be much longer than the lifetime of the civilization which constructed it. Such a satellite might orbit its planet for millions of years after the local civilization had perished. Finally, in the epoch of decay and destruction of the parent civilization, very likely the safest place for such a station would be aboard a satellite. Here, the instruments would be protected not only from wars, but also from the destructive action of wind and water, and from geological changes on the surface of the planet. A large instrumented artificial satellite might be able to transmit the treasures of science and the heritage of culture of a dead civilization into the cosmos for hundreds of millions of years. We draw upon the knowledge and insights of men long dead through the books which they once wrote. Is it not possible that civilizations throughout the universe also draw upon the knowledge and insights of civilizations long vanished? If some technical societies have devised methods for transmitting information to space for extremely long periods of time, longer than their own life spans, the probability of contact among Galactic civilizations is immeasurably enhanced.

II

Technologies

It is worth restating at every opportunity that the negatives of our present situation are not inherent in the technological revolutions as such, but in the conceptual approaches and social attitudes that determine how new technical means will be employed. *We* are the active instruments that create a technological passivity.

—JOHN McHALE,
The Future of the Future (1969)

SOCIETY OF THE SCIENTIFIC BREAKTHROUGH

by THEODORE J. GORDON

ONE OF THE key questions in a recent RAND study dealt with scientific breakthroughs expected in the next fifty years. Some ideas I have discussed elsewhere, for example, chemical control of heredity, which was the item most often predicted independently by the experts, and wide use of personality-control drugs. The ideas suggested were rich and varied and I have made use of some of them in defining this Society of the Scientific Breakthrough.

In this society, no one will be hungry. Computers will have solved the problem of the distribution of goods, what to plant, and when and where to plant it. There will be a central hunger-control agency which will assimilate all of the data needed to predict worldwide food requirements, production, and availability, so that appropriate distribution can be made to all the world's people. This could mean state-operated "missions" throughout the world, guaranteeing the right to eat.

What will they eat? The winner of the race between population and food supply is not clear. However, it has been predicted that agricultural yields can increase by a factor of ten, and ocean farming techniques will augment our food supply even further.

We already have a good start at learning how to increase crop yields. In addition to simply increasing the amount of arable land through irrigation, crop yield per acre will be increased drastically through the use of chemical insecticides and fertilizers, eugenic selection of stock and plants, and new mechanical farming techniques. In a new agricultural process, for example, black polyethylene strips, twenty inches wide, are laid over soil prepared for planting. The seedlings are inserted into holes in the plastic. The effect of the strip is to absorb heat and trap moisture in the soil while discouraging the growth of nearby weeds. This process has been found to double tomato crops and is being used widely on cotton acreage, now that new farm machinery has made the laying of the strips practical over large fields.

Specially processed or manufactured foods will become increasingly important. A food named Incaparina is being manufactured and sold in Central and South America. Its major protein-bearing ingredient is the residue of seed oil extraction processes. A grain such as corn or wheat, vitamin A, and yeast are mixed with a cottonseed, soybean, or sunflower seed-meal to produce a food which is cheap and nutritious. Its ingredients can be grown almost anywhere in the world.

Completely synthetic food is also a possibility. Scientists are learning how to grow specific proteins in the laboratory. Synthetic amino acids are being used in cattle feed in the United States today. Synthetic vitamins are already routine and unexciting. Housewives buy monosodium glutamate, by name, over the grocery counter. Someday, when a man says, "This doesn't taste like my mother's cooking," he may be remembering a silver-haired lady, carefully blending an array of handsomely packaged and well-advertised chemicals, in the twenty-first century equivalent of our kitchen.

Ocean farming will be so important that the ocean bottom may be colonized and annexed as territorial property by the nations of the world. That the oceans can become a more important source of food is clear. Aside from breeding and herding meat-fish, food can be taken from the oceans in the form of plankton and sea-grown vegetables. Plankton, microscopic plants and animals, could be used directly as food, or cultivated as fodder for the meat-fish herds. Those who have tasted it say it is quite palatable, and tastes variously like shrimp, lobster, or vegetables. At the present time, the density of plankton is too low to make its harvesting profitable; future large-scale use of the material would depend on the development of efficient breeding techniques. The cowboy of the future may have a purse-seiner for his mount and plankton for his "dogie."

Seaweed is consumed as food today. While in some countries

it is used in salads or as a vegetable, probably its most important use as a food is in the form of agar-agar. This is a powerful gelatin-like substance which forms the basis of Japanese bean cake jelly. One trouble in using seaweed as a staple food is that it is fairly indigestible to humans. Seaweed seasoning on the table of tomorrow may contain an enzyme which will help our bodies extract more food value from these plants.

Modification of weather and climate will become possible. The exact scale of this modification is not certain. Production of rain from moisture-laden clouds is relatively simple; much more complex is the avoidance of weather extremes such as flood and drought. Perhaps, through the use of solar reflecting mirrors, even the night itself will not fall over large cities.

Accurate prediction of weather is almost a certainty. The Tiros weather satellite program is already moving meteorology in the direction of becoming an exact science. Dr. S. Fred Singer, Director of the National Weather Satellite Center of the U.S. Weather Bureau, feels that within a decade, a scientific theory of the long-range causes for weather variations will be formulated. If anyone believes that accurate prediction of weather is trivial, President Lyndon Johnson estimated the following yearly economic benefits in the United States alone would result from making predictions accurate as little as five days in advance: $2.5 billion in agriculture, $45 million in the lumber industry, $100 million in surface transportation, $75 million in retail marketing, and $3 billion in water-resources management. He pointed out that ". . . continued scientific research aimed at understanding the underlying processes that produce weather and determine climate may lead us in the next decade to control weather and modify climate."

Attempts at cloud seeding to produce rain, and fog dispersal through the use of heat generators or cold-water injection, have not been spectacularly successful so far. But the systems to come will be far more effective. They may involve modification of the solar transmission characteristics of the atmosphere, or changing the rate of natural heat absorption or emission of certain portions of the earth. When modifications are attempted on this scale, they must not be experiments; their outcome must be certain, because they may be irreversible. If the color of the polar ice cap were to be changed by coating it with a spray which permitted it to absorb more heat, not only would the ecological balance of the Arctic life cycle be seriously upset, but the waters released into the oceans of the world might flood the continental coastlines. Winter might be moderated, but in the process the world might lose all of its coastal cities.

On August 15, 1963, the Atomic Energy Commission announced that a Yale-Brookhaven team of scientists had found the last particle of anti-matter, the anti-xi-zero. With this discovery, it can be postulated with some certainty that a family of matter can be constructed with each portion of its atomic makeup bearing properties exactly opposite to matter as we know it. In our world, an electron has certain mass, electrical charge and magnetic moment. In the world of anti-matter, the electron's mass is the same, but its charge is of opposite polarity and its magnetic moment is in the opposite direction. When a "this world" electron comes in contact with an anti-electron, both are annihilated, and only gamma radiation is produced. In an anti-matter world, anti-electrons would circle anti-nucleuses, composed of anti-neutrons and anti-protons. Some scientists have theorized that some stars, and perhaps some galaxies, are made of anti-matter. It is tempting to guess that matter and anti-matter are distributed in equal amounts thoroughout space. It is equally tempting to guess whether the original creation of matter was based on a process which was the inverse of annihilation. Such a process is fairly common in the case of electrons, at least. A high-energy photon, passing near a nucleus, occasionally disappears, and in its place are created two electrons, one common and the other an anti-electron.

There would be great difficulty involved in constructing atoms of anti-matter on earth. Nothing could contain them; they would have to be constructed in some sort of absolute vacuum insulator. What would we do with these atoms after they were built? One obvious answer is use in warfare: an anti-matter bomb which would return the target to its annihilated state of energy. Another is to provide the earth with an ultimate incinerator, a device which would be a bottomless dumping ground for all of our waste products, with useful energy as a by-product of the disposal. A more immediate objective would simply be to learn more about matter itself. One thing is clear; experimentation with anti-matter will intensify.

The search will also continue for simplification of gravitational theory. Since the time of Newton, experimenters have been searching for some anomaly in the universality of gravitation. There appears to be no way to shield against this force, no way to switch it off as in electrostatic or magnetic force fields. Albert Einstein showed mathematically that gravitational forces are the result of inertial forces acting on bodies moving in curved space. A non-rigorous analogy can be made to the force felt by a mass in an accelerating vehicle. As the acceleration increases, the mass is pushed harder in the direction opposite to the acceleration. The force is also increased if the mass is increased. Einstein's equivalence principle extends this idea to space-time. By virtue of the curvature of space, all bodies in space are accelerating; gravitation is the inertial force resisting this acceleration.

If gravitation is then a result simply of existing in our continuum, how can there be anti-gravity? There would appear to be three answers: reduce the gravitational mass to zero; reduce the acceleration acting on the mass to zero; or, develop a force equal and opposite to the gravitational force. We are, of course, well acquainted with this latter approach. Satellites, in orbit around the earth, experience weightlessness. Here, the gravitational force between the satellite and the earth is exactly overcome by the centrifugal force resulting from its motion around the earth. Note that this is not anti-gravity in the sense of eliminating or modifying gravity, but rather a straightforward Newtonian balancing of forces. The chemical energy of rocket propellants also produces a force which counteracts gravity. In this sense anti-gravity machines may be possible. The breakthrough required is the development of an efficient device which will produce force at least equal to its own earth weight over long periods of time. This type of propulsive device is certainly feasible. On the other hand, gravitational shields most certainly require the discovery of some physical principle not known today. Everything behind such a shield would be weightless. Only infinitesimal forces would be required to produce motion. We could roam over our world and the solar system free, and at our leisure. Is this the philosopher's stone of the twenty-first century?

Sunday supplements have long predicted the video-telephone. Two new inventions, the laser and fiberoptics, may make it possible. In July, 1960, Dr. T. H. Maiman of Hughes Aircraft Company fired the world's first laser. This is a device which produces light in an entirely new way, by exciting the electrons of certain atoms to higher-than-normal energy states, and then gathering the light that is emitted when they return to their normal energy level. The peculiar aspect of this light is that it is all of a single color; that is, all energy is emitted at precisely the same frequency. Non-laser light is emitted over a broad band, like a radio transmitter which is not tuned to any frequency, but emits its signals over the entire spectrum. The advantage of the single-frequency laser light is that it can be modulated, tuned, and amplified like a radio signal, and it can be focused with precision by lenses or mirrors. Broad-band light can be focused only approximately, since each color is refracted a different amount. This ability to focus permits delicately controllable concentrations of large amounts of energy at pinpoint spots for use in such diverse fields as welding and brain surgery. The ability to modulate, tune, and amplify light also promises to produce a means of conveying large amounts of information very simply. For example, it has been estimated that a single laser beam could transmit more information than 25,000 television stations all broadcasting simultaneously.

A widely separated field, fiberoptics, may be used in combination with laser light generation. The fibers used in fiberoptics are very fine threads of glass. Light which enters one end of the fiber emerges from the other end with only slightly diminished intensity, over lengths of many feet. These fibers are assembled into bundles of perhaps half a million elements. As long as the fibers are arranged the same way at both ends, any image focused on one end will appear at the other end. These bundles are being used for remote inspection tools, for example, to inspect the lining of the stomach. But this application may be only a beginning.

Picture an underground distribution system in which fiber bundles run from a central point along trunk lines to the users. Along the way, light amplifiers boost the signal to make up for losses in the fibers. One thin fiber enters the home of every sub-scriber, every newspaper, every office, the world over. This thin fiber entering the home could simultaneously carry telephone, facsimile, and video from the laser-central, where the program material would be projected on the fiber ends. It is the laser-fiberoptics combination which could give us practical video-tele-phones, facsimile-transmitted newspapers, and remote libraries which send books over the line to be printed in the home.

New materials of construction will have a major impact on the society of the scientific breakthrough. Theoretically, iron, un-alloyed, can be thirty times stronger than today's structural steel. Our steel is not stronger because of defects in its crystalline structure which form when the molten alloy is cooled. Small samples of the pure, strong stuff which exhibit maximum theoreti-cal strength have been grown in laboratories in the form of thin whiskers. Aluminum theoretically can possess a strength ten times greater than today's steel, and the metal iridium, a strength one hundred times greater. If these ultra-strong materials can be developed, the effect on architecture will be tremendous. Buildings will be lighter, more open. Unsupported spans will curve grace-fully from solid anchors. Cantilevers will be commonplace. Auto-mobiles, if they still exist, will weigh a tenth as much. Such materials could provide the key to the emergence of the ground effect machine, the aerodynamic skimmer which can float on a cushion of air over grass freeways. Aircraft, submarines, ships, and satellites—the design of all of these will be changed by the introduction of stronger metals.

In this society, you may be able to purchase a ticket to travel forward in time. In searching for clues to the aging process, re-searchers have found that biologic age and chronological age do not necessarily coincide during the period of an animal's hiberna-tion. Metabolism slows down to perhaps ten percent of the waking state; heart beat is barely detectable; body temperature can drop by 50° F. Animals can remain in hibernation for four months; living, but not eating; living, but at a slower rate.

It is possible that drugs or freezing could trick the human metabolism into this state, and slow the aging process so that bodies will age only one year for every ten that pass. If this proves to be the case, a person could be "put on ice" for a hundred years. This would be a one-way trip, though, so one would have to gamble on the continued existence of the world during the period of time travel.

THE FUTURE OF AUTOMATION

by HASAN OZBEKHAN

Because "automation" is one of the central events of our time, there have been many speculations in the past decade about what it was going to be, and do, to society or to the individual in another ten or twenty years. Some of these speculations are motivated by fear, others by curiosity. Finally, there are some which attempt to set the foundations of policy. The outcomes they depict vary in their details, depending on the initial motive. All seem to agree, however, that automation is an all-pervasive social phenomenon and that its impact on the post-1975 world will be considerable.

Only a few of these forecasts go so far as to outline the forces which are at work in the field of automation today and to see whether the conclusions that are being suggested are in fact justified by these forces. My aim in this article is to discuss briefly the current meaning of automation, to derive from that meaning some ideas with regard to emerging areas of application and to major expectations and to review these areas in the light of current technological evolution. Finally, I shall examine the impacts which automation will make on society in the more distant future.

Reprinted from *Science Journal*, October 1967, copyright © 1967 by Hasan Ozbekhan. By permission of the author.

The distinguishing feature of automation is that human control is exercised upon machines which control other machines. In the early stages this control was described as corresponding to four types of operation traditional to manufacturing: materials handling, routine judgments in connection with machine adjustments, machine setting, and simple data processing.

For these operations to be done by machine they had to be seen as a continuum or process, an integrated set, having a preestablished internal order or logic and possessing self-regulatory, or feedback, mechanisms. In the light of these requirements, automation emerged as a "system" that can be described with reference to the concept of process control. Today, process control is developing along two lines—"process mechanization" and "situation interpretation"—both of which, after the late 1940's, could be integrated by means of the modern general-purpose digital computer with internally stored programs. Process mechanization and situation interpretation are therefore the two general functions that define the directions and outcomes towards which we are now tending. The first of these is the older and better-known function but situation interpretation does require a brief explanation. It concerns the interface between environment and computer. It is across this interface that interpretation must occur if the computer is to respond properly to its external environment.

Simple programs can obviously interpret only a very incomplete picture of the total environment and one which can be transcribed only in a form of binary code—the only information which computer hardware is so far capable of assimilating directly. But a more complete picture can be interpreted by a more sophisticated program. In effect, this constitutes a new boundary, extended beyond the first. In each case, the boundary is embodied in the language in which the program is written. Situation interpretation, then, is the process of crossing boundaries to provide information to the computer which approaches more and more closely its required internal representation scheme. This can be done with the help of a number of programs in cascade, each of which provides a simpler interface as it nears the stage at which information is actually interpreted by hardware.

By cascading programs we can therefore develop an ability to interpret across more and more complex boundaries. The notion of higher-level languages derives from this fact. Interpretation across more complex boundaries requires more raw processer speed to support more complexity in the interpreting programs. More complexity simply means more work. Higher speed thus allows the accomplishment of complex actions in reasonable times. Conceptually, it is irrelevant whether a given boundary is reached by cascading interpreters or by building a single extremely complicated program the whole of which is directly interpretable by hardware. Here, the relevant point is that extremely complex interpretative behavior can be developed and supported in the future.

Just as the machine interprets a program and this program may interpret another, so man interprets his situation where his "situation" is his perception of his environment. As the computer interpretation interface is extended, the boundary becomes more complex; it is understood less explicitly and more implicitly. The "language" of situation representation becomes less well comprehended and the "situation" tends towards the complexity of man's universe.

The aim in systems such as I have described is to increase the speed of the interpretation both through hardware development— by making faster switching circuits—and by software development, so that a more effective exploitation of the hardware can be obtained. Such developments are necessary to deal with the wider realms of complexity. Thus the basic function of process control is evolving in terms of two general functions, both of which are being driven by the twin forces of higher speed and lower cost.

The combined thrust of this evolution has led to the emergence of a number of new functions which, in turn, define the major areas of expected applications. The function and projected-applications map printed here is an attempt to depict, in as complete a way as is possible, the following points: the functional development which underlies automation at the present time; the main areas of application that are evolving; the main expected outcomes; and the time horizon generally believed to govern the maturation of these outcomes. The last column on the map is a set of comments which represents evaluations of the corresponding forecasts.

The main operational forces that underlie this projective outline are economic, technological and social in varying proportions. I shall describe these forces in terms of six propositions that encompass developments taking place in both the hardware and the software fields. These are the developments in which the forecasts that can be validated are grounded.

1. *By 1975 computer hardware will become at least one and probably two or more orders of magnitude cheaper than current systems, while computer software will decline in cost at a far slower rate.*

This is the fundamental economic expectation. Recent studies of computer characteristics predict a decline in the cost per bit of core storage to 2.5 percent of the current cost and a decline in the cost per bit of tape storage of three to five orders of magnitude. Meanwhile, software costs, depending so heavily upon the production rate of human programmers, can decline only as fast as new tools (mainly higher-order languages) are developed. Because of this trend the 1975 hardware/software cost breakdown of systems, now about 50/50, will be in the order of 30/70. (It was 70/30 ten years ago.)

2. *Computer hardware will become much more powerful than today's in every sense—absolutely, relative to size, relative to cost, and relative to the ability of system designers to use their capabilities.*

Because there is no single measure of hardware power, at least four aspects must be examined. First, a radical decrease in component size is expected from new developments in thin film and molecular circuitry by 1975, making it convenient to install fairly powerful equipment in the normal business office. Secondly, add times are expected to decrease at least three orders of magnitude; memory cycle times to about 6 percent of the current speed; and circuit speed increased to nearly electronic rates. Thirdly, substantial improvements are expected in mass storage: magnetic tapes with packing densities to fifteen thousand bits per inch; large disc capacities with read/write capability on several discs

Basic
Function

Process
Control

General   Speed   General
Function   Function

Process   Cost   Situation   Main Areas
Mechanization   Interpretation   of
                                      Application

DYNAMIC ADAPTABILITY
   Self-Adapting Memory Organization
     Data Arrangement   PLANNING (I)
     Data Base Development   MANUFACTURING (I)
   Taxonomy Generation & Development   LEARNING/TEACHING (I)
   Structure Development   EXCHANGE (I)
     Classification   NEGOTIATION
     Factor Identification
     Relationship Identification

TRANSLATION ACROSS BOUNDARIES
   Interrelating
     Interfacing   INFORMATION PROCESSING
     Internetting   MANUFACTURING (II)
   Communication   LEARNING/TEACHING (II)
     Remote Access   EXCHANGE (II)
     Real-Time Operations   TRAFFIC—Communications (I)
     Remote Control   TRAFFIC—Transportation (I)
     Switching   PLANNING (II)
   Interpretation

ALLOCATION
   Facility Sharing
     Simultaneous Use
       Time Sharing   RESOURCE MANAGEMENT (I)
     Interactive Use   TRAFFIC—Transportation (II)
     Real-time Operations   TRAFFIC—Communications (II)
     Scheduling
       (Time organized planning)
   Flow Control

SELECTION
   Search
     Hill Climbing
     Mini-Max
   Retrieval
     Relevancy Measurement   RESOURCE MANAGEMENT (II)
     Context Sensing   LIBRARY
     Abstracting   LEARNING/TEACHING (III)
     Extracting   EXCHANGE (III)
   Decision Making
     Machine Decisions
       Routines
     Value Decisions
       Heuristic Choice

SIMULATION
   Analytical Modeling
   Artificial Reality Production   PLANNING (III)
     System Evaluation   TRAFFIC—Transportation (III)
     System Improvement   TRAFFIC—Communications (III)
       System Performance Prediction

Main Expected Outcomes	Time-Horizon Dates of Fruition of Outcomes	Probable Obstacles
PLANNING		
Long-range problem solving in all areas of application (I)	1980–2000	
Aids for sensing and understanding environments (II)	1975–1980	Problems of representation of meaning in mechanically interpretable forms
Feasibility testing of long-range goals (III)		
MANUFACTURING		
Replacement of sensory control of worker by more sensitive electro-mechanical devices (I)	1966–	
Self-adaptive inventory, production, and organization control (I)	1975–1980	
Multi- or general-purpose, regional (then global) interlinked tools (II)	Unlikely	Transportation costs high unit process costs
Robots—for production and services (I)	1970–1985	declining
EXCHANGE		
General transaction facilitation and handling using new unit values (I)	1990–2000	
Credit systems, invoice paying, purchasing, international business transactions, particularly at commercial level (II)	1975–1980	
Automated marketing through home terminals and touch-tone telephone systems (III)	1975–1980	Cost of delivery of purchases Communication costs vs. increased leisure
NEGOTIATION		
Bargaining: automation of the search for meanings and of the determination of real issues in dispute	1975–1985	Mechanical extraction of meaning from unstructured information
Real issue identification and conflict identification	1975–1985	
INFORMATION PROCESSING		
All areas of application		
Computer/information "utility"—interlinked Data Banks	1980–1995	Computer "utility" unlikely as processor
Automation of office and institutional data handling	1970–1975	costs declining much faster than
Automated diagnostics (medical, social, mechanical, etc.)	1980–1990	communication costs; also social problems of privacy
LEARNING/TEACHING		
Regional and/or global educational centers accessible through home terminals (II)	1985–	Global or large regional centers unlikely because
Substantive curriculum development (III)	1975–1980	of high communication costs vs. low processor
Generalized computer assisted instruction (I & III)	1970–1975	costs
Man-computer symbiosis (I, II & III)	1985–	
Knowledge development (I)	1985–	Problems of representation
TRAFFIC-COMMUNICATIONS		
Transmission of all communications (I)	Ongoing	
High-speed message switching & handling utility (II)	1990–	Installation of all-digital communication network
Off-line experimentation & testing of networks (III)	1960–1975	
RESOURCE MANAGEMENT		
Complex scheduling systems (I)	1970–1980	
Optimal benefit resource application decisions (II)	1980–2000	
TRAFFIC-TRANSPORTATION		
Mass rapid transit (I)	1975–1985	High speed physical object switching
Air traffic control (II)	1970–1980	
Integrated traffic system problem solving development (III)	1975–1980	
LIBRARY		
Home access and retrieval (reproducing copy)	1985–	Communication costs vs. printing costs
Text abstraction and reproduction	1975–1980	
Question answering	1975–1980	Mechanical interpretation of questions to extract meaning
Automatic bibliography generation	1970–1975	

simultaneously; cheap magnetic cards capable of millions of bits of storage; and photographic devices with densities of more than a million bits per square inch. These are expected to make storage capacities of 1000 million bits economically attractive by 1975. The availability of very large memories and low-cost, high-speed circuitry will permit the transfer of data between external and internal storage in large blocks at high speeds. Finally, the availability of cheap circuitry should permit hardware producers to introduce far greater parallelism in data processers and systems, and to include considerable circuit and component redundancy so that the overall system reliability will be greatly enhanced. The effect of increased hardware power depends, of course, on the application. For example, simulation and modeling experiments will take far less time to run and will include many more variables and complexities than today. Great hardware power at lower cost also means that it will be economical for less sophisticated users to interact directly with the computer.

3. *Computer design will achieve far more diversity and modularity in systems, permitting much greater flexibility in assembling them.*

One of the major effects of the first two trends is that hardware producers will have far greater freedom in designing the configurations of their computers. This will profoundly affect software design. Hardware producers will also be able to offer a wide selection of memory sizes and speeds at a wide range of costs. Multiprocesser systems, consisting of a number of individual computers each capable of performing on an independent program but linked together in a way that permits cooperative operation, are now being worked on. They show promise in applications which require occasional facilities greater than any single module, or when the usual mode of operation requires individual independent storage. Yet, while increasing portions of the housekeeping requirements of multi-processing systems will be built into the hardware, the software problems are likely to continue to provide serious difficulties over the next five years at least.

4. *More powerful, flexible and inexpensive man-machine interface hardware and software will be available by 1975.*

Partly as a result of the above trends and partly as a result of what might be called an escalation of expectations from computers, many new classes of users, mostly non-programmers, will want to interact with computers "on-line." This will be made possible by optical character readers and point-of-origin devices; faster and more versatile print readers, able to accept a wide variety of type faces and to operate reliably at speeds of ten thousand characters per second; cheap and flexible keyboard devices and display terminals, using light guns and graphic display inputs where needed; high speed printers using cathode ray tubes to produce hard copy economically at three thousand lines per minute or more; document reproducing systems tied to computers so that multiple copy outputs can be prepared as needed; display devices with better resolution, greater light output, smaller equipment requirements and much greater flexibility.

Similarly, software development tends to respond to the demand for increased man-machine interaction with more flexible and powerful higher-order languages and a great variety of special-purpose languages. These will make it possible for non-programmers to interact with different modules of the computer and even different computers in languages with which the user feels most comfortable.

5. *Time sharing technology will evolve into the linking of several or many time shared (and non-time shared) computers in networks tied together by common-carrier communication channels.*

Today, the formation of computer networks is technically feasible but is being held up by economic and administrative considerations. However, with hardware costs decreasing and the demand for very large data bases that can be queried from remote points growing, it appears reasonable to surmise that the so-called "information utility" will be a reality by 1975.

6. *Processer costs will decrease drastically relative to common-carrier communication costs.*

The information utility will evolve as a number of shared information stores which are part of a dispersed network of processers and information stores. The total costs of processers relative to communication channels will preclude development of a computer utility consisting of processers shared over long distance phone lines. Some processers will certainly be shared, but the sharing users will generally be within normal toll free calling distance of the processer by 1975. Only in those cases where information is volatile relative to average interrogation rates will it be economic to share access to remote storage facilities.

It is clearly impossible to say that everything which has been forecast will necessarily occur. However, a general forecast of this kind can usefully predict the range and set the boundaries of the possible. The forces that I have reviewed and the possibilities they create make it evident that the range of automation is growing in such a way that impacts capable of altering some parts of the social structure ought to be expected. And we should also keep in mind that adaptation to these changes might be quite difficult because change is occurring at a more rapid rate than it did before.

Among the many issues that have been raised, three seem to constitute the focus of general concern. These are: will automation "take over"; will large scale automation destroy what we today usually refer to as "the privacy of the individual"; and, finally, will large scale automation create massive unemployment?

The first issue arises from a general sense of fear and is, therefore, badly stated. What it really attempts to express is the extremely complex phenomenon of man's "displacement" in relation to his perception of reality. All major changes in the content and organization of knowledge create such a philosophical displacement. The point to remember is that the full impact of automation, as we are beginning to understand it today, might lead to a displacement comparable to the Darwinian revolution.

The question of privacy is also important. In some sense it restates the preceding concern with reference to displacement

within the political structure—it asks whether, thanks to automation, those in power will "take over." Basically, the issue is one
of dossier technology—namely, of the lower cost of personal-
dossier handling that may result from centralizing such information in large government data files. This raises the possibility that
information which is now considered private (such as incomes,
expenditures, individual life histories and individual work histories) will be publicly "stored" and, consequently, be accessible
to public authorities to a greater extent than we would now be
prepared to condone.

At the technical level, this confronts us with interesting problems of how to ensure privacy and security and how to design the
required identification devices that will permit access only to those
who need to know, and at times and in circumstances when they
have to know. However, technical progress has not been spectacular mainly because, in order to solve the technical problem, social
norms must first be established and defined. Work leading towards
such definition has hardly begun. We do not yet know what
properties of privacy have social value and need to be preserved.
We do not know how to sort out with any precision the kind of
information to which access must be prohibited. We do not quite
understand the complex legal, jurisdictional and, ultimately, constitutional mechanisms that are involved.

The third problem—that of employment, or unemployment—
was the first to receive the attention of experts when cybernetic
control in manufacturing became a distinct possibility. The classic
analysis of this issue was given in 1965 by Professor Herbert
Simon in his book, *The Shape of Automation*. Nothing that has
happened since then has seriously contradicted his conclusion
that automation will not lead to massive unemployment. Nor,
as of today, has automation (in the United States, anyway) led
to spectacular increases in productivity, except perhaps in agriculture.

However, some degree of discomfort remains, probably because
we sense that until now automation has not gained its full, expected, momentum. When that happens, probably after 1975, its
impact on the nature and structure of human work will tend to
become cumulatively more telling. Ultimately, there is little doubt
that the existing foundations of the economic system will, under

such an impact, have to be rethought and, as a result, a restructuring or reconceptualization of our basic institutions of production, consumption, income distribution, work and leisure will have to take place. It is clear, if we look far enough into the future, that the traditional tie between work and income upon which our current system is based cannot be maintained under large scale automation. It seems self-evident that in an economy of high and automatic productivity the distribution of income can no longer be regulated by our current market criteria but that new social criteria will have to be invented to regulate it. This leads to an important and profound prediction: for automation to come of age and be fully integrated into the world of man, an entirely new system of ethics is needed which will allow the individual to adjust himself to the manifold displacements with which he will soon be confronted.

THE BANISHMENT OF PAPERWORK

by ARTHUR L. SAMUEL

IT MAY COME as a surprise to some to be told that the modern digital computer is really quite old in concept, and that the year 1984 will be celebrated as the 150th anniversary of the invention of the first computer, the Analytical Engine of the Englishman Charles Babbage. 150 years is really quite a long period of time in terms of modern science and industry and, at first glance, it seems unduly long for a new concept to come into full fruition. Unfortunately, Charles Babbage was ahead of his time, and it took 100 years of technical development, the impetus

Reprinted from *The World in 1984,* vol. II, edited by Nigel Calder. By permission of Penguin Books. First published in 1964.

of the Second World War, and the perception of John Von Neumann to bring the computer into being. Now, twenty years later and with several generations of computers behind us, we are in a position to make a somewhat more meaningful prognosis than appeared possible in, say, 1948. We can only hope that we will not be as far off in actuality as we believe George Orwell to be, or as far off in our time scale as were Charles Babbage and his almost equally famous interpreter, Lady Lovelace.

Where, then, will the computer be in 1984? Computers are not going to get much bigger; in fact, they are going to get very much smaller, that is smaller in physical size, while retaining all of their presently envisioned computational capabilities. They will, of course, have access to very much bigger memories, memories which in fact can contain the total sum of man's recorded information—but this is already technically possible today. Nor are computers going to get much faster. They may be faster by a factor of a hundred or even by a thousand, but not by anything like the factor of one million which has characterized the last twenty years' development. The finite velocity of light, and the discrete nature of matter and of energy, conspire to limit the attainable computational speed. Because of these limits the speed of our computers is not apt to change very much. We are learning a great deal about computer organization, and we can expect some startling changes along these lines, but these changes will be more apparent to the computer designer than to the user.

The large changes, and they will be large, will come in the way in which computers will be used and in the extent to which they will permeate the entire fabric of our society. Let us try to visualize these changes.

In the first place we have good reason for predicting that two rather basic problems will by then have been solved. The first of these has to do with learning, or rather its absence. At the present time, computers do not learn from their experience. Given a new problem to be solved, no matter how similar it may be to a previously solved problem, we, as humans, must write a new set of instructions, a program in the jargon of the trade, to specify the solution procedure. Not only this, but unless we make special arrangements to save old information we frequently have to rewrite an identical set of instructions and even waste machine time by recomputing previously computed data. By contrast, when similar tasks are given to a human assistant, he is expected to learn from his experience; and a clerk who has failed to do so is likely to be looking for another position. This problem of machine learning should certainly have been solved well within the next twenty years, and the computer will then become a very much more useful device.

The second difficulty resides in the nature of the instructions which must now be given. The computer, today, accepts only imperative statements; it is a slave which executes our commands, and this without any ability to ask questions, volunteer information, discuss pros and cons with respect to solution methods, etc. In short, one cannot converse with a computer. Here, too, we can confidently look to a practical solution within a period short compared with twenty years.

Meanwhile, as a result of these two difficulties, we now find it necessary to employ a veritable army of people called programmers to write instructions for the computer. When these problems have been solved, programming as we now know it will have ceased to exist and the computer will then be a truly "intelligent" and reliable assistant.

A third current difficulty of a less basic sort will also have been solved within the next few years. It concerns the construction of simple input and output equipment for both oral and visual communication with the computer. This is already largely a problem of cost and, with time, we can expect to have extremely cheap and convenient terminals which will also be highly portable. Communication with a computer will then be easy and natural—as easy and natural as communication with an intelligent servant of the human variety.

Given computers that are perhaps a hundred to a thousand times as fast as the fastest present-day computers, computers with larger memories, computers which occupy perhaps one one hundredth the volume that they now do, computers that are much cheaper, and, finally, computers which learn from their experience and which can converse freely with their masters—what can we predict?

To be completely realistic, we must postulate two quite different situations, the one in which nearly everyone has his own private computer, and the second situation in which the private ownership of computers is banned by law, but in which each person has access to a small terminal connecting him with one or more large state-owned computers giving him most of the advantages of a small privately-owned computer, but without the opportunity for private or, perhaps some would say, clandestine operations. Capitalist countries will tend in the first direction while communist states will doubtlessly go in the second direction, although even in these countries the "big brother is watching" aspect will be very much less pronounced than was predicted in 1948. Lest we of the West view this dichotomy with complacency, one must note that a trend towards the large central installation is also evident in the western world. One might, therefore, expect that an intermediate situation will develop in the West with private ownership of computers of limited capabilities which also serve as remote terminals to communicate with the centrally located computers for the solution of larger problems. Computers will in any case be as convenient to use and as readily available as the present-day telephone.

Telephones will, of course, be portable and connected via radio so that one need not be at any special location to obtain phone communication only with one's computer. Tele-video-phones via radio will be well developed although not yet in widespread use, and the terminals will still be rather bulky, so that one may still have to go to fixed locations if one wishes video-communication with a computer.

Connection to a central location will be very necessary to perform another function which will, by then, be delegated to the omnipresent computer. I refer to information retrieval. The entire contents of the large central files (or at least that portion which the government elects to make available) will be readily retrievable by anyone at a moment's notice. One will be able to browse through the fiction section of the central library, enjoy an evening's light entertainment viewing any movie that has ever been produced (for a suitable fee, of course, since Hollywood will still be commercial), or inquire as to the previous day's production figures for tin in Bolivia—all for the asking via one's remote terminal. Libraries for books will have ceased to exist in the more advanced countries except for a few which will be preserved as museums, and most of the world's knowledge will be in machine-readable form. Perhaps it would be more correct to say, all of the world's recorded knowledge will be in this form since the art of programming computers to read printed and handwritten material will have been fully developed. However, the storage problem will make it imperative that a more condensed form of recording be used, a form which will only be machine-readable, and which will be translated into human-readable form by one's computer on demand.

The consequences of this compilation and ready access to large amounts of stored information will be truly profound in many diverse fields, such for example as agronomy, jurisprudence, and medicine, to name but three. But all this is another subject.

Computers will perform yet another major function—that of language translation. Not only will one be able to obtain information from the central files in the language of one's choice, but automatic translation via the telephone will also have come into use—although perhaps not general use, because of the cost and because of the gradual drift towards a universal language. It will, nevertheless, be possible to dial anywhere in the world and to converse with anyone speaking a different language with only a slight translation delay to allow for the differences in sentence structure and word-ordering between the languages.

Perhaps we should say something about teaching machines, which will have been developed to such an extent that master-computers of large capacity will be needed, each to direct many slave-teaching machines and to compile data from them. These master-computers will alter teaching methods on the basis of experience. They will up-date the material and its ideological slant as dictated by scientific advances and the changing *mores* of society. While it will be entirely feasible to obtain an education at home, via one's own personal computer, human nature will not have changed, and there will still be a need for schools with laboratories, classrooms, and individual teachers to motivate the students.

So far, we have talked primarily about the individual user and his personal use of the computer. But the digital computer is destined to play an even bigger role in the real-time control of projects and processes. The coordination and scheduling of any large endeavor, whether it be running a business, operating a factory, constructing a large building or running a government, now takes a fantastic amount of paperwork. This paperwork will cease to exist in twenty years. Instead, direct inputs and outputs to the computer will provide information, initiate the necessary processes (all computer-controlled by a lesser breed of computers), and finally issue what few instructions are needed for the few people who are still involved.

Process control with the attending automation, while delegated to simpler computers, will have reached a very high degree of development so that the number of factory employees will drop precipitously. These displaced people will be going into the service industries, and a few into the design and maintenance of the machines which replace them. Science and the arts will be flourishing. The working week will have been shortened to four days, but we shall have an unemployment problem. Making this due prediction will, of course, help to nullify it. Many people (including the author and his associates) are taking steps to make the transition to automated production an orderly one without socially undersirable side-effects.

Finally, a word regarding solid intellectual achievements of computers. The world checkers, chess, and go champions will, of course, have met defeat at the hands of the computer, but strangely enough this will not have ended these three games either as intellectual pastimes or as professional career activities. It is true that matches between people will be less common, but nearly everyone will know his precise rating as a player and he will endeavor to improve his ability by playing against his computer. Computers will have largely taken over the task of composing and arranging music, at least for popular entertainment, and many people will vie with each other in regard to the quality of mood music which their own personal computer or personal program can produce. As far as literature is concerned, the computer will still be a neophyte although whodunits will be turned out by the million. Computers will not have contributed as much as some people have predicted, with respect to making basic contributions to mathematics and science and, somehow or other, all attempts to invest them with truly creative abilities will have failed.

There will still be a place in the world for people!

DESIGNING THE MATERIALS
WE NEED

by ROBERT ALLEN SMITH

M ATERIALS science is passing through a marked
transitional period at present so that prediction is a chancy
business. However, many trends are discernible and some fruits
of a changed attitude to the means of developing new materials
have already been gathered. In the past, such development has
been largely empirical and it is amazing how much success has
been achived by this means. For example, steels used in the Middle Ages by swordmakers in Japan, Damascus, and Spain have not
been bettered as regards tensile strength (except in the form of
cold-drawn wire). The development of these steels took a very
long time with much trial and error and in this modern industrial
age the time and effort are just not available. The transition which
is taking place is from empirical methods to the controlled construction of man-made materials and has come about largely
through the great advances which have taken place in solid-state
physics. There are still many basic problems to be solved and the
need for fundamental research is greater than ever.

Steel will still be with us as a widely used material in 1984 but
will have been improved enormously, since we now understand
many of the functions of deliberately added impurities. Steel will
not, however, meet all our needs in 1984 for a high-tensile ductile
material; it loses much of its strength at high temperatures. For
the leading edges of supersonic aircraft it would be inadequate,
and for spacecraft, where kinetic heating on re-entry into the
atmosphere will raise the temperature to well over 1,400° C., the
approximate melting point of most steels, it would be useless. Here
it is likely to be superseded by alloys of the refractory metals such

Reprinted from *The World in 1984*, vol. I, edited by Nigel Calder. By permission of Penguin Books. First published in 1964.

as zirconium, niobium, molybdenum, or tungsten. Metals in use in 1984 may well be composite, consisting of minute globules of metals with lower melting points embedded in the refractory metals. Composite materials of this kind have shown promise of giving the ductility needed for forming them into the required shapes, are much less brittle, and retain a fair measure of these properties as well as their strength at high temperatures.

An entirely different approach to this problem comes through the development of new ceramic materials. These have many of the heat-resistant properties required but lack the strength and ductility of metals. Until recently the development of ceramics has certainly been an art rather than a science, but this phase is passing. Basic studies of the structure of ceramics have shown that defects on an atomic scale are largely the cause of the failure of ceramics to stand up to the strength requirements. Control of these defects should lead to greatly improved materials of this kind.

An important class of composite materials consists of aggregates of different substances. Concrete is a rather crude example. More subtle examples are in the form of fibrous materials. It is found that many materials, made in the form of thin filaments, can be very free from defects and exceptionally strong. These fibers can be embedded in a matrix and may form the basis of new materials. Flexibility and freedom from fatigue come about from the fact that the thin fibers may be bent very easily and frequently without breaking. In this class of composite materials also come "solid foams." These have a high strength-to-weight ratio and could be glazed to give a protective finish. Such materials made from high-melting-point oxides have been suggested for the leading edges of wings of supersonic aircraft but will have a multitude of other uses, including that of providing heat insulation at high temperatures.

Although the material requirements of aviation and space flight have given rise to some of the most difficult problems and have tended to have much of the limelight, these represent only a very small fraction of the requirements for the technological advances twenty years from now. By then we shall see great changes in building construction which will require lighter, tougher, and more elegant materials than we have now. For all but special buildings where expense is no object and traditional design is desirable, the use of stone and brick will largely have disappeared by 1984, and happily we shall have passed out of the gray concrete age.

The new materials will mainly be derived from high polymers and, in addition to strength and beauty, they will provide thermal and sound insulation and ease of working. These will be a consequence of the present basic studies of the processes and of the control of polymerization (the making of big molecules out of little ones). This class of materials will also give us a much better type of paint for both decorative and protective purposes. The emulsion paints now in use are only a beginning of a movement toward this type of material based on controlled polymerization. The continuing need of new fabrics for dress and interior decoration should also be met by new types of fibers based on polymers. Glass is an excellent material for transparent construction and is unlikely to be superseded. It is likely that much less brittle forms will be developed.

The need for fuels for space travel and for other requirements where bulk is a severe disadvantage will undoubtedly lead to the development of new solid fuels which are much more concentrated than those currently in use. This is a very large subject which we cannot discuss in this brief article. The development of an entirely new type of material is, however, of very great interest, and should be mentioned. This type of material is the converse of a fuel. A fuel consists of material which when reacted chemically, usually with oxygen, produces a strongly exothermic reaction, the heat of which is used to produce motive power or just heat. The new material is one which produces a strongly endothermic reaction and by this means can absorb heat. A rather crude example of this type of material is a plastic which absorbs heat when charred. Materials of this kind will be developed to absorb the intense heat generated on the nose-cones of spacecraft re-entering the atmosphere, and may have a number of other uses.

In addition to constructional materials, many new materials for special technological purposes will be in use in 1984, for example, for electronic equipment, the use of which will be even more widespread than at present. These new materials will be like either the germanium used in transistors, first made ultra-pure and then modified with minute controlled amounts of impurity, or man-made materials like indium antimonide. Special new optical materials, of which the existing laser materials are just a crude beginning, will have revolutionized optical systems, and new superconducting alloys will enable very high magnetic fields to be generated without dissipation of large quantities of electrical power.

One very important field in which great advances may be expected in the next twenty years is that of biological materials. Some of these materials, originally studied in a form obtained from living organisms, can now be man-made; many more will be made, with controlled variations, in the next twenty years. The potential consequences of this in medicine are tremendous either for evil or for good, depending on man's moral attitude to their use. This is far too big a subject for this article but also far too important not to be mentioned.

The new materials of 1984 will largely be the ones that man needs most urgently. The days of "cut and try" are nearly over and materials science is moving into an age of control. Man should be able to design the materials he needs, and the next twenty years will see great steps in this direction. It will not be achieved, however, without extensive research in physics. Many of the basic facts about how solids hang together, what are the factors that weaken them, that give them ductility or make them brittle, and so on are gradually being brought to light. An important development of this age is the cooperation of staff from different academic disciplines, such as physics, chemistry, and metallurgy, in so-called "interdisciplinary laboratories" to make a determined attack on some of the basic problems of materials science. On the biological side we are just beginning to see the cooperation of biologists, chemists, and physicists in a similar attack on biological materials. By 1984 we should be picking some of the fruits.

COMMUNICATIONS

by JOHN R. PIERCE

Technological readiness must reflect itself in the nature of the planning we should do and in the role that communication will take as a part of man's life in the future. It is important to consider here two very different fields of communication: mass communication, typified by television, and personal communication, typified by telephony.

As technological readiness improves, there is a clear tendency to personalize mass communication by serving smaller and smaller segments of the mass and to generalize personal communication by effective communication among larger and larger groups. This tendency is a challenge to both fields. Nonetheless, the gap in nature between mass communication and personal communication is still wide.

It is also important to consider a number of technological innovations which are at hand, or nearly at hand, but which have not yet found their full use either in the field of mass communications or in the field of personal communications. These innovations include surprising extensions of the solid-state technology inaugurated by the transistor and, especially, innovations of two natures—extension of operation to higher frequencies, and the production of many devices interconnected to form an integrated circuit on one chip of silicon, at a cost and with a reliability characteristic of a single transistor.

Innovations also include the possibility of providing hundreds of television channels and hundreds of thousands of telephone channels by millimeter wave transmission through hollow tubes or waveguides, the extension of microwave radio transmission to frequencies above 10 gigahertz (or wavelengths shorter than 3 cm), the extension of microwave radio to communication by

Reprinted and abridged from "Forecasting the Future," *Science Journal,* October 1967. By permission of *Science Journal.*

means of satellites, and the possibility of attaining communication channels of great capacity by the coherent light of lasers. What impact are these technological advances likely to have on society?

First, let us consider mass communication. One advance which technological improvements will certainly bring to this field is a little more variety. Near a few large American cities, such as New York and Los Angeles, there are a dozen or so TV channels, and there is a good deal of variety. But there are insufficient TV channels to have a dozen in everyone's home town and this would, in any case, lead to interference.

Some Americans wandered into a very good idea without at first quite understanding it. This arose because towns in valleys and behind hills were unable to receive TV programs. Local enterprises began to put big antennas on the top of a nearby hill, amplified the TV signals these picked up, and brought them into the town via cable. Sometimes they rented distribution facilities from common carriers, sometimes they built their own. They found that people were willing to pay a few dollars a month for good clear signals from nearby TV stations. And this made money for such Community Antenna Television (CATV) operators.

This is the way CATV was born. But it has gone further. CATV people found that they could pick up distant TV broadcasts by using large hilltop antennas and thus provide their subscribers with programs from several cities. And because CATV cables will carry around a dozen programs—they could carry more in the future—occasionally there were channels left over. As these had been virtually paid for by the other channels they could be used for local programs of limited interest and low cost—local news and weather, for instance.

The only way I see of getting a great variety of programs to small towns as well as large cities is through wired distribution. And this could provide cheap channels for local use as well as for network use. The only foreseeable alternative approach to providing greater variety is through the use of communication satellites. These may well have a profound effect in the developing countries where there are few, if any, TV stations and networks. But I do not foresee them producing such a revolutionary effect in an advanced area such as North America or Western Europe.

Extra CATV channels could bring other advantages. Overnight, one channel could pour all the newspapers in the country into a home, if there were a means of recording them. This is not practical today. Paper would be an impractical recording medium but perhaps newspapers could be recorded on microfilm or magnetic tape. In this way they could be viewed on a screen like that of a TV receiver or the receiver could be set to record just those papers that were required. If such techniques are to be economic, they still require a good deal of development. They call for invention, innovation and technological readiness.

So far, I have talked about mass electrical communication—electrical communication from the few to the many. I see this broadening through wired distribution, and perhaps extending to storable material, printed or taped. But what of other sorts of communication?

One expanding development is closed circuit communication over private lines. This includes TV to monitor industrial operations such as cable laying at the bottom of the ocean. It includes TV linking classrooms or rooms in hospitals. This will grow in importance but in the long run will not make as large an impact as has the telephone or the television set itself. One thing that is growing in importance, however, is private industrial communication networks, often made up of circuits and switching facilities rented from common carriers.

Fundamental advances will be made possible by the technology of integrated circuits. These are already in use in laboratories but not yet in the home or the office. But when they do become commercially available on a much wider scale, it will be possible to have devices as complicated as a small electronic computer in the telephone set, in the car, or even in the pocket. They will be inexpensive, will use little power, will last for decades, and when they fail will be thrown away, not repaired.

What advances do such devices promise? If sufficient radio frequencies are made available, they could lead to telephones in all cars, and perhaps to telephones in the pocket. But the telephone itself will extend beyond its old functions, whether in the office, home, or car. One thing that telephone lines will do increasingly is to put us in touch with electronic computers.

This trend is already becoming apparent. A clerk can determine the state of airline bookings or bank balances by direct interrogation of a computer. And if he asks for a stock market quotation the computer may reply in recorded voice over the phone. And the clerk queries the computer by using the same "touch-tone" keys he uses for dialing a number. The pulses a dial produces will go only as far as a central office, but the touch-tone signals can be transmitted over any connection to operate a computer.

This use of computers is due to expand, first in business but eventually into the home. Instead of trying to solicit a limited amount of information from one man—hotel porter or tourist guide, for instance—we will be able to make enquiries about hotel accommodation, weather forecasts in any area, restaurant facilities, sporting facilities and many other items simply by interrogating a computer.

Some of this could be done with touch-tone keys and voice reply. But some would require a full keyboard and a visual display of text. Microelectronics promises to provide these at a reasonable cost. They will be used first in business and eventually in the home.

Such a device could open up access to books and other recorded material, transcending libraries and encyclopedias in scope and ease of use. In business it could do far more. It could store a secretary's typing, print it out, allow her to make a few corrections and type out the corrected text without her retyping the whole thing. In schools it could allow the student to interact with a teaching program in a computer, as is already done in some universities. In the future such programs may be made available in the home.

All these things will be done by means of simple terminals which microelectronics will make widely available. But they will also make available TV phones. In the United States the Bell System is working toward this through a "see-while-you-talk" service called Picturephone. I have an early design terminal in my office. It connects me with about thirty people at Murray Hill, New Jersey, where I work, and at Holmdel, about thirty miles away. This service will be made commercially available when the development problems have been solved.

Integrated circuits are vital to any TV phone system, as is a very large capacity communications link. A Picturephone conversation will use in each direction about as much communication capacity as a hundred telephone conversations. To make this service cheap we will need cheaper ways of transmitting broadband electric signals.

We have in prospect ways of doing this. High speed solid-state devices and integrated circuits make it possible to encode the signals economically, as sequences of on-or-off pulses, by pulse code modulation. Such pulses can be transmitted over a variety of media, including coaxial cables.

But advances in solid-state physics have also opened up higher radio frequencies to economical use—frequencies above 10 gigahertz (10^{10} c/s). Also, by using millimeter waves, thousands of TV phone lines could be transmitted through a 5 cm pipe or waveguide. And in satellite communication, pioneered by American Telephone and Telegraph Company with the *Telstar* satellite, advances in space boosters and in electronics indicate that it is possible to launch a communication satellite weighing a ton which could provide hundreds, and later thousands, of TV phone channels between various telephone offices in the country.

When the traffic is large enough, these new advances will make feasible broader band communication circuits which will make TV phone transmission cheaper—and will make telephone and data transmission cheaper as well. The technique of transmitting many more signals over one system is the road to economy in electrical communication. Thus in personal communication I foresee more complicated and versatile communication terminals and more economical communication circuits. And these will be tied together with faster and more versatile electronic switching systems, again made possible by integrated circuits.

An economical common carrier network could go beyond telephony and serve all our needs and senses—sight and perhaps touch as well as sound. It will enable us to control computers and manipulate machines at a distance. And I am sure that it will make it possible for groups of people to confer effectively without traveling, using voice, data, charts, blackboards—all the media we use in conferring face to face.

The telephone, the car, TV, and electric power have made possible a uniformly high grade of human life throughout all developed lands. We no longer need to live in the heart of a city to live comfortably. But we still travel by plane to meet other people, to use rare facilities or to see or participate in special events. I believe that, in the future, improved communication will enable us to avoid much onerous travel. We can live where we like, travel for pleasure and communicate to work.

How will we get into the world of the future? Planning will be necessary, but planning is not easy. It is hard to tell when the fantastic rate of growth characteristic of the effective introduction of a new service will begin, and it is hard to tell when and at what level the initial rate of growth will level off. Even more than wise planning, we will need readiness of resources—financial and technological—in order to provide new forms of communication and to respond flexibly to the demand for them. We must plan as hard and wisely as we can, but we must be ready for the inevitable unplanned deviations and unexpected opportunities.

CHEAP COMMUNICATIONS

by J. L. HULT

THE FABRIC of any society is communications, and the dominant means of communication in the past has been the transporting of people or the written word. With the advent of more economical communication capabilities, we may have the opportunity to change the degree as well as the style of communications. We are also offered the opportunity to automate many activities or to participate in them with remote sensors.

The choices available will frequently involve consideration of

Reprinted from *The Futurist*, June 1969. By permission of the publisher and the author.

more than economic factors, and it may be difficult to predict the relative social acceptance of the various alternatives. For example, in choosing between a personal visit or video and audio transmission for various communication purposes, what values would society associate with the physical presence involved in personal visits or with the various possibilities of electronic transmissions?

A different kind of consideration may be illustrated as follows: Most of the inter-actions of society that generate communications have been linked with the transportation of people, things, or information at a cost that increases with distance. In most cases this has led to a rapidly diminishing volume of communications as distances increase. If a capable mode of communications is introduced that can dominate and control the cost rates for all types of communication, and if its costs are relatively independent of distance, what difference will this make in the style of communications and in the distribution of traffic with distance?

These types of questions can become important in determining when and whether society will accept various possible applications. An additional factor to be considered is the variety of vested and special interests which could impede change in methods of communication. The discussion that follows outlines some interesting *possible* applications and some social implications.

Business frequently requires communication between remote locations. For example, the better part of two days, a lot of inconvenience, and travel expense are now involved in accomplishing a few hours of communications between people on the opposite sides of the United States. If appropriate private, secure contact could be made through electronic linkage, much cost, time, and inconvenience could be saved, and even better communication might result than with a personal visit. This could be particularly true for multiperson conferences, where there might be advantages (beyond the elimination of travel costs) from the better contact and individual information access that would be possible. For example, each individual could have access to the information in his own office while having greater opportunity for visual and aural contact with every other individual in the conference.

By arranging for face-view cutouts of all the participants to appear around a central, larger view of the speaker on the display, every participant could have better eye contact with everyone at all times than would be possible at a conference table. Furthermore, it would be possible to expand the contact to any desired degree—to intensify it, or to provide separate private channels for conferences within, or exclusive of, the main conference.

Representation is frequently required at remote locations for private or government business. With the availability of greatly expanded electronic communication facilities, better access with less delegation of authority could be provided. This would permit greater global representation with less personnel and other costs. This is particularly true for government activity on the international level as well as within nations. With a more informed public and with the possibility of automatic opinion-sampling or voting, a much greater degree of direct participation at all levels of government would be available.

The home could probably generate the greatest potential demand for communications of all types. Although most of this demand is likely to be for local services not requiring satellite relay, these services could stimulate enormous increases in circuit demands that could involve satellite relays, if they developed adequate two-way circuits and terminal facilities. If adequate communication facilities were available, much of the transportation of people and recorded information would be unnecessary. This would include most private social visits and group participation activity. The latter could be broadcast with such features as audience participation, program rating or reaction information, and social contact within the audience to exploit any feature of "live" audiences that is desired. Selection shopping, banking, and a host of errands could be done electronically. All mail services for communication purposes could be completely replaced. Every reference service could be made available by remote control to the home. This would include libraries, newspapers, magazines, every kind of broadcast stored and available on call, and any kind of computer facility.

Finally, education received directly in the home is a dramatic possibility. There seems to be no technological reason why any educational technique could not be automated and made more efficient through video, audio, and data-link communications, with appropriate coupling to large computers. If broad-band communication coupling is required for every home, as might be specified in the building codes, two-way circuit capacity for bringing education directly to the home would be available. Such an educational system could be adapted to any teaching technique, curriculum change, or educational innovation. It would have practically unlimited capacity and qualitative growth potential. It need not exclude any degree of physical social contact or benefit from team experiences. It could be made a continuous, lifelong process, standardized and available without discrimination, but adaptable to each individual to maximize his benefits according to his capabilities.

Although standardized opportunities would be available to everyone without discrimination, the system could minimize conformity and maximize individualism. However, any application of these educational techniques to a significant segment of society must, in addition to the satisfactory development of the facilities and techniques, be concerned with the resistance from teachers, and the problem of suitable employment for those that would be displaced.

If a significant fraction of the possibilities indicated for communication systems in the home were accepted, how would this affect many of the traditions and values of society? It would emphasize residential activity and information access and provide an opportunity to make the family a more important factor and influence in society. However, the greater communication capability would also permit complete access to any terminal, and social grouping of individuals need not emphasize family. In fact, the technological capabilities will provide great opportunities for individualism, and we may find a tendency toward smaller *physical* grouping for social contacts. It would then be easier to avoid a "captive audience" for the development of the family as a group. For example, the large number of TV channels that might be made available at any location could provide the equivalent of direct, immediate global access to any theatrical, entertainment, cultural or educational activity. This broad choice is apt to lead to more conflicting interests the larger the group.

Since technology can provide small personalized TV sets that would permit independent simultaneous reception of a number of programs at little extra cost over the larger TV set reception of single programs for larger groups, we should expect a trend in this direction. How would our society be affected by the simultaneous general increases in the *number* of people in one- or two-way communication contact and in the *effectiveness* of those contacts, and a general decrease in the size of the groups in *physical* communication contact? It could lead to greater social understanding and greater access to and transfer of information, while improving the opportunities for both freedom and privacy!

The first impression of many concerning the effect of broadband access to the home is the fear of the loss of privacy; the homemaker visualizes the possibilities of being caught improperly dressed or with a messy house. The broad-band access could be used to provide greater privacy and greater freedom for all parties by simply providing the facilities for greater control and choice of mode of response.

The predominant means for the transmission of bulk information has become recorded communications—mostly recorded on paper. We are in fact threatened with inundation by mail, newspapers, magazines, and books. As more and more of this communication is converted to unrecorded transfer or selected terminal recording, we will be faced with problems of employing the displaced personnel involved in recording and distributing or delivering the communication, for example, mailmen and post office personnel.

It will be very difficult to dispense with any of the mail services or personnel until most addresses are uniformly equipped with facilities to accept and record the communications. The provision for electronic transmission between post offices will provide very little relief for the congestion and bottlenecks in the system, since these bottlenecks are primarily related to the sorting and distribution of the mail and not to the transportation of the mail between post offices.

Public-order surveillance seems to be an activity that could benefit from automation or remote operation. An illustration will serve to define some possibilities and social implications. Optical sensing systems might be installed near street intersections in urban areas and be designed to scan or provide surveillance of the activity on the streets and in the environment within a block, for example, in all directions. With the appropriate distribution of such sensing systems coupled to an adequate communication network, it should be possible to maintain better monitoring and surveillance of any given area from central locations with less manpower than is needed for current surveillance practice. However, would such a system be socially accepted? Many would feel that it would constitute an invasion of privacy, while others would be concerned about a lack of "presence" of help.

There are a number of possible applications for automatic identification of people as they perform everyday tasks. It could be used for authorized, quick, private access to people, places, records, or information of a privileged or proprietary nature. It would be of value in conjunction with the prolific use of credit cards; and it would be necessary for what has been casually referred to in the literature as the "cashless society," in which "money" transactions would take place without the physical transfer of negotiable material. There are many attractive features that a cashless society might provide, but its viability depends on its ability to ensure reliable nonnegotiable identification and a satisfactory, continuous, private surveillance of resources. This seems to require as a prerequisite a very comprehensive and competent communication network and a variety of terminal record transducers. The purpose of this brief discussion is to provide a taste of the possible nature of automatic identification in such systems and its potential impact on communications and society.

It should be much easier to design an identification device for unambiguous, secure, automatic identification than to adapt a mechanism to perform this function automatically on conventional money (either coin or paper), which was never intended for this purpose. Thus, for example, it should be possible to use cards with specially designed magnetic signatures that could be read more easily, automatically, and unambiguously than the coins presently used in telephones, parking meters, bus or commuter transportation systems, stamps, change-making machines, and a host of other coin-operated systems. Not only should it be possible to eliminate most counterfeit use of these systems, but it should also eliminate the opportunity to rob the systems of the negotiable deposits that have accumulated.

In order to protect the identification system against unauthorized use as a result of loss of identification or against coercive extraction, some security measures could easily be employed. For example, several charge accumulation thresholds and identification measures could be used which are not overtly indicated. An identification card alone might be used to accumulate charges up to $10, for example, before a higher level of identification is required, such as a specified fingerprint or voice print to be compared with a stored reference. Then at another accumulated threshold level, for example, $300, a great identification data transfer might be required, such as a video communication containing specific signature requirements. By the appropriate use of these types of measures with the possibility of card, threshold level, or identification requirements changing with time, it should be possible to guard against unauthorized or illegal use.

The private surveillance of resources could be provided with the use of the same identification system. It should be possible to provide on request through the communication system a discreet private statement and running review of resource status. It might be convenient, for example, to provide a daily statement which could be transmitted at night during low traffic periods and recorded at home or at any terminal or address (or at a central library or exchange). This information could then be selectively retrieved and extracted from the recording on request with the appropriate identification. When such retrieval is accomplished, automatic acknowledgment could be made. The various types of information that might be made available in this manner could be arranged to be erased at a given age, upon retrieval, or at some other specified time to prevent accumulation of unwanted information.

All the various operations and techniques for automatic identification would add to the general communication systems burden. Not only would the system require many additional terminals, but a great variety of bandwidths and types of data or information would also need to be handled, justifying an earlier statement that a very comprehensive and competent communication network and a variety of terminal record transducers would be required.

As a final indication of a clearly defined application possibility, with well-defined conflicts of interest and uncertainties of acceptance, consider tourism. It would not be difficult to provide within any country, areas which are typical of the physical environment in another country: for example, a hotel with eating, drinking, and living facilities and service, representative of what would be experienced by a tourist in the country represented. If two-way, full-video communications to the represented country were also available and under the control of the "tourist," he could have nearly any desired capability to communicate visually and aurally with the country being toured and he could also experience many of the essential features of the physical environment. Thus for many "tourists" there could be more extensive and comprehensive "tours" at less cost, and this might promote greater global understanding. However, this new kind of tourism would encounter strong resistance from vested interests such as transportation and personal service organizations for obvious economic reasons. National governments might be concerned about the regulation of or access to information, even though it should be easier to control this than to control the activities of physical tourists. But finally, it is difficult to assess the "tourist's" acceptance of this means of tourism. Would it reduce or promote tourist travel?

There can be a variety of motivations for tourist travel, some of which may not be satisfied by electronic communications. For example, one motivation component may be the subjective feeling of prestige or the impression made on other people, and this may be lacking in an electronic "tour" until it has been established as a prestigious or impressive action. Until proven otherwise, some may feel that it is not an acceptable alternative to the physical presence.

It is perhaps pertinent to ask if there are any fundamental limitations to the communications that society can use. How much more information transfer can society effectively absorb?

What portion of society's total communications might be to and between machines rather than to individuals?

As we automate more and more functions and reduce the physical body requirements for more of our activity, we will need to guard against physical atrophy. However, as we develop our environment so that the physical exertion required for survival is reduced, we will be freer to pursue those activities which are most enjoyable or conducive to our physical well-being.

The communication capacity that we currently provide by relatively primitive means falls far short of the limit that society may effectively use. However, many important problems of our society today—inadequate roads, mass rapid transit, smog, airport congestion, supersonic transport, inadequate post offices and school systems—either exist or are aggravated because we are transporting people or recorded information in order to communicate. Why shouldn't we take advantage of electronic communications, the fastest, most effective and efficient communication means that our technology can provide?

TRANSPORT

by GABRIEL BOULADON

THE CHAOS OF today's transport systems is the result of anarchic growth. Spectacular progress in aviation has been to a great extent counterbalanced by urban congestion. Even if the super-train to commute between town and airport in ten minutes is built, some thirty minutes might be needed to reach the railway station and even then only if a taxi could be found which managed to avoid hold-ups or if we used the overcrowded underground. Within a time lapse of one hour, we are

Reprinted from *Science Journal*, III/10, October 1967. By permission of the publisher and the author.

pampered, cosseted, and fed in a supersonic plane but deafened, jostled, choked, and exhausted in town getting to it.

Clearly, there is something fundamentally wrong with our transport systems. Those systems which are in demand by the greatest number of people are currently the most inefficient and uncomfortable to use. Yet demand for these urban transport systems will increase the fastest. By the end of the century the world population will have doubled but the number of people living in urban areas will increase by a factor of four. Supercities some four hundred kilometers long will appear similar to the Boston-Washington megalopolis which will house eighty million people and the Tokaido strip which will house eighty-five million. The people living in these cities will have large incomes and, with their longer life spans and increased leisure time, will have more time to spend them. One result will be greatly increased travel. The youth of today, following our example, will travel fifty or one hundred times more mileage per year than did their fathers. The requirement for goods transport will increase just as fast. How are these new demands to be met?

The future of transport is susceptible to most techniques of technological forecasting and I do not intend in this article to elaborate on them further. What I will do, however, is to try and assemble the most salient results in a scenario of the kind of transport systems, and the way in which they would integrate, which technology could offer. The systems are already undergoing an evolution guided by three main forces: the passenger requirement, advances in technique and "service legislation" forced on governments by the public. The precise way in which these three forces interact will determine how much of the scenario which follows will actually become reality. But the important point is that we should have a clear idea of what is technically possible. What follows is deliberately provocative; equally, all of it is based on sound extrapolation amply documented in the transport literature.

In an earlier article ("The Transport Gaps," *Science Journal*, April 1967) I showed that all transport systems, from pedestrian to the rocket, could be classified according to their optimum range of use and combined in a unified theory of transport. This theory has revealed a very simple statistical law of which all town dwellers are subconsciously aware: there is a time duration which we consider acceptable for covering all distances. This law varies as a function of time. In 1925, for instance, we might have been content to spend three hours traveling 100 km but only twelve hours traveling 1,000 km—in other words, four times as long to travel ten times the distance. But in 1955 we were prepared to spend only three times as long in covering the extra distance; in 1975 it might be twice as long and in 2000 we will accept only a 50 percent increase in journey time. To achieve this, speeds will have had to increase 2.5, 3, 5, and 7 times respectively. Thus in the year 2000 only three times the time will be required to go by hypersonic ramjet from London to Sydney (16,800 km in 60 minutes) than to the airport (40 km in 20 minutes).

Most urban travel involves distances of two kilometers or less. The pedestrian will not consent to walking distances even as short as this. His "refusal distance" will then, as today, be about four hundred meters. Thus, as soon as traffic level justifies it, a whole category of assisted pedestrian systems will be put into use, even for shorter distances. Such systems are practically nonexistent in 1967. The original slow-speed transporter belts will have been replaced by accelerated conveyors, operating at a speed of 10–16 km/h. Passengers will, however, step on and off, walking slowly as they do with existing escalators.

These continuous systems, referred to as transfer systems or HVCS (High Volume Continuous System), will have a capacity of up to ten passengers per second (36,000 per hour). Each system will save passengers ten minutes per mile traveled. With twenty hours' operation per day, allowing a 30 percent load factor, this makes 36,000 hours saved or £80,000 daily (at the rates applicable in the year 2000) which is ample proof that the system will be a worthwhile proposition.

An HVCS network with entrance and exit every five hundred meters will cope effortlessly with traffic in the central business district, which will be closed to cars. The technique of transporter belts is reliable, safe, automatic, silent, and economic. Recent studies show that with only 20 percent load a performance of 38 passenger-miles/kWh is obtained. These figures have been confirmed by the British architect Brian Richards who refers to a running cost of 0.025 pence/passenger-mile for the moving belt; this is 10 to 20 times less than for any other means of transport.

These studies are based on existing techniques: moving belts supported by rollers, with a friction coefficient of 2 percent. It is quite possible to use a very thin film of low pressure air to reduce friction still further. Such a system could bring about a revolution in transport similar in magnitude to the one that resulted from the combination of steam engine and rails some one hundred years ago, or from the internal combustion engine and the tire fifty years ago.

Air lubrication will reduce energy demands; it will also mean that tension is no longer necessary so that the weight and cost of the belt can be considerably reduced because the energy is brought to the exact spot where it is required—underneath the belt and no longer in it. With a slight difference in level of little more than one meter per kilometer, a thin belt could transport two hundred tons of passengers (3,000 people) with no tension and without the need for any propulsive unit; their own weight would act as the energy source.

What new systems could cover distances between two and fifteen kilometers? The traditional underground, derived from the horse-drawn omnibus, will remain in existence only in "small" towns of less than five million inhabitants. Today's underground systems are condemned by their very principle: with stations close together (500 meters) they are convenient but inevitably slow; with stations farther apart (2 km) they are inconvenient and still not fast because passengers waste time and energy in having to walk to and from the nearest stations. What is more, they waste precious and costly space: even during the rush hour, when the town is choked, 86 percent of the underground tunnels is empty—and these tunnels, in fact, represent two-thirds of the investment.

One alternative for big cities will be the continuous underground train—a concept which has been investigated and patented by P. Zuppiger and myself at the Institut Battelle in Geneva. This new system will be noiseless, automatic and non-stop. It will offer eight to ten times more floor space (to be used in increasing comfort or capacity, or both) than does our current underground system even though it will use the same tunnels.

To reach this stage, the technique of the HVCS will have been extended by about 1980 to improved accelerators, called integrators, which will give passengers safe access, without any waiting, to a continuous-belt transporter. This will travel at 30–40 km/h, sufficient to transport passengers more rapidly than at present, where more than 50 percent of the time is wasted in waiting, slowing down and stopping at stations.

What of other types of ground level public transport? The last buses (electric, of course, because of the antipollution laws of about 1980) will have disappeared around 1990. Labor costs will have come to represent 90 percent of the operating costs of buses, which will still be plagued by strikes of the dissatisfied drivers. Buses will finally become too heavy and cumbersome to be able to be integrated into the centrally and electronically controlled traffic flow which will gradually extend to all the main arteries and, by reducing the distance between electric cars to less than three meters, will increase the flow by a factor of four.

Most ground level traffic will, however, be represented by small electric cars, cubic in shape. The urban branch of the car will have terminated its evolution and adopted the simplest and most functional shape: that of a smooth transparent plastic cube with no chromium plating and no protuberances, but standard rounded corners to facilitate handling and storing. The length of the cars will also be standardized to make them easily transportable in standardized containers. These silent, efficient cubes will have helped town dwellers forget the noisy, evil-smelling vehicles that proliferate today. They will be propelled by high speed electric motors running at 35,000 rpm using alternating current without brushes or commutators. They will be fed at variable frequency by miniaturized thyristors. Transmission systems will still be necessary to convey the power to the micro-wheels. But such progress will have been made in construction materials that it will be possible to drive the wheels by a single gear ratio with an efficiency of over 95 percent. These successors to gears will be flexible, deformable and practically everlasting.

The energy supply for these electric cars will be batteries storing eight to ten times more energy per unit weight than existing types. The most popular will probably be slurry batteries which can be recharged at service stations by forced recharge/drainage taking roughly the same time as it now takes to fill a petrol tank. These batteries will, rather like fuel cells, consume oxygen from the air and hydrogen, the best fuel, which will be stocked in the form of metal hydrides.

Speed will be restricted to 50 km/h in town. But this will be a real speed of 50 km/h, as compared to the average city speed of 15 km/h at present, for traffic will be a non-stop flow, crossing at different levels. Traffic lights will be a thing of the past. And even town cars will not, for the most part, belong to their users but will be rented. Self-service taxicabs will be made available after legislation to reduce urban congestion.

The average town traveler will proceed as follows: when he leaves his office, he will go to the nearest "linear mobile park." The latter will be situated along all the main arteries (ordinary parking will not be allowed). Self-service taxicabs, the supply of which will be computer-controlled, will be hooked magnetically on to a conveyor-chain under the pavement, forming a slow procession as they await customers. The traveler will insert his credit card, made of magnetized plastic, into the appropriate slot and will be able to open the car door and sit at the steering wheel. Pressure on the accelerator will release his car from the conveyor.

If he is going to the suburbs, he will be able to drive himself, but if he is going to the university and has to cross the town via the main thoroughfares he will have to integrate into the atomatic driving system, after indicating his destination by word of mouth to the central computer. On arrival he will park his car in the nearest linear mobile park.

What new solutions will be found for longer distances? The car will remain the only means of transport available at one's home. The increase in numbers will have been so phenomenal that it will have become necessary to regulate its use, first in towns in the early 1980s and then on all motorways (by 1985?) which will become electronically controlled. With four or six lanes in each direction the motorways will handle approximately 80 percent of the traffic at a rate of 15,000 cars per hour per lane; this will represent a vehicle density three times greater than at present. The speed limits in these lanes will be: lane 1: 160 km/h—turbo lorries; lane 2: 185 km/h—delivery vans and cars more than five years old; lane 3: 210 km/h—conventional family cars; lane 4: 240 km/h—fast and sports cars.

The "driver" will be able to read, relax or talk with his passengers. The automatic driving system will see that the space between cars is constant. Cars will follow a few meters behind one another in batches of twenty. Between the batches sufficient space will be left to enable a car which has broken down to be evacuated automatically into the slower lane, and so on until it is at the roadside. In the same way, drivers wishing to change lanes or leave the motorway will indicate their intention to the central computer and the maneuver will be carried out automatically a few seconds later. Such a system will be truly safe. After having accused cars, public opinion and governments will finally have realized that the dangers of driving result less from cars themselves but more from their being driven by emotive, slow-witted, and imperfect human beings.

About 30 percent of cars will still use the old internal-combustion engine. Although much lighter, its popularity will be diminishing for two reasons. First, "pollution cars" will not be allowed in the central business district. Secondly, motor fuel will be three times more expensive than today; the taxes that represent 80 percent of the price of fuel in 1967 will be increased to subsidize the electric car which is 100 percent "clean" and uses national carburant (nuclear electricity produced by high-temperature fast breeder).

Fuel-cell vehicles which give 60 percent more miles per gallon will therefore be more popular. What is more, they will be tolerated in town. These fuel cells, based on solid electrolyte, will be relatively cheap and light in weight (less than 2 kg/kW). They will, however, be subject to fierce competition from the rechargeable batteries that have ventured outside the towns.

Finally, sports cars will be equipped with high-temperature gas turbines with high power/weight ratios and fuel consumptions halfway between those of the internal-combustion engine and those of fuel cells. One drawback: because of the danger of pollution, turbines will not be allowed in towns even though they may be almost noiseless.

Fuel cells and gas turbines will also be used in trucks, or rather enormous multi-trailer lorries (over 100 tons) which will handle half the freight traffic. Diesel engines of the required power will be too heavy, too slow, too noxious, and too noisy and so will gradually die out.

In the year 2000, there will be 360 million private cars in the United States (1.1 car per inhabitant) and about the same number in Europe (seven times more than at present). But saturation will be in sight and the market will have become solely a replacement one. Manufacturers may even turn towards the private aircraft, which will have become the maid of all work and will undergo enormous expansion. Needless to say, these private aircraft will have little in common with existing ones. Their garages will be roof tops and they will be automatically driven, with automatic vertical take-off and landing, assisted electromagnetically from the ground. In flight, the planes will always be propelled by directional-jet gas turbines, which will have become extremely light (100 kg thrust per kg) which will make possible a considerable range of speeds (60 to 1,000 km/h).

The main competitor of road freight transport will not be the train but vehicles totally enclosed within a tightly fitting "tube." Such tubes may be made from new forms of glass free from surface faults, giving them a strength/weight ratio three to four times higher than steel. Glass wire tubing will be impregnated with transparent synthetic resin, concealing the structure itself. These tubes will find applications overhead and underground, where they could be used to speed the postal service and the removal of household refuse. Tubes will carry not only liquids, as in 1967, but also solids in standardized containers moving on an air film. The same air will be used to propel them.

Tubes will also be used for passenger transport up to 800 km/h. The passenger carriages will be transparent capsules about the same size as the fuselage of a present day aircraft. These containers will be floated on an air film. Air entries and exits will be at blowers at regular intervals along the tube but to conserve energy and increase efficiency air distribution will be controlled by sensing devices which let air out only when the container is passing over them. This technique has already been worked out

in some detail at the Institut Battelle in Geneva and is already
in commercial use for the transport of goods. Extended in scale,
it will give rise to the Pneumatic Logic Tube Train which will be
more efficient than the traditional forms of pneumatic transport.
It will be preferable, too, to the other kind of pneumatic train
known as the Foa system or Project Tubeflight. The idea here is
to float the passenger container in a tube by means of air pads
extending on arms from the container itself. Disadvantages of
this system are that it needs tubes of twice the diameter of the
container as well as noisy, pollution-causing turbines for propulsion. This would cause difficulties in providing fresh air for
passengers and after a few days of running the exhaust would
obscure the view through the transparent glass tube. It has also
been shown that the passage of each 10,000 horsepower train will
increase the temperature by about 10° C., making it impossible to
keep trains running continuously during the summer.

The Pneumatic Logic Tube Train will therefore become the
most widely used for reasons of safety and cost. The key components will be fresh air pulsated by low-pressure ventilators and
thousands of plastic valves. The latter will be inexpensive logic
elements, designed to bring the air beneath and behind the train
and evacuate it in front, thus reducing drag. In a sense this invention is the three-dimensional equivalent of the invention of the
railway in the 19th century, whose most important contribution
was the elimination of rolling resistance along one plane.

But the railways will not remain inactive as the following evolution shows:

1961: discussions as to the possibility of increasing speed
limits of trains from 150 to 160 km/h.

1964: the Tokaido line in Japan is opened to the public (190–
210 km/h).

1967: in France the Bertin Aérotrain prototype reaches a
speed of 300 km/h.

1969: Shin-Osaka line in Japan opened to the public at 240
km/h.

1970/71: turbotrains in use successively in Canada, United States,
France, United Kingdom and the Soviet Union at speeds
up to 270 km/h.

Railway speed will have practically doubled in ten years. Pendulum suspension, automatic driving and signaling and the invention of automatic control of rail adjustment will make it possible gradually to increase train speed to 400 km/h by about 1985. Nevertheless, the revival of the railways will be only a swan-song, particularly since there will be a noticeable reduction in the amount of heavy low-value goods being transported. Factories handling large quantities of raw materials will be set up along the coasts, receiving their ores by tube from the ocean seaports capable of handling million-ton super ore carriers.

The usual unit for maritime transport will be one million tons. Ships will be divided into two types: first, there will be the almost conventional giant transporters for low-value goods (ores, petrol, and grain). They will be operated by nuclear energy (100,000 h.p.) and screw-propelled at speeds not far exceeding those of today (20/22 knots). A crew of eight will be sufficient to control them, and will be replaced by STOL plane.

These giants will require installations at sea called seaports, which will consist of enormous floating surfaces made up of standardized barges of plastified steel, assembled on the spot. Shipbuilders will find an unhoped-for opening in the mass-production of such barges, which will also be used for floating airports, floating motorways and even floating hotels.

Goods of higher value will be transported by container ships, completely different from those of today. These will be air-cushion vehicles, more successful on sea than on land because they will not have to contend with water resistance, and there will be hardly any limit to their speed; as in aviation, speed will prove economical. Catamarans of 100,000 tons, lifted by surface-effect air pressure between the two hulls, will move at 60 to 80 knots with three to four times greater productivity than today. Port installations will also have undergone complete transformation. It will have become routine to unload a 100,000-ton container ship and re-load it in 1.5 hours by means of trays carrying 240 containers at a time, gliding on an air cushion. These container ships will be propelled by a row of ducted propellers, made of reinforced plastic honeycomb; each propeller will be driven by a gas turbine, and a single 100,000 h.p. gas generator will supply all the propellers in parallel.

But the aircraft will become the great rival of ships for long-distance freight transport. World traffic in air freight will increase from 4,000 million ton-kilometers in 1965 to 320,000 million in 1985 and then to 5.6 million million in 2000. Freight will represent 80 percent of air traffic as compared to 20 percent at present. Computer piloted, 1,000-ton air freighters capable of carrying 450 tons of containers on each trip will fly at Mach 2.5. Speed and size will be shown to be the most profitable considerations in accordance with a law confirmed in 1973 when the Boeing SST supersonic aircraft comes out, carrying three times more passengers three times faster than a Boeing 707 with a total weight only twice that of its predecessor and less fuel consumption per passenger. Much of these freighters will be made of reinforced thermostable plastic, heat-resistant up to 450° C.

Passenger traffic will have progressed in a less spectacular manner: 14×10^{12} passenger-kilometers in 2000—only 60 times more than in 1967. The average size of aircraft will, however, be multiplied by 20 (the average will then be 2,000 passengers per plane) and freight will be completely separate from passenger transport. Air congestion will thus still be fairly acceptable. Electronic guiding and automatic landing in all weathers will have been generalized for some time and pilots, of which there will have been a shortage, will now be replaced by navigation controllers. Take-off and landing will, of course, be vertical or nearly so since space for airports will be in very short supply.

The supersonic 650-passenger plane flying at Mach 6 and propelled by scramjet (supersonic combustion ramjet), the study of which has already begun, will be available about 1985. A lapse of eighteen years will still be necessary to transfer to the civilian sector the lessons learned in military aviation from record flights.

The most advanced aircraft will be a 2,000-seat plane flying at Mach 10, available in the late 1990s. Considerations of comfort, due to the maximum acceleration (about $0.3g$) to which passengers can comfortably be subjected, will restrict its use to long distances. On the London–New York run which will take fifty minutes it will have time to reach only Mach 9 before deceleration.

Although military pilots are already equipped with anti-g suits and trained to stand continuous acceleration up to $2.5g$, military aviation will find high g values an increasingly severe problem after the 1980s. An aircraft capable of reaching Mach 35 will have to go halfway round the world to reach such a speed. In the absence of effective gravity control, any further progress will be illusory. It is for this reason that a vast program of basic research will be launched by WASA (the "world" successor of NASA) in 1980 with a view to gravity control. This research might show results by the year 2000 and world aviation, after scaling the sound and heat barriers, will then be girding itself to clear the gravity or acceleration barrier.

Throughout this outline of the future of transport I have referred frequently to electronic control techniques. These, together with the obvious uses of computers in the transport field, will be of very great importance to the future of transport. Equally, I have also mentioned the factors of safety, noise, and pollution. To these should perhaps be added a fourth factor—disfigurement of the environment. These factors, as much as technical development and demand for more and better transport systems, will shape the future of transport. Their importance is already beginning to appear and stricter governmental controls on all four factors have already been implemented. As the century progresses, such controls are likely to become still stronger as we learn better to value the environment in which we live. There is today reasonable hope that we will never again allow industrial development to disfigure the environment as it did in the nineteenth century or the railways to disfigure large sections of cities as they did when they were built. Certainly transport systems of the next fifty years will differ from those of today much more than today's do from those of fifty years ago. But we can hope that this time technical progress will be coupled with concern for our environment and will not be pursued for its own sake. The vital role, then, may depend on new legislation. This may be the most important innovation of all.

AIRPORT PLANNING

by J. BLOCK

AIR TRANSPORT must be thought of as a whole, i.e., in terms of a "system." It would be pointless to have improved aircraft if they could not move in airspace or land at airports. Similarly, it would be useless to have airports if they could not be operated because of noise or congestion of their surface access facilities. Aircraft, airspace, airports, and ground environment are therefore parts of a system which must necessarily be analyzed and planned together, otherwise the shortcomings in one area may disrupt the whole system. Something like this is in fact now happening in the Northeast of the United States owing to the congestion of airspace.

Thus the future of airports cannot be imagined without studying the future of the other parts of the system and trying to identify the bottlenecks that are likely to jeopardize development.

With regard to co-ordinated planning, major efforts are being made everywhere in the world to associate aircraft manufacturers, airlines, airport authorities, and those responsible for town planning, more closely. True, there will be many problems, but a good start has been made and the solidarity of the interests involved may help to solve them. The trend towards increasing the capacity of conventional aircraft has the twofold effect of delaying airspace congestion and cutting operating costs, thus making it possible to meet demand as well as attracting new passengers. There seems to be no limit to this increase in aircraft size; weights of 700 metric tons, fuselage lengths of 100 meters and spans of 85 meters are now conceivable and such aircraft will probably be available for freight before passenger traffic.

As a result, difficulties may arise at airports with regard to the bearing strength of runways, the strength of bridges, and the geo-

This article was first published in *Futures*, Volume 1 Number 4 June 1969.

metric dimensions of taxi-ways and aircraft loading stands. But these problems will not be insoluble if manufacturers increase the number of wheels on landing gear and ensure good aircraft maneuverability on the ground.

The progress in engines and aerodynamics of conventional aircraft has ended the race to lengthen runways. Noise control has also entered an active phase; certification of the noise of aircraft is going to be imposed on manufacturers and initially this will represent a cut of about 10% in sound levels as compared with existing machines, which will be reduced still further with technical progress. Not all the noise problems around airports will be solved by this but certainly they will be alleviated, making it possible to guarantee that the increase in traffic will not worsen the present situation. Certain flight restrictions, particularly on night operations, may also be lifted, which is very important for the development of freight.

Even more important for the future is the development of new, non-conventional aircraft. These are mainly supersonic (SST), short takeoff and landing (STOL) and vertical takeoff and landing (VTOL) aircraft. The first will enable the very-long-distance market to be developed by raising quality of service: covering 6,000 km in 2–3 hours instead of 7, or 10,000 in 5–6 hours instead of 12, has considerable appeal for anyone traveling frequently by air. SSTs create scarcely any particular problems at airports, apart from the probably high noise level owing to the power of the engines (thrust/weight ratio of 45% as against 25% for subsonic aircraft).

STOL aircraft are at present undergoing a period of development which is justified for several reasons:

They enable the aircraft to be introduced in regions where it would be impossible to set up conventional airports either because the topography is unsuitable (mountains, islands, etc.), or because there is not enough traffic to justify the cost (developing or desert countries).

They enable the use of airspace to be increased in very busy regions through their ability to operate outside conventional airways and landing and takeoff paths (see tests with the Breguet 941/McDonnell 188 in the Northeast of the United States).

They are a good replacement for the helicopter on short routes because their operating costs are much lower. However, they require a bigger infrastructure than helicopters, which limits this advantage to favorable sites (for example, links between the New York and Washington airports and services for the Los Angeles region).

STOL aircraft will certainly facilitate the development of air transport by conquering new markets in regions with a difficult terrain, in virgin territory and on short routes. But in this last resort their operating cost, which is higher than the conventional aircraft's, can only be offset if they permit a gain in time over competitive transport. This supposes that stolports can be located near traffic-generating centers. The shortness of the runways required (about 450 meters long) may in fact permit their location nearer to urban areas than major conventional airports, but in many cases it will be impossible to accommodate them in the center of towns.

Only VTOL aircraft really appear as capable of taking over the short-distance transport market for aviation. This is an important market as most journeys are over short distances.

VTOL aircraft require only very small areas and are not demanding with regard to obstacles. The location of vertiports in the center of cities—on the ground or on terraces—is therefore perfectly feasible provided the VTOL noise level is acceptable. This problem has not yet been solved, but prospects are good.

Then there is the economic aspect: the helicopter has hardly been developed commercially because of its price, but future VTOL aircraft, whether derived from the helicopter or not, will be much less costly to operate. A study conducted on services by helicopter for the Paris region has already shown that if a heliport could be located in the center of the business district the time saving compared with surface methods of traveling would justify the extra cost.

There is no doubt that the breakthrough of economic and quiet VTOL aircraft, which is considered probable between 1980 and 1985, will be just as great a revolution in aviation as the advent of jets in 1958, since these machines will be able to compete effectively on very-short, short and even medium distances. They will in fact be using a network of vertiports placed very near to the traffic-generating centers and will thus solve the problem of economic penetration into the center of towns, which the other transport methods cannot do. They will make possible rapid direct links between a large number of points, with limited expenses on infrastructure and reduced terminal delays, which will be particularly advantageous and necessary in the conurbations of the future.

The optimum utilization of airspace poses problems that the growth in the number of aircraft will make increasingly difficult. Fortunately, solutions can be considered through increasingly complete automation of control and improved accuracy in identifying the exact position of each aircraft, its path and its speed. Extension of such automation to landing systems will give the aircraft the main quality it is still lacking, namely regularity. Once this is provided, there will be a further reason for even more traffic growth. The automation of aircraft guidance on the ground will pose quite difficult problems at very big airports where the taxiway network will grow increasingly complex and become similar to a railway network on which several dozen machines may be moving at the same time.

The problems the airports will have to overcome will be mainly traffic flow and financial; the aim will be to cope with a considerable amount of traffic at the least cost. Today's area and investment ratios required per passenger are incompatible with the foreseeable development in traffic. But the technological mutation of aircraft will enable this contradiction to be partly overcome. The development of STOL and VTOL aircraft for short and medium distances, i.e., for 90% at least of future air trips, will make it possible to replace giant airports which eat up space and money and whose very size creates increasingly insoluble problems for the neighborhood, by a large number of small, inexpensive stolports and vertiports.

Thus, to handle the foreseeable 600 million air passengers a year in the Paris region in the year 2000 (i.e., 60 times the present figure), will not require ten giant airports each handling a traffic of sixty million passengers a year, which would be impossible to build owing to the lack of suitable sites, but rather 200 vertiports and stolports whose area would range between 0.5 and 200 hectares and each of which would serve a region with 100,000 inhabitants and account for an annual traffic of three million passengers a year, with about 100 aircraft movements a day, posing no noise, access, congestion or cost problems. One or two conventional long-runway airports will be sufficient for long-haul supersonic or hypersonic aircraft.

Generally speaking, the way to reduce costs will be to specialize facilities as much as possible, so that they can be adapted to their functions with maximum output and minimum waste. The development of air freight will, in particular, make it possible to consider in the future airports specializing in goods traffic. This is out of the question at the present time since the bulk of freight is still carried in passenger aircraft holds which, incidentally, are continually increasing in volume. These all-cargo airports will give birth to large industrial complexes, an idea of which is given today by major seaports, together with container-sorting terminals which will form the main junction points in overland transport networks. Similarly, aircraft maintenance operations will probably be centered on aerodromes like those which already exist near major aircraft factories.

The subject of facilities required for private flying has been deliberately ignored. Foreseeable growth in this area will be comparable to that for the private car, i.e., enormous.

In all air terminals, automation will make it possible to speed up procedures which cannot be eliminated. Preparations are already being made to solve the urgent problems of handling high-capacity aircraft: automatic check-in, entirely automatic baggage handling and passenger movements, simplified or computerized administrative formalities for passengers and freight, generalization of the use of containers, etc.

Problems involving the airports of the future will, in fact, probably come under the psycho-sociological field more than the technical field. A very detailed investigation has been conducted by the Paris Airport Authority to analyze the behavior of the future air passenger when air transport has become absolutely commonplace and completely depersonalized by automation. It appears that air terminals will have to be especially designed to create around the passenger an environment meeting his continually increasing and often contradictory requirements for rapid efficiency and a friendly atmosphere, individual independence and high-quality personal service.

Like any transport infrastructure, the airport is both part of a transport system and part of an urban system. It must therefore be planned coherently in both systems, which is difficult, for their interests are often contradictory. The town, for example, rejects the airport which eats up space and creates noise, but the town demands the airport which, as a center of trade and a creator of jobs, is a factor in economic development; or else the airport users demand convenient means of surface transport, but the problem cannot be settled separately from that of traffic in general in the urban region in question. It seems, however, that these conflicts may be solved better in the future than in the past because of greater awareness of the importance of air transport in economic and social development.

Airports do not run the risk of acting as a brake on growth in aviation. But the giant airports of today have become victims of their own size and its resulting limitations and will probably disappear and make way for smaller, more numerous, more specialized airports that are better adapted to the environment of the future. These airports, serving STOL and VTOL aircraft, will reduce the disturbance in urban neighborhoods and terminal delays, and will be cheaper and more efficient. Because air transport is a very dynamic field particularly subject to development, airports often lead the field in innovations for transport infrastructure. The dynamic nature of air transport has meant that it is peculiarly susceptible to innovation. The developments in airports are likely to remain the torch of innovation that has guided other transport infrastructures such as railway stations and bus terminals.

TELEVISTAS: LOOKING AHEAD
THROUGH SIDE WINDOWS

by J. C. R. LICKLIDER

IN PLANNING to improve the use of television for educational purposes, most people have accepted the basic framework of conventional "broadcast" television. That framework determines the basic structure of their thinking and in the process delimits it. For example, a person who thinks of educational television as a set of educational functions supported by the framework of conventional broadcast television is unlikely to think of television as a medium for two-way communication or as a way of transmitting the text of a book or the stimulus material for a course of programmed instruction.

The main purpose of this paper is to explore some of the possibilities that come to mind when one deliberately looks aside from the central line of thought about educational television and rejects the assumption that educational applications have to be built upon the framework of conventional broadcast television. It is not part of the purpose to argue that what is to be seen out the "side windows" is more attractive than the view along the central path. The intention is merely to examine briefly a collection of ideas that seem interesting from a technical point of view and to consider how they might fit into the future of education supported by technology. It seems important to do this because the modern technology of information and communications is opening up a wide horizon of bright prospects, most of which seem to be technically achievable. These prospects should be held in mind, and brought into active interplay with pedagogical, psychological,

Reprinted and abridged from *Public Television: The Report and Recommendations of the Carnegie Commission on Educational Television.* Copyright © 1967 by The Carnegie Corporation of New York. Reprinted by permission of Harper & Row, Publishers.

economic, and philosophical factors, during this crucial period of planning and deciding the course of educational television.

"Interactive" and "Selective" Television

The great simplifying characteristics of conventional broadcast television are that it is broadcast and that the broadcast stations transmit to viewers who do not transmit back. Under past technological constraints, those characteristics were a *sine qua non* for a wide-band medium. That is to say, to justify the use of a medium capable of carrying a very large amount of information each second, one had to reach a mass audience and therefore could not provide channels through which the many individual members of a large audience could talk back. In the future, technology will constrain less severely. We should therefore think about what educational television might do and what it might achieve if it could afford to present a much wider range of programs, direct its services to small and highly selected audiences, and even engage in two-way communication.

From an educator's point of view, the main intrinsic defects of broadcast television are that it offers everyone the same thing and does not give its viewers a direct way of participating in its programs or interacting with its program material. It is likely that advances in technological capability and changes in social perspective will multiply the channels available to educational television, making it possible for educational television to offer a wide variety of programs and services to meet diverse educational needs selectively and responsively. Indeed, it is possible that facilities will become available to educational television that will permit people to participate directly in educational programs and to interact directly with subject matter. These possibilities evoke concepts that I shall call "selective television" and "interactive television." Since interaction is such a strong factor in learning, let us consider it first.

Viewers do, in a sense, participate in conventional television programs. If the program material is dramatic and matched to a viewer's motivations, the viewer may sit on the edge of his chair, empathize overtly, and utter words of encouragement. That kind of participation fails, however, to qualify as *inter*active participation, since the actual course of a broadcast television program depends in no way upon the concurrent behavior of its viewers. The criterion for what is here called "interaction" is that both the program and the viewer be capable of influencing each other.

From a psychologist's point of view, there is an important difference between interactive and noninteractive participation which is crucial to the development, as distinguished from the exploitation, of motivation. Noninteractive participation stems from previously established drives, but it does not contribute effectively to the development or augmentation of motivation. Interactive participation, on the other hand, is regenerative. It stems from already established motivation and may in turn strengthen and even restructure that motivation.

It is obvious enough how viewers can react to a television program, but how can a television program react to its viewers? If it is a set piece, it can do nothing that is not set into it. If it is a contingent program, on the other hand, it can in principle adapt itself to its audience as a lecturer adapts himself to his. Indeed, if the "program" is an array of contingent programs—a "multiple-track" program, in the parlance of programmed instruction—it can adjust itself simultaneously in different ways to achieve and maintain resonance with each of several or many sectors of its overall audience. The trouble, of course, is that the difficulty of selective adjustment increases with the size of the audience. Obviously, there is an essential incompatibility between viewer-program interaction and mass media.

For a viewer of educational television, the next best thing to having the program itself react to him may be to select from an ensemble of transmitted alternatives the one that is most appropriate to his needs or interests. The viewer of conventional television can, of course, select a channel and change his selection whenever he likes. That is good as far as it goes, but it does not go far enough to give the viewer any sense of participation in a program. The idea of "participating by selecting" involves the assumption that broader and more systematically organized sets of options can be offered to the viewer and that more convenient and more sophisticated ways of selecting among the options can be provided.

On *a priori* grounds, to augment the electability of program material seems less likely to open significant new opportunities than does the establishment of true interaction between the viewer and the program itself. However, selectability does not suffer as severely the essential incompatibility with mass-audience broadcasting that handicaps interaction, since the entire process of selecting can be carried out at the receiver and no feedback channel from the home to the television station is required. Let us, therefore, consider a few approaches that involve selection by the viewer—approaches that might achieve some of the same advantages as interaction without giving up mass audiences.

Selective Broadcast Television

The approach to improving the effectiveness of educational television that requires the least modification of the framework of conventional broadcast television is one that takes advantage of increased availability of television channels to broadcast a large amount of carefully scheduled and coordinated material, from which individual viewers can select what meets their needs and interests. Each broadcast program, for example, could be an array of subprograms, from which each viewer could select one. From time to time, either at specified points in the program or at moments of his own choosing, the viewer could switch from one subprogram to another. A few of the ways in which this general method could be applied are suggested by the following ideas:

1. Several cameras are used to cover a group discussion, a play, or a football game. All the signals are broadcast and received by the television receiver. Associated with each receiving set is a control by means of which the viewer selects the camera through which he wishes to watch.

2. The picture of a work of art or of a scene on a large stage is transmitted in such a way as to preserve very fine detail. A control on the receiver permits the viewer to select whatever part he likes of the overall picture for display upon his screen. Having mastered the control arrangement, the viewer can let his eyes

explore a painting almost as though he were before it in the gallery or follow spontaneously the action of a dynamic scene.

3. The news broadcast has two main parts. First there is a summary in which the essence of each item is presented very briefly. During this presentation, the viewer presses a button each time he sees or hears something he wants to learn more about. Then, during the second part of the broadcast, when fuller and more penetrating accounts are given of the various developments, his receiver selects for him and presents to him a program custom tailored to his interests.

4. Instead of broadcasting a "moving picture"—a succession of still pictures, each minutely different from its predecessor—the transmitter sends out a sequence of still pictures in which one is quite independent of the next. The still pictures, coming at a rate of thirty per second, constitute a vast informational resource from which each receiver can select. The receivers are designed to pick out certain images and to hold each one for view until its selected successor arrives. Thus the viewer sees a succession of still pictures, each selected from a large set of alternatives.

The first two schemes would be interesting only if means were developed through which viewers could control the selection and display of received images very conveniently and very naturally, almost as a part of the act of viewing. The third scheme does not appear to involve any problems of adjustment by the viewer that would require the development of sophisticated means, but it does invite development of sophisticated arrangements for controlling the selection of program elements on the basis of the viewer's pattern of interests and preferences. The basic idea, suggested in terms of an augmented newscast, was to offer a variety of program elements, transmitting them in several parallel sequences so that each viewer's receiving set could make its own selection. If the entire schedule of offerings were preannounced, each viewer might of course piece together his own news program by operating a simple channel selector. To make the scheme practicable, however, it would be necessary to provide, for each receiver, a programmable selection controller. This notion, which tends to develop itself into a concept that might be called the "control subsystem" of the home information system, will be pertinent also to other ideas to be introduced later.

Assuming a sophisticated control subsystem, one can envisage application of "custom tailoring" to other things than news. It would be especially appropriate for announcements of forthcoming events and, indeed, for any subject matter that naturally divides itself into elements of which some are likely to be of interest to one viewer and others to another. Inasmuch as materials and services offered for sale to the public constitute precisely such a subject matter—and the development of sophisticated control subsystems would open new fields of advertising for commercial television—one can look forward to the actual appearance in the home of such selective means as we have been envisioning.

In the fourth scheme, many sequences can be carried by a single television channel of normal bandwidth because they are sequences of images separated by seconds of time rather than by milliseconds. The basic idea—not very appealing on first thought —is to give up the motion-picture quality of conventional television in order to make room for the many alternatives demanded for certain applications of selective television. If for each viewer there were one image every ten seconds, on the average, instead of thirty images every second as in conventional television, the same channel that carries a conventional moving television picture could carry three hundred entirely different sequences of images. Selecting from those three hundred sequences, each home television receiver could assemble its own unique program.

If the images had to be selected deliberately by the viewer, through some explicit control action taken each time he wanted to see a new picture, the idea of trading the dynamic motion-picture quality of conventional television for the high degree of selectability under discussion probably would not seem attractive for any purpose. However, if we recall and extend the concept of a control subsystem introduced earlier, we see that the viewer need not concern himself with the individual selections. The procedure governing the selections can be programmed into the control subsystem and, what is most important, the procedure can be made contingent upon relations between the viewer's responses and criteria transmitted along with the sequences of pictures. This notion of making the selection of the next picture contingent upon the viewer's responses to preceding pictures—responses he might make by pointing to part of the picture with a stylus or by pressing buttons on a portable response unit—can, in effect, convert television into a radically different and very interesting new medium.

The new medium would be especially appropriate for programmed instruction. Each receiving set would be equipped with a "light pointer" (a stylus connected to the receiver in such a way as to communicate the viewer's responses to the control subsystem), and scoring criteria would be transmitted along with the picture and sound of each "frame" of instruction. The result would be an extremely sophisticated teaching machine capable of presenting self-scoring multi-track instructional programs with automatic path selection. With such a medium, and with the aid of sophisticated programming, one should be able to involve each individual "telestudent" in an active participation that would verge upon true interaction with the program material.

Any scheme that requires the television receiver to hold an image for several seconds requires a receiver somewhat different from conventional receivers that use short-persistence picture tubes and embody no other means for storing the image than is inherent in the luminous phosphor of the display screen. However, devices and techniques now under development offer hope that receivers of the kind we have been discussing will be technically and economically feasible within a few years. Several different "buffer storage" devices have been tested successfully, and storage tubes are available that will hold their images until deliberately erased. An early development version of a "meshless" storage tube capable of displaying pictures with high resolution (i.e., the reproduction of fine detail) was demonstrated recently.

The dynamic—or, to put it more precisely, the kinematic—quality of moving pictures and conventional television is so obviously valuable that the thought of sacrificing it to achieve some other quality, such as the selectability just discussed, is likely to require a considerable amount of urging, even though assurance be given that the idea is to supplement rather to replace the standard medium. But it is important to keep the mind open to periodic reassessment of the values and costs of various ways of using the resources available to television. It is important to face the fact that the cost of the kinematic quality is high. Another costly quality is what we might call the "full-pictorial" quality of the conventional television image. Conventional television does not provide very high resolution, but it does reproduce more or less faithfully the hue, the saturation, and the brightness of each small area of the scene before the camera. Typically, there is a large amount of information in a detailed picture, and it takes a wide channel to transmit such a picture in a short time. With the facilities required to transmit one image of full-pictorial quality, one could transmit many pages of letters and numbers or many line diagrams, graphs and sketches. Text and line drawings can of course be transmitted, received, and displayed either with motion or without.

The development of low-cost video recorders and recordings adds important new dimensions to educational television. The impact of these components will depend upon the quality and reliability of their performance, upon their cost, upon the merit of the programs available to and through them, and upon the effectiveness of the program distribution systems. The potential seems very great, for it includes both a marked increase in the number of programs from which viewers may select and freedom from the constraint of having to synchronize the viewers' schedules with the broadcasters'.

Although we are used to thinking of the output of a television set as ephemeral pictures ("soft copy") and sound, it is interesting to consider also some of the possibilities and problems suggested by the phrase "hard-copy television." The change of domain from soft copy to hard requires that we make a corresponding change in the range of functions considered. Perhaps the most appropriate functions for hard-copy television overlap the functions now served by newspapers and magazines.

The concept of the newspaper delivered by wire has been discussed widely enough to need no elaboration here, but it may be worthwhile to relate it to ideas presented earlier about selection of program material by the viewer. The essential things are to give the viewer a way of specifying what he wants to have put into his newspaper and to incorporate into his receiver the means for selecting and recording, and later playing back upon demand, the appropriate items. Those requirements can be met by a blend of "ordering from menu" (as suggested earlier in connection with the augmented newscast) and "matching to profile" (as used in systems for selective dissemination of information). In one approach, for example, the televised newspaper would periodically broadcast an index to forthcoming news items, on the basis of which "subscribers" would make selections and designate them to the control sections of their receiving sets. Each control section would add to the list of designated selections a list of calculated selections, the latter being arrived at by comparing viewers' expressed interests with available news items. (The calculating might be done by a multiple-access computing service and fed into the receiving set via telephone lines. Indeed, the control section of the receiving set might reside mainly or even exclusively in a central computer somewhere.) The receiving set would then copy the desired items "off the air" and present them in the form of a custom-made family newspaper or custom-made newspapers for individual members of the family.

The basic theme of the foregoing discussion is of course selectivity, and the basic problem is the one already encountered and discussed: the problem of broadcasting enough alternatives to provide a basis for truly sharp selection. It is important to note how much that problem is simplified by the switch from the moving pictures of conventional television to the mainly alphabetic text of the news article. The amount of space in the frequency spectrum (a bandwidth of about 5 million Hertz) required to transmit a conventional television program will carry about a million alphanumeric characters (letters, numbers, punctuation marks, etc.) per second. A standard newspaper column of text contains about four thousand characters. Thus one conventional television channel could carry the alphanumeric contents of a thirty-page newspaper each second. Indeed, if a recent estimate is even approximately correct, one television channel could transmit —on a continuing basis, as it is published—every bit of text that is published in any newspaper, magazine, journal, or book that finds its way into any recognized library or document room in the world. (J. W. Senders's estimate in 1963 was about two million bits per second.) Evidently, if we limit the discourse to alphanumeric text, it is not lack of bandwidth that stands in the way of offering the world's fund of news and knowledge to every man in his own home.

All the news may fall within it, but not all the world's fund of knowledge falls properly within the domain—even within the here considerably extended domain—of broadcast media. The categories of content that do seem worth considering include, in addition to news, all the schedules and advance announcements and all the background information and evaluative commentary that pertain to situations or events of widespread interest, for no other medium than television has the potential capacity and selectivity to make available to each person at the time and place of his choosing his own self-prescribed subset of the whole.

Most of the foregoing "prediction" is simply projection into the future of what now exists and is familiar to many. Nothing in the list of statements is beyond the range of technical feasibility. The uncertainties are mainly uncertainties of time scale, and they stem mainly from difficulties in predicting the interactions among economic, social, and psychological factors. On the one hand are those who see in modern informational technology a firm promise of making education not only universally available but universally achievable and universally attractive. On the other hand are those who hold that our rate of progress toward any such goals is limited essentially not by any lack of material resources or facilities, but by lack of basic understanding of the educational process. The position of wisdom no doubt lies somewhere between the polar extremes, but wherever it lies, it calls for continual examination of the full range of possibilities offered by technology and periodic reassessment of our plans and courses of action in the light of those possibilities.

As a conclusion to this paper, let me presume to offer a tentative assessment. The main trend of educational television is somewhat too conservative in its estimation of the feasibility of selective, interactive, and intercommunicational television systems and of the achievability, with the aid of such systems, of a significant breakthrough in education. The main factor that is not sufficiently appreciated, I believe, is the effectiveness of interactive participation in a well-designed, strongly reinforcing educational process. Advances in technology are making it possible for the first time to set up such a process without depending upon lavish use of scarce human resources. Other advances are making it at least conceivable that we may be able to set up such processes on a broad enough scale to reach almost every educable member of the society. My conclusion, therefore, is that the situation calls for intensive research in two complementary fields: the exploitability of informational technology in support of education, and education within the new context offered by informational technology.

ARTIFICIAL THINKING AUTOMATA

by ROGER A. MAC GOWAN
and FREDERICK I. ORDWAY, III

I⊤ is becoming apparent that within a very few years it will be possible to build an artificial automaton having superhuman thinking ability, just as it is now possible to build a machine having superhuman mechanical strength. Although artificial automata may also be endowed with superior mechanical abilities, their significance will not lie in their mechanical but rather in their information-processing capabilities. The majority of an automaton's components will be fabricated from inorganic compounds and no naturally evolved life need be associated with them after the fabrication and perhaps an initial education. The first intelligent artificial automata on Earth will consist principally of electronic circuitry. It becomes appropriate to inquire as to the characteristics of artificial thinking automata and what advantages may be anticipated for them over naturally evolved life.

Reprinted from *Intelligence in the Universe* by Roger A. MacGowan and Frederick I. Ordway, III. © 1966 by Prentice-Hall, Inc. Reprinted by permission of the publisher.

Characteristics

Probably the most important characteristics of artificial automata will be simplicity (relative to biological life) and modularity. Biological organisms, as a result of evolution, tend to be highly integrated systems, but the trend in electronic systems design is toward a high degree of modularity. The trend toward modularity in electronic systems design results from both design and construction considerations. The processes of biological evolution inevitably resulted in extreme biochemical complexity in achieving maximum results with very limited control over local environments. The great environmental control due to the application of human intelligence implies that similar results may be obtained artificially with orders of magnitude less complexity.

In designing an automaton it would be desirable to have a highly flexible optical input system. Much information concerning our surroundings is detectable through electromagnetic radiation in the visible light range. It is interesting to note that human beings often resort to the use of eyeglasses, magnifying glasses, telescopes, and microscopes to supplement their optical input systems, which indicates that a much more flexible optical system than is found in humans would be desirable. This should not be interpreted as being contemptuous of the human optical system, which is quite remarkable in many respects; but, since it is an integral part of the body and nervous system, it is virtually unmodifiable—except indirectly by altering its input.

The lenses in the optical input of an automaton could readily be replaced in the event of damage or improved technology. Any automaton that might be designed today should have telescopic and microscopic vision as well as superior normal-range vision. This could be accomplished by automatic adjustment of lens systems and even the automatic switching of lenses and whole lens systems. The number of retina cells in the optical system, determining the input pattern information content, could be made as large as desired, assuming that the central information-processing network has a compatible capacity. An automaton could also be equipped with such exotic sensors as infrared, ultraviolet, and x-ray detection devices.

An automaton could be equipped with an input device capable of transducing sound waves over any specified frequency ranges and with specified sensitivity (within technologically achievable limits). As is the case with optical input systems, human beings often find their sound wave input systems inadequate for many needs. Amplifiers are used with hearing aids to increase the intensity of sound and many scientific instruments change the frequency of sound waves in order to make them audible to humans. Many other animals (for example, dolphins, bats, and even dogs) are noted for their superior hearing in frequency ranges beyond those audible to humans.

Touch, and more especially taste and smell, are relatively much less important to humans than vision and hearing. Early designs for artificial automata will probably ignore these sensors, although they could certainly be developed for any desired characteristics and any sensitivity within the limits of current engineering technology.

Human beings have made very extensive use of some external engineering devices to supplement their own input devices. One such device is the radio transmitter, which converts sound waves to electromagnetic radiation to facilitate long-range transmission. Then, the radio receiver converts the electromagnetic radiation back to sound waves to permit human perception. Television incorporates radio transmission and also permits the scanning of optical patterns so as to convert them to a serial set of electromagnetic signals. The television receiver re-creates both the sound waves and the visible light pattern. The frequency of the optical scanning rate is such that normal rates of movement perceivable to the human are preserved. The telephone is another well known engineering device that supplements the natural human input and output by converting sound waves to electronic signals, transmitting them over wires, and then regenerating the sound waves. Automata will be sufficiently modular so that receivers for electromagnetic radio and television signals may be installed as an integral part of the automata, inputting directly into the central processor, rather than being peripheral conversion devices, or transducers.

Human output devices are relatively much weaker than their input devices. Both writing and speaking are slow and essentially serial outputs. Unfortunately, human beings have no output capability comparable to their parallel optical input system; no automaton would be designed with such a weakness. A display device capable of displaying two-dimensional optical output patterns directly from the central processor will undoubtedly become a feature of many automata. Built-in electromagnetic radiation transmitters for transmitting internally generated serial symbolic characters and two-dimensional information patterns, directly from the central processor, would be another attractive feature for automata. With this type of output an automaton could communicate information as rapidly as it could be processed by the central processing unit, thus eliminating much of the slow, laborious speaking and writing that is characteristic of human beings.

An automaton designed for communication with human beings could be given both printer output and sound-wave output for the human frequency range. Some existing printers can print 600 lines per minute, which is about 150 times faster than a human can type, and research has begun on printers having a print rate of 30,000 lines per minute. This would yield a printing speed 7,500 times faster than a human with a typewriter keyboard.

Locomotion ability, which is an unimportant characteristic compared to thinking ability, could easily be provided in an automaton if desired.

Unquestionably, the most important aspect of automaton design is the capability and capacity of the central processing unit. One of the basic parameters of thinking is the information capacity in the patterns being processed. For simplicity's sake it is convenient to visualize the maximum size information pattern of a particular automaton as a two-dimensional square array of binary information elements. In essence, the size of this maximum information pattern represents the maximum complexity of ideas with which the automaton is capable of dealing.

In a neural network type automaton the complexity of information patterns may be increased by increasing the number of elements in each layer of the network. The only problem, then, is that of manufacturing more neuron models and enlarging the network, or manufacturing modules containing larger numbers of neurons per module. Additional modules may be added to each layer in a neural network, and additional modules may be assembled into additional layers.

If an increase is sought in the complexity of ideas processable by an automaton which is already "educated," then special precautions must be taken to avoid loss or disturbance of existing knowledge. That is, the neural network must be designed so as to facilitate future expansions with a minimum of disturbance. This implies that new neural elements should be added gradually and that they should be highly dispersed throughout each layer. Special wiring features should permit use of these expansion methods, and also might enable the new elements to be prebiased with the biases of logically adjacent neural elements. An engineering design allowing gradual, dispersed, biased expansion will permit a maximum expansion rate with a minimum distortion of existing stored information.

The complexity of information patterns in a digital computer type of automaton may be increased by simply altering the sequence of instructions in the program so as to permit the processing of larger patterns. This could result in an increased storage requirement, since every stored pattern would also be larger. The processing and retrieval time for each pattern would also be increased due to the serial nature of digital computer processing. However, a digital computer automaton would achieve a high degree of parallelization by operating many digital computer modules simultaneously. Thus, a lowering of the overall processing rate for a digital automaton could be avoided by adding more digital computer modules to the system for more parallel operations. The theoretical limit to this increasing of pattern complexity, without paying a penalty in overall processing time, is a situation in which every digital computer module is processing only a single pattern. This extreme will, of course, be beyond economic reason for a long period of time. However, a very large number of parallel digital computer modules is already conceivable.

The speed of associating and processing is one more important parameter of the thinking process. In neural network type automata the speed is dependent on the speed of transmission of wave fronts of pulses through the layers of neural elements. It could be increased by increasing the operation speed of the individual neural elements, or reducing the number of layers of elements. If the operating speed of individual neurons is to be increased without loss of sensitivity, then an improvement in electronic technology is implied. Electronic miniaturization permitting more dense packing of the neural elements could also make some contribution to increased speeds. A reduction in the number of layers of neural elements would also increase the speed of processing, but this is not a feasible alternative since it would interfere with the quality of the processing.

The speed of thinking in a digital automaton also depends on electronics technology in that more dense packing of electronic elements reduces the distances the signals must travel, faster switching devices produce faster processing, and lower power requirements mean less problems with heat dissipation and thus denser packing of electronic elements.

Another factor in the speed of digital automata processing is the parallelization of calculations, which can be increased by increasing the number of digital computer modules in the system. An excessive increase in pattern complexity, simultaneous with this increase in computer modules, could, of course, offset the potential increase in processing rate. As was noted previously, the theoretical limit to increases in processing speed by increasing the number of computer modules is the assignment of only one pattern to each computer module; this limit is way beyond presently conceivable economic practicality. The speed of thinking or pattern processing could also be reduced by shortening the program of instructions which is contained in every computer module, but this is not a feasible approach since it would necessitate a poorer quality of thinking. In conclusion, both the speed of thinking, and the complexity of ideas being processed in a digital computer automaton, may be increased significantly by adding digital computer modules to the system (this is manifestly a mass production manufacturing problem).

Another parameter of a synthetic thinking automaton is storage or memory capacity, which can be increased in a neural net system by increasing the number of neurons in the network. A neural net has an integrated or distributed memory which means that the condition of all the neural elements in the system are a component of every stored information pattern. Thus, both the number of neural elements per layer and the number of layers per network contribute to increased differentiability of patterns and therefore increased memory capacity. The previously mentioned methods for increasing the complexity of ideas being processed by a neural network automaton, by increasing the number of neural elements, will simultaneously increase the total storage or memory capacity of the automaton.

In a digital computer automaton the memory capacity may be increased by expanding the storage contained in each computer module of the system, but this implies a reduction in overall processing rate for the system since each digital processor must now process more stored patterns for each input, with no increase in processing capability. However, if more digital computer modules, with their attached memory units, were added to the system, then increased memory would be gained without loss in system processing speed.

The associative level of a thinking automaton is a very important characteristic. In a neural net automaton of fixed size the associative level is determined by the profuseness of the interconnections between neurons and the dispersion or fanout of the interconnections. Increasing the number of layers will, of course, also improve the associative ability. Electronic technology related to compact, mass-produced, flexible circuitry connections is the controlling factor in associative level of neural net automata.

In a digital computer automaton the associative level may be improved by altering the digital computer program of instructions in every computer module. This will naturally increase the number of calculations necessary for each association and result in a loss in processing speed. Such a potential loss in overall processing speed could be counterbalanced by an increase in the number of digital computer modules permitting increased parallelization.

The differing characteristics of synthetic automata and animals are profound in some respects. The possibility of having remote inputs and outputs of high quality would greatly reduce the importance of locomotion for an automaton. There would be no point in traveling to another planet or to an extrasolar system simply to observe, if sets of replaceable eyes and ears could be shipped there. Similarly, remote outputs could be sent to accomplish any desired manipulation of the remote environment. This concept assumes that adequate communication is possible between the remote inputs and outputs and the central processor of the automaton. It can readily be imagined that a very large number of remote input and output units could be permanently stationed at points of interest, and could be switched on and off at will by the central processor.

The problem of communication with other synthetic intelligent automata would not even require the transportation of input and output units. Direct communication of ideas between automata by electromagnetic radiation in the form of radio and television type signals would be possible.

Advantages

Intelligent artificial automata have several very important advantages over intelligent biological life.

One obvious advantage of an automaton over a biological species is the possibility of preloading the former's memory with high-order generalizations. A human being generally requires about 20 years of learning and induction before he is able to perform mature thinking. The human neural network is almost completely disorganized at birth; that is, the neural elements have not been systematically biased so as to store any information patterns. The processes of learning, and generalization or induction, cannot exceed some maximum rate due to memory-decay (time) factors. Efforts to exceed the maximum learning rate could lead to saturation of the neural net and loss of stored information. However, it might be possible initially to load the memory of an automaton with the highest order generalizations known at the time of construction, meaning that an automaton should be able to start operation at the peak of knowledge for a given time, and progress from there with learning and induction processes.

Another significant advantage which synthetic automata have over biological automata is ease of maintainability. As a result of the processes of biological evolution the human organism is made up of extremely complex aggregations of very complicated organic molecules. At the present level of technology it is impossible to produce synthetic duplicates of most of these biological components and attach them directly to the biological organism. It is impossible to repair much of the damage that occurs to biological organisms, although natural biological processes accomplish some repairs automatically. Thus, totally effective maintenance of the human organism is impossible at present.

This lack of maintainability of human beings results not only in their rapid aging and death, but in all manner of irreparable physical defects during their lives. Human nerve cells die regularly throughout life and they are not replaced naturally nor are they yet replaceable synthetically. Therefore, human mental life may be described as a struggle to achieve a maximum knowledge production through processing of information, using a constantly decaying information-processing device. It is interesting to note that the various details of biological aging processes are still poorly understood.

The human life span is ridiculously short compared to astronomical time scales; death itself seems quite unnecessary when looked at as the result of the gradual failure of components required to perform simple physical functions. Since there is no reason that they should face death, except as the result of some catastrophic occurrence, all synthetic intelligent automata should have indefinitely long life spans.

The relatively simple electronic and mechanical components of an automaton (as is the case with any engineering device) can easily be duplicated and replaced when a failure or accidental damage occurs. If the central thinking system of an automaton were properly designed, it would be possible for the automaton to maintain itself; that is, it should be designed so that the removal of small modular units of the central processor for repair or replacement would not interrupt or interfere with the overall performance of the thinking automaton. These small modular units containing many neural elements in close physical proximity would certainly disturb the normal operations upon removal unless the neural elements were wired in such a way as to be logically dispersed. Another feature facilitating maintenance in a neural net automaton would be automatic jumpering of all potential circuit gaps caused by removal of any network modules.

The maintenance of a digital computer type automaton during continuous operation would be a much simpler problem. Assuming that the system has a large number of parallel computer modules, the failure of a couple for short periods would only temporarily prevent the recall of a small percentage of the memories. Precautions should also be taken to prevent the possibility of any malfunctions erasing all of the memory in a computer module. If it were possible to switch a replacement computer unit to the memory module of the unit being repaired, then no interference with operations would result.

Special precautions would have to be taken with the master control computer module to prevent interference with normal operations in case of a breakdown. One or more of these modules would have to be kept on continuous standby for emergency use.

The ability to control the parameters of its thinking process would be useful for a synthetic automaton. This is presently impossible for human beings, due to the complexity and unalterability of biological organisms. It would be a relatively simple matter to design parameter controls into a synthetic automaton, making it possible to optimize its parameters for any particular environmental situation. The provision for parameter control in a digital computer type automaton would involve modifying the computer programs in all of the computer modules. Parameter control might be more difficult in a neural net automaton because an independent control system would be necessary to permit the operating characteristics of all the neural elements in the network to be changed during continuous operations.

A somewhat less significant advantage for artificial automata would be their greater tolerance to environmental factors. For example, they would not require a specialized gaseous environment and narrow temperature range as does man. An automaton could be designed to function perfectly in a vacuum and in a variety of gaseous atmospheres, as well as over a much wider range of temperature. Similarly, an automaton could be designed with other superior environmental tolerances to many factors such as radiation and acceleration.

A more impressive attribute of artificial intelligent automata would be the control of their own growth. Not only would it be possible for an automaton to direct the production of its own replacement parts, but it could also design and produce additional components for its own growth. Unlike biological organisms, an intelligent artificial automaton could continue to grow indefinitely both in mental and physical capacities. The continued growth of intelligent automata would be limited only by the availability of materials, production facilities, and energy. Consequently, it may be expected that, compared with human beings, an automaton would quickly expand its mental capacities to literally astronomical values.

Methods for accomplishing controlled growth in both neural net and digital computer automata have been pointed out previously. Expansions of digital computer automata require additional computer modules, additional or expanded memory modules, and modified digital computer programs. Growth in an operating neural net automaton requires careful engineering design so as to facilitate the gradual, dispersed, biased expansion of the neural elements. The logical dispersion of neural elements (lying in close physical proximity) in the same module, and the automatic jumpering of circuit gaps for removed modules, would certainly reduce the magnitude of the problem.

An automaton could easily control its own evolution as well as its growth by gradually incorporating new technological developments. New technology could be incorporated by removing one major module at a time and either replacing it with a more advanced module, or modifying it so as to assimilate the new technology. This would eliminate obsolescence in synthetic automata and consequently make it unnecessary to reproduce in order to evolve. Evolution could thus take place in a single artificial automaton, whereas biological evolution requires random mutations and natural selection over many generations involving multitudes of individuals. While it is probable that biological evolution will be controllable in the not too distant future through social controls and chemical means, the effects of this control will be insignificant when compared with the effects of growth control and evolutionary control in intelligent artificial automata.

The ability of synthetic automata to modify their makeup leads to an interesting possibility in the case where two or more artificial automata exist in close proximity. It may become possible for these automata to gradually, but completely, integrate their central information processing systems, while preserving their combined knowledge. By such a voluntary coalition each individual automaton would appear to gain tremendously by greatly increasing its directly available stored knowledge and by similarly increasing its capability for processing information.

It is conceivable that the individual and organizational competition that exists between biological organisms and societies may not occur between intelligent artificial automata. Biological organisms cannot fully integrate in this way, although social organization may be regarded as a trend in this direction. Advancing communications permit ever larger and more efficient social organization, the end result of which may be attempts toward gradual integration of human organisms. However, this is far more difficult in complex biological organisms than in artificial automata, as has been noted already.

In summary, the evolutionary potential of intelligent artificial automata is astronomical when compared to the evolutionary potential of biological organisms. Replacing the mutations and natural selection in biological organisms are the controlled growth, constant technological improvement through parts replacement, and complete information-processing system integration in intelligent artificial automata.

THE SOLAR SYSTEM AND THE FUTURE

by ISAAC ASIMOV

IN LESS THAN ten years after the first satellite was placed in orbit about the earth, men have been placed in orbit

Reprinted from *The World Book Year Book.* © 1966 Field Enterprises Educational Corporation. By permission of the publisher.

and remained there for up to two weeks. Some of them have emerged from the space capsule to "walk" in space. Unmanned satellites have made soft landings on the moon, and others have skimmed Venus and Mars to make observations that could not have been made from earth's surface.

What lies ahead of us now? If mankind can advance so far in space in less than 10 years, where will he go in the next 10 years? In 20? In a century? Is there anything we *cannot* do in space by 2100, for instance?

Suppose we begin by asking where we stand on the matter of unmanned exploration of space. There the greatest barrier was overcome in 1959, when, for the first time, a rocket was hurled upward by man at a speed of more than seven miles a second. At such speed, a rocket is not confined by gravity to an orbit about the earth. It "escapes," and goes into orbit about the Sun. The faster a rocket is hurled, the larger is its orbit about the sun. If it is made to slow down, it will drop closer to the sun. By carefully adjusting a rocket's speed in a mid-flight maneuver, we can place spacecraft close to Venus or Mars, even though these planets at their closest are many millions of miles from us. Mariner II executed a passage within 22,000 miles of Venus in 1962, and Mariner IV passed within 6,000 miles of Mars in 1965.

It would not take much more refinement to plot the course of an unmanned probe to Jupiter, Saturn, and beyond. This is something that could be done now if our space scientists were not committed to other tasks of greater importance.

It is not enough, however, simply to send a piece of metal toward Jupiter. If a planetary probe is to be useful, the ship must send back signals. The signals tell us its position and provide us with other vital information. From how far out in space can we reasonably expect to be able to receive such messages?

Already space scientists have sent radar waves to Jupiter and have (possibly) detected the reflection. The distance of such a round trip to Jupiter is about 800,000,000 miles. This is quite an advance over the time, just after World War II, when it was a great feat to bounce radar waves off the moon—a round-trip distance of less than 500,000 miles. It seems possible that by 1975 or so, our techniques will have developed to the point where we could produce a radar beam that could bounce off a body 4,000,-

000,000 miles away—the distance to Pluto, which is the most remote planet known in our solar system.

We will soon be in a position, then, to explore the entire solar system with unmanned probes. By the year 2000, we might well have launched one or more probes toward every one of the planets in the solar system. The results of these probes will not, however, all be known by then, for trips to the outer reaches of the solar system take a great deal of time. Mariner IV took more than eight months to reach the vicinity of Mars. If it were traveling to Pluto, many years would be required for the flight.

Can we explore beyond the solar system? After all, if we propel a rocket at a speed of more than 26 miles a second (escape velocity from the sun at our distance from it), it will no longer remain in orbit about the sun. It will leave the solar system forever. If we aim it correctly, it will eventually approach Alpha Centauri, the nearest star to our system, or, for that matter, approach any other object toward which it is aimed.

Unfortunately, though, even the nearest star is almost 7,000 times as far away as Pluto. The flight of an unmanned probe to Alpha Centauri might well take many centuries. Nor does it seem that we will be able to develop communications beams of sufficient power to track a probe all the way to the stars. Certainly we will not, in the next century or so.

And what about manned flight? A lunar probe taking pictures of the moon does not compare in excitement with a man landing on the moon. And will reaching the moon be the end? Can we expect human beings to land someday on the surface of Mars or Jupiter? Where can we draw the line and say: "Here man is not likely to go in the next century and a half?"

Man can explore space in four stages: in journeys that last days, months, years, centuries. The first stage, a trip of a few days, has taken him to the moon. And now that we have reached the moon, there seems to be nothing to prevent us from ferrying machines and supplies there to build a permanent base.

By 1980 or 1985, such a base may exist. From an astronomical observatory on the moon, knowledge can be gained which can smooth the way for more extensive voyages of exploration. What's more, the moon with its lesser gravity could eventually be used as a more economical launching pad for extended voyages than the earth itself would be.

The second stage of space exploration—trips of a few months—will place the inner solar system within our grasp. This includes the planets Mars, Venus, and Mercury. Of these, Mars is the least forbidding. Despite its extremely thin and arid atmosphere, Mars just possibly may have simple life forms on its surface.

The main difficulty in reaching Mars involves the length of the journey. Before men can reach Mars, they must spend six months or more in space. Can they remain in isolation that long? Can they carry sufficient supplies? Can they endure weightlessness that long?

Let's consider these problems. Isolation need not have serious effects. Four or five centuries ago, men made voyages that lasted several months across wide oceans under conditions almost as dangerous for them as a flight to Mars would be today. They were even more isolated then than a space traveler would be now. They were truly cut off from home, whereas an astronaut would be in radio communication with the earth at all times—with the encouragement of all humanity constantly in his ear.

The problem of supplies is one for which solutions are being found. First of all, it will not be necessary to pack aboard a spacecraft to Mars the several tons of water and oxygen each man would need during the trip. Instead, the spaceship would carry a miniature chemical plant which would distill and purify waste water and process carbon dioxide to recover oxygen for breathing. It is not contemplated, however, that food would be produced aboard ship. Food would be brought along in freeze-dried packages.

What about weightlessness? It would seem that a man in a state of weightlessness for six months or more would suffer physical harm. If, however, a specially designed spaceship (or part of one) could be spun steadily, a centrifugal effect would be produced within it that would push the astronaut out toward the walls. This would have the same effect upon him as a gravitational field. It would take no energy to keep the ship spinning once it was put into such motion, and the effect might well be to keep the astronaut healthy and comfortable.

If these problems are solved, astronauts may land on Mars by 1985, and there may be a permanent station there by 1995. Stations might also be established on the two tiny Martian moons, Deimos and Phobos, which have no atmosphere and virtually no gravity.

What about the danger of radiation on these month-long trips? The principal danger would come from high-energy particles emitted at unpredictable intervals from flares on the sun. Although spaceships to Mars would be moving away from the stronger radiation of the sun, radiation shields would have to be provided to protect the astronauts during periods of intense solar activity. Mars itself has no detectable radiation belts to worry about once the spaceship nears the planet.

Trips to Venus and Mercury would take no longer than the trip to Mars, but those to Mercury would take considerably more energy because of the orbital mechanics involved (maneuvering an orbit in the presence of the nearby sun's gigantic gravitational field is difficult).

Neither Venus nor Mercury is expected to have any radiation belts to speak of. Both are, however, in the direction of the sun, whose radiation increases dangerously as it is approached. If the radiation danger can be overcome, and, in all probability it will be, Venus and Mercury can be reached before 2000.

Establishing permanent bases there is another matter. The surface temperature of Venus, as measured by Mariner II, is about 800° F. This is the temperature all over the planet's cloud-shrouded surface, both day and night, so it must be at least that hot under the surface. There would be no escaping the heat by burrowing underground. Unmanned probes could reach Venus's surface, and a manned expedition might make a temporary flight beneath the clouds, but it seems unlikely that a permanent base will be established on Venus in the foreseeable future.

Mercury is a better prospect since it has no atmosphere to conserve the heat and spread it over the entire surface. Until very recently, it was thought that Mercury presented only one side to the sun, so that one side was always unbearably hot, while the other was almost at absolute zero. If that were so, we could land on the cold side. It is simple to establish an artificially heated base, whatever the cold. Now, however, we know that Mercury slowly rotates with respect to the sun, so that each part of its surface has a day and a night about 59 earth-days long.

During the night, however, any spot on its airless surface has ample opportunity to cool down. This means that any expedition landing on Mercury would have to do so at a point far enough into the night shadow for the surface to have cooled down. An underground base would then have to be dug before the landing point had circled into sunlight again.

Mercury approaches to within 28,000,000 miles of the sun. Can men ever expect to approach even closer? One possibility exists. There is a tiny asteroid named Icarus, which at times passes within a few million miles of the earth. It has a very flattened orbit. At one end, it reaches halfway to the orbit of Jupiter, but at the other it falls in toward the sun, speeding about it at a distance of only 19,000,000 miles. If an expedition could reach Icarus while it was passing near the earth and implant the proper instruments hastily, marvelous observations could be made of the neighborhood of the sun, the charged particles it emits, and the magnetic field it produces.

Any closer approach to the sun by man than Icarus would seem unlikely. Spaceships, manned or unmanned, could be made to skim about the sun at closer distances, but the heat and radiation would very probably be fatal not only to men but even to instruments, unless they were particularly well protected. It seems doubtful, therefore, that in the next century and a half, men will succeed in doing better than Icarus.

The third stage of space exploration—that which will involve voyages lasting years—will carry us to the vast outer solar system. This can be done in graduated steps. Between the orbits of Mars and Jupiter circle thousands of asteroids. A few of them are a hundred miles or more in diameter. Ceres, the largest, is 480 miles in diameter. Once we get to Mars, we will be able to reach the asteroids without too much additional trouble. Perhaps as early as 2000, man will have landed on Ceres. Step by step, other asteroids may be reached. One of the most interesting is Hidalgo. It has a very elongated orbit. At one end, it approaches to within 24,000,000 miles of the orbit of Mars. At the other end, it recedes as far from the sun as does Saturn. Hidalgo's orbit is quite tilted as compared to the orbits of the various planets, so it comes nowhere near Jupiter and Saturn. Still, if an expedition could land on Hidalgo when it was near Mars, men could remain in space for years, studying conditions in the outer solar system at their leisure, knowing that they would eventually return to the neighborhood of the orbit of Mars.

Astronauts could tackle the outer planets one by one, establishing themselves firmly on one, then progressing to the next one. To make these trips, however, even under the best of conditions, astronauts would have to spend many years in space, if spaceships are equipped with the chemical rockets of the kind used today. Unless a new kind of rocket is developed, it may well be that man will never pass beyond the asteroids.

The use of nuclear rockets is a possibility. Rockets might be driven by a series of atomic explosions or by exhaust gases expelled by the heat of a nuclear reactor. In either case, rocket ships could be kept under acceleration for longer periods, and would attain higher speeds.

Then, too, there is an ion rocket now being developed by scientists. Ordinary rockets achieve their thrust by hurling large quantities of heated gases backward. This brute force is necessary to lift the spacecraft above the atmosphere and push it into an orbit around the earth. Once in orbit, however, and surrounded by a vacuum, a ship might make use of electrically charged atoms (ions) instead. These can be hurled backward by the action of an electric field. The thrust of the ions is very weak, so the rocket's speed increases very slowly. The ion rocket is, however, much more efficient in the long run than an ordinary rocket. Acceleration can be continued for indefinite periods, and speeds approaching that of light itself (186,282 miles per second) could, in theory, be attained. By 2000, when men will have reached Ceres, both nuclear rockets and ion rockets may be in operation. If so, it may be with these that the outer solar system will be explored.

A generation later, say by 2025, we may well have landed on one or another of Jupiter's satellites. A century from now, a landing may have been made within Saturn's satellite system, with plans in the making for reaching the satellites of Uranus and Neptune. By 2100, perhaps men will stand on Pluto, at the very limits of the solar system.

Notice that I mention the satellites of Jupiter, Saturn, Uranus, and Neptune. What about those planets themselves? These four planets are giants with conditions that are far removed from those on the earth. They are frigidly cold and have deep, thick, poisonous atmospheres that have incredible storms and winds of unimaginable violence. Pressures at the bottom of these atmospheres must be thousands of times greater than ours. Nor are we certain as to the kind of solid surfaces they have.

If astronauts ever did reach the solid surface of the outer giants (through the use of a spaceship with some of the properties of the bathyscaphes with which we now explore the oceanic abysses) they would be subject to gravitational pulls much stronger than those which are experienced on earth. These pulls would largely immobilize the astronauts and make the problem of getting off the planet almost insuperable. The difficulties in sending manned expeditions to the surface of the giant planets are so great that for a long time space scientists will be satisfied to send unmanned probes spirally toward Jupiter, Saturn, Uranus, and Neptune. Manned exploration of these planets will not take place in any foreseeable time. But small Pluto can be landed upon.

The fourth stage of space exploration—voyages lasting centuries—will take us to the planets of the nearer stars. As was said previously, the nearest star is almost 7,000 times as far away as Pluto. Why bother?

Well, nowhere in our solar system is there another planet on which man could live comfortably. He would have to live underground or beneath domes (which, however, may turn out to be an exciting forward step in man's progress). Nowhere else in the system, outside the earth, can there be anything more than very primitive life forms. Out there among the stars, however, there are sure to be other earthlike planets, which may very likely bear life. Some of them might even bear intelligent life. Unfortunately, we cannot be certain a particular planet bears life until spaceships get fairly close to the stars that these planets circle, so that if other life is what we seek, we must explore blindly.

But can other stellar systems be reached?

Certainly the task of reaching even the nearest ones is many times as difficult as that of reaching even the farthest planet of the solar system. A major problem in making such a trip would be to ensure protection against the lethal high-energy particles that would collide with a spaceship, endangering its passengers and instruments. No solution to this problem is yet known. Moreover, even the most advanced rockets we can imagine cannot go faster than the speed of light, and, even at the speed of light, a round trip to the nearest star would take nearly nine years. Round trips to more distant stars would take hundreds of thousands of years.

Even by 2100, when mankind may well be in occupation of Pluto, it seems doubtful that any serious attempt would have been made to send out an expedition to the stars. Does that mean, though, that men will *never* reach the stars?

"Never" is a pessimistic word. Scientists have speculated on several means of reaching the stars. The first necessity, of course, is the ability to reach speeds approaching that of light. These may be reached by means of ion rockets or some other technological developments not yet visualized.

Einstein's theory of relativity explains that all internal motions slow down in objects moving at great speeds. Astronauts, therefore, might experience the passage of only a few years in the course of voyages which to men on earth might seem to be lasting hundreds of thousands of years. Men could therefore reach even distant stars in the course of their own lifetime, though that would mean saying farewell forever to the earth they left behind.

If it turns out that speeds near that of light are not practical, it may be possible, nonetheless, to live long enough to reach the stars. To achieve this, astronauts could be frozen and put into a kind of suspended animation for decades or generations until their destination was in view. We cannot say as yet, however, whether such suspended animation by low-temperature hibernation will ever be practical.

There is a third way out. In place of the small ships used for exploration and colonization of our solar system, a huge ship might be built for voyages to the planets of the stars. Actually it would be a small "planet" itself. On such a "star ship," there might be hundreds or thousands of men, plus room for agriculture and for herds of animals. Whole generations of men and women might be born, grow old, and die while the star ship traveled from one star to another.

When expeditions are sent to the stars—by whatever system —we need not expect to see them come back. Even a successful expedition to any but the very nearest stars cannot possibly return to earth in the same century, as we count time. Nor will it be possible to communicate with any human colonies that may be established on the planets of other stars in ordinary fashion. Even if we develop the ability to transmit communication beams intense enough to reach other stars, it will take dozens of years, even centuries, for such beams to reach the colony and an equal amount of time for the colony to answer.

Let us summarize then. A reasonable guess is that by 2100, mankind will have explored our entire solar system and will have landed on the surface of any planet, satellite, or asteroid he has tried for, except for Jupiter, Saturn, Uranus, Neptune, and Venus. He will have studied the sun from close range, but not more closely than from a distance of 19,000,000 miles. Mankind will *not* have made any attempt to reach or colonize planets outside our solar system.

After 2100, a long pause may be enforced on mankind. He will probably have gone as far as he can go without developing technical abilities far beyond what he will possess even then. Those space feats which mankind will not have accomplished by 2100 (a landing on the giant planets, a very close approach to the sun, a voyage to the stars) may not actually be impossible, but they are so difficult that mankind may not even attempt them for many centuries after 2100.

III

Environments

In lieu of the after-the-fact curative reforms, trending to highly specialized individual offender case histories, my philosophy urged the anticipatory avoidance of the accident potentials through invention of generalized highway dividers, grade separators, clover-leafing and adequately banked curves and automatic traffic control stop-lighting systems. I saw no reason why the problem shouldn't be solved by preventive design rather than attempted reforms. My resolve: Reshape environment; don't try to reshape man.

—R. BUCKMINSTER FULLER, *World Design Science Decade: Document 1* (1963)

MAN AND NATURE AND MAN

by ANTHONY J. WIENER

I

For centuries, man's intrusive and expansive civilization has caused increasingly radical changes in his environment. Until recently, it was not noticed that many of these changes are detrimental to man's future, and that some may even be irreversible or reversible only at great cost. In the last decade there has been a great deal of public discussion regarding the dangers of radioactive wastes deposited in the air and water as well as the danger of contamination of streams and rivers by sewage, industrial wastes, pesticides used in agriculture, and silt from construction sites. There has also been a growing concern over the health problems and consequent loss to industry that may be attributed to chemical pollutants in the air, especially exhaust products from internal combustion engines. However, extensive as this contamination may be, it is only part of a much larger picture: man's beneficial alteration and harmful misuse of his environment. Unfortunately, most of the criticisms that have been leveled against present trends have been characterized by a moralistic or romantic approach to "nature unspoiled." What is badly needed, however, is an unsentimental, balanced, realistic, and long-term view of man's impact on his environment, in order to "lobby for the future" in terms of projections that include benefits as well as costs resulting from various kinds of ecological changes caused by human activities.

The following list (prepared by Robert U. Ayres) may convey something of the scope and complexity of the overall problem:

A. Planetary Scale

1. Continued large-scale burning of fossil fuel may create a "greenhouse effect," possibly raising the temperature of the earth,

Published by permission of the author. First published in 1969.

melting ice and snowcaps, creating macroclimatic changes and raising sea levels.

2. Meteorological effects may also result from smokes, fumes and aerosols produced by combustion processes or water vapor ejected from cooling towers of large power plants. Also biological effects of toxic "smogs" can occur.

3. Properties of stratosphere and ozonosphere may be altered significantly by jet and rocket exhausts (increasingly important as space program continues).

4. Modification or diversion of ocean circulation may result from undersea topographical engineering. Tempting targets include the Gulf Stream, Bering Straits, Gibraltar, Gulf of Siam, and the Amazon River.

5. The evaporation rate from oceans may be inhibited by a floating monolayer of high molecular weight, e.g., from petroleum residues attributable to undersea drilling operations.

6. Absorption of solar heat by ice and snow may be increased deliberately or accidentally by creating ice or soot smogs.

7. The albedo (reflectivity) of the earth may be changed as a result of widespread surface changes (plowing, land clearing, etc.), with long-term consequences for climate, weather patterns, and secondary effects.

8. Reduced photosynthetic activity in estuaries and coastal waters may result from DDT in runoff from continental land masses. This could shift the balance between carbon dioxide and oxygen production.

9. Weather and climate modification schemes will have other impacts.

B. *Continental and Local Scale*

1. Because of population pressure, non-conservative agricultural practices may lead to alterations in the micro-climate and the meso-climate, e.g., as a result of wind erosion due to overgrazing, exposure of laterite soils to the sun in tropical areas, etc.

2. Instability of river banks, increased flood hazard, silting of flood plain, and marshy delta formation are consequences of upstream erosion caused by strip mining, logging, overgrazing, plowing of dry lands, road building, etc.

3. Excessive use and pollution of fresh water resources—due to rapid industrial development and population growth—results in accelerated eutrophication of lakes, and salt encroachments in rivers as ground water tables rise.

4. Ecological changes and the creation of resistant mutant strains of pests result from the use of broad-spectrum agricultural pesticides. Problems have also arisen from other non-biodegradables such as detergents.

5. Problems are created by fire suppression: for example, hazardous buildup of inflammable trash in Ponderosa forests and the spread of unpalatable brushy vegetation, e.g., mesquite, in former grasslands.

6. Ecological problems follow the lowering of the water table due to increased water use; conversely, higher water tables and even creation of marshes can result from deliberate burning of brush and trees.

7. The widespread use of water for irrigation projects can result in a build-up of salt in the soil; it also leads to increased local humidity.

8. Pest species and/or disease vectors are frequently introduced to new environments through various human agencies. Notable examples include the importation of the rabbit to Australia, the giant East African snail to Indonesia and Micronesia, the Dutch Elm disease, the sea lamprey and the alewife to the Great Lakes, and the Japanese beetle to the United States.

9. The decline or extinction of some species of fauna, due to excessive hunting or elimination of breeding grounds, is a common occurrence. The American eagle, the rhinoceros, the orangutan, the gorilla, the polar bear, and many less-well-known species are rapidly declining.

10. Suppression of some predator populations such as fox, chicken hawks, lynx, etc., lead to a buildup of their natural prey—rodents, rabbits, etc.

11. Serious ecological problems may be associated with disposal of radioactive and chemical wastes; for instance, certain radioisotopes are preferentially accumulated in animal tissue (e.g., Iodine 131 in the thyroid). Thus, ecological consequences arise from any use of nuclear explosives for topographical engineering.

12. Important psychic costs may be consequences of over-

crowding and widespread aesthetic deprivation, e.g., ugliness in slums: noise due to automobile traffic, jet planes, etc.; unpleasant odors from wastes, garbage, effluents, etc.

13. The efficient disposal of bulky solid wastes, e.g., auto bodies, trash, ashes, salt (from desalinization projects), slag, tailings from low-grade ore processing, subsoil from construction projects, etc., often leads to major external costs.

II

The development of some technologies creates hazards or by-product costs to society. These are primarily nuisances rather than matters of potential life and death for hundreds of millions of people, but nuisances that might grow serious enough to threaten man's individual health or survival, or his general economy, comfort and/or happiness.

Pollution is one of the effects of technological "progress" most in the news today. We continually read of streams, lakes, and even ocean shores becoming so polluted by the activities of our people, industries, and cities that the water sources constitute a hazard and can no longer be used for the benefit of society. We lose sources of drinking water and recreational facilities: serious ecological tolls are taken as fish and wildlife are killed or forced to migrate elsewhere. In recent years we have had to mourn the "death" of Lake Erie by pollution-induced oxygen starvation. Even in cases where man has made an effort to control the effects of indiscriminate waste disposal, his efforts have been stymied by side effects of other technological advances. For instance, the development of detergents was hailed as a great boon. However, it then became apparent that detergent, unlike ordinary soap, which is an organic material, resists bacterial decay. It also contains a great deal of phosphate builder which accumulates in surface waters, subsequently acting as a powerful nutrient for algal "blooms." Modern sewage plants are designed to convert organic matter to inorganic salts which can be safely disposed of in our waterways. However, the algal blooms reconvert the salts to algal organic matter. The algae then die, polluting the waterways and thereby defeating the purpose of the sewage-treatment plant.

Other objects of our progress have caused a disposal problem too, either directly or indirectly. For instance, our roads have been cumulatively marred by automobile graveyards. The substitution of aluminum for steel in beer and soda cans makes possible the pull-top, but it creates an object that will last, by the roadside or in the woods, for a matter of decades, rather than a few years. The no-deposit, no-return glass bottle represents another significant increase in litter made economical by the affluence of purchasers who can no longer be induced in large numbers to take the trouble to return bottles for a few cents each, and by a legal situation which makes it possible for the bottlers and the consumers to shift the resulting costs of litter disposal to the general public.

We might also note that waste heat, while not greatly publicized, may become an important pollution problem. There are nuclear power plants and even commercial steam plants which give off enough heat to raise at least the local temperature of a river such as the Colorado by several degrees. As the number and capacity of power plants increase, the issue of heating these rivers can become quite important. Similarly, in large urban areas the temperature generally runs 5, 10, or more degrees higher than in the surrounding rural areas, largely but not completely because of the rejection of heat from man's urban activities. It seems likely that as urban life becomes more affluent, larger in area, possibly more dense and more dependent on energy-consuming (and therefore energy-rejecting) devices, this problem will increase in importance. (For example, the air conditioning for an apartment house rejects much more heat to the outside world than is removed from inside the house, because of inefficiency.)

A third type of pollution is noise. Automotive vehicles have polluted not only the air in our cities, but also have raised the noise levels, often to points of discomfort. Medical and scientific studies have been made of the effects of higher-than-normal exposure to noise levels to which teenagers expose themselves by means of blaring-loud music; the results have proved to be damaging to some extent, depending upon the exposure.

A final and obvious example of this kind of pollution is the sonic boom that would be produced by supersonic jet transports. Some proponents of the SST expect that the difficulty will be alleviated by more efficient aircraft design and/or special operating procedures. But this remains an open question, and most experts believe the "boom" constitutes a very serious problem. It has been suggested that supersonic transportation may have to be restricted to routes over water or other uninhabited areas and that, even in that case, shock waves might be excessively disturbing to ships at sea or to other aircraft, not to mention possible unforeseen effects upon sea life.

There are other special activities, some of which are not widely publicized, which can cause serious problems. Some experts feel that the burning of gasoline in the upper atmosphere by high-altitude jets may trigger odd and possibly dangerous reactions in a zone of many delicately balanced processes and delicately stabilized situations.

The contamination or degradation of the environment does not necessarily have to be gradual or local. In a nuclear war (or even nuclear testing), it could be both spectacular and multi-national, or perhaps affect the entire planet. Bacteriological and chemical substances are not only dangerous as potential weapons, although they have within recent years been shown to have serious effects. For instance it appears to be an established fact that whole villages of people succumbed to poison gas attacks in Yemen and, more recently, there has been grave concern about the possible long-term ecological effects of our defoliation of Vietnamese lands.

Widespread damage might also occur as the result of an accidentally produced but uncontrollable epidemic. The death of several hundred sheep in the neighborhood of an Army testing site in Utah in the spring of 1968, later acknowledged to be caused by a nerve gas the Army was testing, may be indicative.

In this connection we must also mention an issue which has received much publicity and which we would argue has probably been exaggerated in discussion—at least as far as conditions of today are concerned—viz., the use of chemicals and other artificial additives at various places in the food production chain. Of course, while there may have been excessive apprehension about this issue in the past, conditions could clearly get a great deal worse, and probably would, if it were not for such campaigns of "exaggeration." The year 2000 may see not only the presence of harmful additives but a sacrifice of taste and of other aesthetic qualities to increased economic efficiency. This has already happened in the United States where commercial fruits and vegetables are inferior in taste to those which once were available (and still are in parts of Europe). However, the decreasing importance of economic efficiency lends some hope that such trends might be reversed. . . .

III

In thinking about the future interaction between man and his environment it is useful to distinguish between trends which are probably effectively irreversible and changes which can be reversed in principle. In the first category one would have to include population growth, life expectancy, mortality, intensity of land utilization, energy requirements, consumption of fossil fuels and other "exhaustible" resources, utilization efficiencies for such resources, topographical modifications (both deliberate and inadvertent, including erosion, silting, delta formation, etc.), reductions in the diversity of species in the biological environment,* and so forth.

While the cumulative effects of the foregoing are probably permanent or quasi-permanent, the *rates* of change of some of the above phenomena may be amenable to deliberate modification. Thus population increase can be stemmed by technological means of birth control such as the use of intrauterine devices, or by altered legal or social codes, as in Ireland after the potato famine of 1846–47, or Japan after World War II. The rapid increase of average life expectancy in the U.S. since the 1850s is already slowing down, probably because an intrinsic limit is being approached. (The *maximum* lifespan for humans has not changed, so far as can be determined, but remains about 115 years. A few individuals have achieved ages close to this limit in all genera-

---

* The interference of man has rapidly increased the "extinction rate" of rare species, and probably simultaneously decreased the rate of evolution of new species. This phenomenon, so regretted (when it is noticed) by naturalists, is an inevitable consequence of the rapid interspersal and "homogenization" of species which originally developed independently in separate parts of the world, but which now compete for the same ecological "niches" if brought into contact with each other through the agency of man. Many species also suffer as a result of direct human competition (for a limited habitat) or direct exploitation by man. Ecologically the world is rapidly becoming "one." Deliberate cross-breeding of agricultural plants and domestic animals may partially counteract this trend, however, by artificially speeding up evolution.

tions for which we have reliable data.) New energy sources, such as nuclear fission, make possible the gradual replacement of fossil hydrocarbon fuels by others which will not produce unwanted combustion products. Energy conversion efficiencies may be increased by technological progress. Inadvertent topographical modifications (i.e., erosion) can certainly be slowed down to some degree by various means of protecting watersheds. Biological diversity can be maintained by active conservation, game management and protection, border controls, quarantines, and restrictions on the uninhibited importation of unfamiliar species to new areas.

Other types of interference with the environment can be reversed, in principle, with no serious penalty attached. The pollution of rivers and streams by industrial wastes and untreated sewage, and air pollution by combustion products are the two most obvious examples. To a lesser extent, damage to the land and the biological environment can be repaired. Soil can be refertilized and enriched by various artificial means—sometimes to a point where it is better than it was originally, sometimes not (if it has been badly eroded as in the Tennessee copper basin)—but the process takes many years and can be expensive.

Ecological damage is sometimes repairable at low cost, but (in our present state of knowledge) more often not. No means has yet been discovered for successfully eliminating or controlling the rabbit population in Australia (where it was established by accident a hundred and fifty years ago), or of controlling the Dutch Elm disease, or the giant East African snail, or the water hyacinth, or the brown rat. There are also some dramatic successes, however, such as the total elimination of the screw-worm fly from Florida and the permanent control of the Japanese beetle, the gypsy moth, the Klamath weed and, most recently, the sea lamprey in the Great Lakes.

The cumulative effects of contamination of the environment by certain toxic chemicals or radioactive substances is difficult to reverse by deliberate means, but the effects tend to decrease more or less rapidly with time. In the case of the isotopes Carbon-14, Strontium-90, Cesium-137, and the fissionable materials themselves, e.g., plutonium, the actual decay rates are so slow that the contamination is, in a sense, semi-permanent; however, the degree of availability to organisms may tend to decrease rather rapidly with time. Other radioisotopes of practical importance generally decay to a negligible level in a few weeks to a few months at most. The situation with regard to toxic chemicals is roughly parallel. Some inorganic poisons such as arsenic remain indefinitely and—as in orchard soils where calcium arsenate has been used as an insecticide for a number of years— may reach a sufficiently high level of cumulative toxicity to affect the trees or other forms of life in the area. Simple chlorinated hydrocarbons such as DDT also seem to linger almost indefinitely, although there may be slow biological degradation. Fortunately the newer more toxic insecticides of the organic phosphate group do decay fairly rapidly into harmless forms, if subjected to sunlight and weathering. Such chemicals may, however, be accumulated (and preserved) in fatty tissues in the bodies of animals until dangerous levels are reached. Technological approaches to this problem are varied: means of "denaturing" dangerous accumulations in the soil may be found. Insecticides which are harmless to other species may conceivably be discovered. More plausible, however, would be a more sophisticated use of chemicals in such a way that the environment is not contaminated, or replacement of chemical by biological or other controls. Thus current trends may be reversed in this area. . . .

IV

It is clear that Western man now has Faustian powers, which are impossible to renounce. Realistically, the possibility must be faced that man's unremitting Faustian striving may ultimately remake both his inner and outer environment, to the point where he will be de-humanized or where his life on earth will be altered in some disastrous and irrevocable way. Already, awesome choices are before him. For example, we already have some power to alter the weather. Suppose that in the future we can divert a hurricane. With this ability will come the responsibility of deciding where to send it. The choice will have to be made, for we will have foreclosed the option of leaving the decision to nature. In this area, as in many others, whose property will be destroyed, whose lives will be jeopardized or lost, will become matters for administrative decision. On what bases should the choices be made, and by whom? We are not yet able to answer such questions, but ultimately these issues should and must be the subject of legislation.

There is a widespread Luddite response to such problems in which the artifacts of technology themselves become the targets of hostility. Also prevalent is the simplistic view that technology now presents man with an either/or choice between immolation and utopia. But evils may not be stark and obvious; they may be subtle, slow-acting, uncertain—and well distributed among all the available options. A series of decisions can be taken separately, for good reasons, and yet produce an ultimate condition that, had it been foreseen, no one would have wanted. Practically all the major changes since the beginning of industrialization have brought unexpected and unwanted consequences. Research that began as an expression of the value of the individual human life could easily become a step toward the treatment of men as disposable objects.

One of the great tasks faced by society is to facilitate intellectual preparation for the kinds of social decisions that will be required in the affluent, technologically accelerating, rapidly changing society of the future. Clearly, we must attain a better understanding of the kinds of technical power over nature (including human nature) that may come into human possession, and a better public understanding of the issues involved in deciding what should be done with such capabilities.

What we need is a better grasp of how social action may lead to unanticipated or unwanted results. We need a better understanding of the effects of social policies. If we cannot learn not only to take full advantage of our increasing technological success, but also to cope with its dangerous responsibilities, we may only have thrown off one set of chains—nature-imposed—for another, in one sense man-made, but in a perhaps deeper sense, as Faust learned, also imposed by nature.

MATERIAL RESOURCES FOR THE NUTRITION OF MANKIND

by FRITZ BAADE

Provided that there will be no World War III, we can predict that in the remaining 32 years from today to the year 2000 the world population will double, increasing from now approximately 3.3 to 6.5 billion.

With a world population of 6.5 billion in the year 2000, food production would have to be increased two times merely in order to provide as much food per person as is available today. But a large part of mankind is at present undernourished, and hunger can be done away with only by tripling the world's food supply.

In order to triple the world food supply we must mobilize all the food production reserves. Such reserves must be sought mainly in four groups:

1. Expanding the arable surface.
2. Additional irrigation.
3. Exploiting the food reserves in the world's oceans.
4. Increasing the yield per hectare of the already cultivated areas.

Group 1

The earth's arable land can be tripled. The dry land surface of the earth measures about 13,500 million hectares (one hectare = 2.5 acres), of which so far only about 1,500 million hectares have been under cultivation as farmland, gardens, or plantations.

The arable surface may be expanded to some extent by tilling part of the pastures and grazing lands that now take up almost

Reprinted from *Mankind 2000*, edited by Robert Jungk and Johan Galtung, No. 1 of Future Research Monographs from The International Peace Research Institute Oslo. Published by Universitetsforlaget, Oslo, Norway, and George Allen & Unwin, London. By permission of Universitetsforlaget. First published in 1969.

twice as much space as arable lands, but possibilities in this direction are strictly limited. A large part of the remaining pastures throughout the world are located in areas too arid to be tilled.

An additional 400 million hectares are shown in FAO statistics as "Unused, but usable for production." Tilling these 400 million hectares and adding them to the tilled land from former pastures would increase the world's arable land area by between 700 million and 800 million hectares.

An incomparably more significant reserve, however, is contained in the world's forests and jungles. About one half of the nearly 4,000 million hectares of "wooded area" recorded by international statistics (i. e., approximately 2,000 million hectares), consist of tropical and subtropical jungles. By cultivating half of this jungle area and adding it to the between 700 million and 800 million hectares mentioned above, we would easily double the world's total arable land area. In case of extreme need, it could even be tripled by clearing all forests not essential to the climatic stability of the locality.

But in the next 32 years mankind will not be forced to convert a major part of the forests and jungles into crop land; for the possibilities inherent in raising the per-unit yield of the total area presently in cultivation are so enormous that only a little proportion of the available soil reserves will be needed by the end of the century.

Group 2

Only a very small fraction of the world's total water resources available for irrigation is actually being put to use. The amount of water from rain and snow that flows off, seeps into the ground, or pours into the world's oceans adds up to something like 27 billion cubic meters. Present irrigation techniques make use of only 1.5 billion cubic meters at the very most, be it through diverting water from streams and rivers or drawing upon ground water reserves. If we consider a number of rivers and their importance in the irrigation of their respective valleys, it soon becomes obvious that the potential of only a very few of them has been exploited to any significant extent. A famous example is the Nile, half of whose available waters are at present being utilized for irrigation. Other famous rivers such as the Tigris, the Euphrates, the Ganges, and the Indus are being exploited only up to at most one-fifth of their water potential.

But in Mesopotamia, Pakistan, India, and China big progress in taming the rivers is under way. By the end of the century, the Nile, the Euphrates, the Tigris, Ganges, and Indus will certainly be under control along their entire courses, rendering unto mankind the three great services a river can give: irrigation, flood control, and hydroelectric power.

The possibilities in the U.S.S.R. and in China are enormous. By the end of the century, the U.S.S.R. will probably have brought the project of a Siberian inland sea into reality; at present the vast rivers of Siberia, especially the Ob and the Yenisey, pour enormous quantities of unused water into the Arctic Ocean. But with relatively limited investments these could be dammed up to create a central Siberian inland sea, whose waters could then be diverted southward. This, in turn, would make it possible to irrigate millions of acres in the Turkomanian steppes.

The People's Republic of China is planning control of all major rivers, most particularly the Yangtze Kiang, Hwang Ho, and Si-Kiang, along their entire courses. It is planned to construct 46 dams along the Hwang Ho, from its source high up in the mountains all the way down to the sea.

China's achievements in the realm of irrigation are already truly remarkable. The effectively irrigated area was expanded between 1952 and 1960 from 21 to 56 million hectares, an increase corresponding in size to four times the total area irrigated in the United States. Within the next few decades, irrigation will supply water to some 100 million hectares in China, twice the irrigated area that 10 years ago was available to the whole world.

Group 3

Deep-sea fishing up to the last decade was in a paradoxical situation, since approximately 98 percent of the fish brought to market had been caught in waters of the Northern Hemisphere, while the Southern Hemisphere accounted for only about 2 percent, although its total water surface area is almost twice that of the Northern Hemisphere. Furthermore, fishing was confined almost entirely to the colder zones, while tropical and subtropical zones have been left practically untouched. This is certainly not because of any scarcity of fish in those waters; the high yields—up to 1,000 kilos of fish per hectare—achieved in Java's artificial ponds certainly demonstrate the fertility of warmer waters. Plankton, basic to an adequate fish supply, is abundant in many parts of the tropical and subtropical oceans.

The reason why this abundance has so far remained almost entirely untapped is simple. The fishing grounds in southern latitudes and in the tropics are remote from the main centers of consumption, and as long as fishing boats had to rely on ordinary water ice to preserve their catch, they could not possibly afford to risk fishing too far out of port.

The technique of deep freezing opened truly revolutionary possibilities. Full utilization of this process, however, has been assured only by the construction of floating factories to combine fishing and processing so that the catch is automatically filleted and deep-frozen on the spot, while the offal is turned into fish meal and fish oil.

The Soviet Union adopted the new process in 1956. Orders were placed with the Howaldts Shipyards in Kiel, Germany, for 24 such factory ships, each of about 3,000 tons. Another revolutionary innovation was the so-called stern-hauler; where conventional boats haul their nets up along the sides, with the crews lined up at the railing and getting drenched by the breakers, these floating factories let the nets trail in their wake until, through a large opening astern, the catch is hauled up an inclined platform to the top deck, from which it is dropped by chutes directly into the filleting machines.

In the summer of 1960, the Soviet Union ordered 2 combination whaling and fish-processing ships of 11,000 tons each. During the Antarctic season these whalers have to process their catch in Antarctic waters; at other times of the year they move to tropical or subtropical areas and concentrate on other species, particularly sardines, tunnies and bonitos. In 1965 the Soviet Union ordered 8 floating factories of 15,000 tons each.

Another innovation pioneered by the U.S.S.R. is that of leaving the factory ships in place and letting specially equipped cargo ships transport the frozen catch back to port. Along the practically unexploited western coast of Africa, they discovered spots so abundantly stocked with sardines that their dragnets were able to catch 10,000 kilos per hour.

Until recently, the U.S.S.R. had a big lead in the exploration of food reserves in the world's oceans. But the West is now trying to make as good a showing as possible in this peaceful race. The initial effects of these revolutionary methods began to be reflected in the statistics on the world fishing industry. The total catch, a mere 4 million tons at the turn of the century, rose to 35 million in 1959 and 52 million in 1964. Fishing production along the coast of South Africa rose from near zero to more than 1 million tons. The director of the FAO Fisheries Section, D. B. Finn, found that progress in fish-production made during the past 30 years exceeded that made in the preceding 3,000. But it will be still overshadowed by the advances possible during the next 30 years.

In the decade from 1954/55 to 1964/65 the total catch of fish increased by 42 percent against an increase of only 31 percent of the production of agriculture. If this development is to go on during the next two decades the total catch may even surpass the 100 million tons line by 1987, thus providing 20 kilos of fish per capita for a world population of about 5 billion.

Group 4

The food reserves obtainable by an increase of the per-unit yield of arable land are enormous: they are chiefly based upon more intense cultivation, plant feeding, pest control, improvement of species, and irrigation. In most parts of the world today, agriculture is still in an almost incredibly backward condition. Of the approximately 350 million families presently engaged in farming, at least 250 million, i. e., more than 70 percent, possess as their one and only tool either a hoe or a wooden plow.

Aside from the 250 million peasants using the wooden hook, about 90 million work with an iron plow drawn by horses, mules, cows, or oxen. The future belongs to motorized agricultural machines. At present the total number of motorized plows in the world is only approximately 13 million.

Motorization of agriculture has another favorable effort upon the balance of food supply because, by eliminating the need for animal traction, it brings about considerable savings in animal fodder. In the United States the reduction in the number of horses and mules has freed an area for growing human food that corresponds in size to the total arable surface of the four Scandinavian countries plus the three Benelux countries and Great Britain.

The greatest contribution toward feeding a world population about to grow from 3.3 to 6.5 billion within a few decades will be made by modern methods of plant feeding. Nearly 150 years ago, our knowledge concerning the fundamental laws of plant nutrition underwent some decisive changes when, in 1840, Justus von Liebig published his basic work on plant nutrition. The most important nutritive factors are nitrogen, phosphate, potassium, and lime. More recently it has also been shown that certain types of soil require such so-called trace elements as manganese, copper, boron, magnesium, aluminium, cobalt, titanium, lithium, iron, molybdenum, iodine, bromine, and zinc; they are referred to as "trace elements" because very slight traces of them can produce amazing results if their lack was responsible for unsatisfactory yields. Fortunately we have learned to produce in practically unlimited quantities the nutritive factors such as nitrate, phosphate, potassium, and lime as well as the trace elements.

But the application of this 150-year-old discovery in the agriculture of our world is very incomplete. Today the world consumption of nitrogen is only in the magnitude of 25 million tons, i. e., a fraction of what it should be. But of these 25 million tons no less than 18 million tons are consumed in the highly developed parts of the world, i. e., Europe (without the Soviet Union), North America, Japan, and Oceania, with an acreage of crop land of only about 400 million hectares. On the other side the less developed or the underdeveloped regions, i. e., Asia, Africa, and Latin America with an acreage of crop land of more than 1,100 million hectares, are applying only 7 million tons.

In order to increase the yields per hectare in the underdeveloped countries, the input of fertilizer would have to be raised from the now applied 4 million tons of nitrogen to 60 or even 80 million tons, and the total application of fertilizer to 150 or even 200 million tons. By such heavy fertilizing combined with the needed progress in the use of seed, of pest control, of soil conservation and irrigation, the yield per hectare can be raised to 4 or even 6 times the yield of today.

Summary

The arable surface of the world can be brought from 1.5 to 3 billion hectares, and if necessary to 4 billion hectares. Using high-yield plants, fertilizing them adequately, and providing irrigation wherever needed, we can obtain an average yield of between 3 and 4 tons per hectare throughout the world. This way an arable surface of about 4 billion hectares could produce between 12 and 16 billion tons of grain value. An addition of 3 billion tons of grain equivalent produced by proper fertilization etc. of grazing lands would then bring about a possible world production of between 15 and 19 billion tons of grain value. We may assume that one ton of grain produced by crop and grazing land will feed two people, provided part of the required protein is supplied by the ocean reserves. Therefore a world production of 15 billion tons of grain value may feed 30 billion people, while 19 billion tons may feed 38 billion people.

In our analysis of the next decades we can confine ourselves to the relatively modest task of examining the food problems of a population growing from 3.3 to between 6 and 6.5 billion. This would necessitate the exploitation of merely a fraction of the world's food reserves.

The Big Paradox in the World Food Economy

The material resources for nutrition of mankind are tremendous, but in spite of that, hunger has still been increasing in the world. In 1965 (according to FAO statistics) there was no growth in world food production, while the population increased by 65 million. Only in a few countries is food production increasing faster than the population, and these are the countries with an already heavy application of fertilizer and other inputs. In other countries—and these are especially the developing countries—with an absolutely insufficient application of modern agricultural techniques, the growth of food production is lagging far behind the growth of population. In some of these countries, for instance in India, not only hunger but even starvation is widespread. The main reason of this big paradox lies in the fact that the mobilization of material resources is not possible without the mobilization of human resources, especially of better education and a more effective extension service among the farmers. This is one of the most crucial problems for the future of mankind.

Varieties of wheat and rice developed in Mexico and in the Philippines by the Rockefeller Foundation and the Ford Foundation are now spreading over large regions in Asia and North Africa. Due to the response of these varieties to high application of fertilizer a real "green revolution" seems to be starting. By the application of the new varieties of wheat, production in Pakistan already increased from four to six million tons, i. e., by fifty percent. Application of nitrogen in India increased from 63,000 tons in 1948/49–1952/53 to 1,136,000 tons in 1967/68. If this "green revolution" continues and spreads on other developing countries, the picture of the resources for nutrition of mankind will become much brighter in the second half of the 1970s.

FRESH WATER

by BURNHAM PUTNAM BECKWITH

LAND, air, sunshine, and fresh water are the essential bases of all human life, and fresh water is the least abundant of these in areas most suitable for human habitation. In arid and semi-arid regions, which occupy a large share of the earth's land area, the growth of agriculture and cities has always been severely limited. And the rapid growth of population and modern industry in agricultural areas with a once-ample water

Reprinted from *The Next 500 Years* by Burnham P. Beckwith (Exposition, New York, 1967). By permission of Exposition Press.

supply has already produced serious shortages of unpolluted fresh water and will soon produce many more. Fortunately men have become more and more efficient in increasing supplies of cheap fresh water in all regions. Their growing efforts to increase such supplies will have major effects on the growth and location of agriculture and industry.

Annual United States water use increased 700 percent from 1900 to 1960. It will continue to increase at a rapid rate throughout the next 500 years, due to growth of population, agriculture, industry, real incomes, etc. It cannot, however, long continue to grow at the 1900–60 rate, because the marginal cost of additional water has begun to rise and will continue to rise for decades in most coastal areas and for centuries in most inland areas.

Fresh-water supplies will be vastly increased in many nations by simultaneous use of three major alternative methods: the importation by canal of fresh water from ever more distant sources; desalting sea and other salt water; and water purification and radical restriction of water pollution. Moreover, much waste of fresh water will be eliminated by ending price discrimination in water rates.

During the past century continuous technological progress has made it economic to transport fresh water by canal over ever-longer distances. In the American Southwest large amounts of water are now transported over two hundred miles, and a much longer canal is under construction. As its population continues to grow, one river after another north of San Francisco will be dammed and its water diverted to the Southwest. By 2050 water from the Columbia River will be diverted to the Colorado River. By 2100 water from the Peace and Yukon rivers in northwest Canada will be flowing to the Great Lakes, the American West, and northwest Mexico. The canal conducting water from British Columbia to the Great Lakes will be navigable, and huge blocks of hydroelectric power will be developed en route. An artificial lake over four hundred miles long in the Rocky Mountain Trench —just west of the continental divide in Montana and British Columbia—will store seasonal water surpluses until needed.

Such long-distance movement of fresh water will steadily expand in many other parts of the world. All the large Siberian rivers which flow into the Arctic Ocean will be dammed and their water diverted to arid regions in Mongolia and Turkestan before 2200. Water from the Amazon will be diverted to arid areas in Argentina, Peru, and other countries, as well as to other parts of Brazil. Water from the great rivers of central Africa will be diverted to the Sahara and Kalahari deserts. Long before 2500 all the rivers of the world will be fully used as sources of fresh water for near or distant areas.

The world supply of river water is fixed, but the supply of sea water is unlimited, and the cost of desalting sea water is declining rapidly. In some coastal regions desalted sea water is already cheaper than transported river water, and the number and size of such regions will increase steadily throughout the next 500 years. Owing to recent and prospective breakthroughs in desalting methods, the use of desalted sea water will skyrocket during the next century; but in most inland and upland areas it will always be cheaper to use and reuse available river water than to desalt, lift, and transport sea water over long distances. The boundaries between the areas where river water and desalted sea water are used will depend upon relative costs, which will vary from region to region and decade to decade.

Desalted sea water will of course be consumed largely in low-land coastal areas, because this will minimize transport costs. As the use of desalted water in coastal areas grows, more and more river water will be reserved for inland or highland use. Later the use of desalted sea water will gradually spread inland, and river water will be increasingly reserved for ever-higher or more remote inland regions. By 2500 over half the world supply of fresh water will come from the sea.

The inland movement of desalted sea water, the repeated repurification and re-use of river water, and the improvement and spread of flood-control and irrigation dams will gradually stop or reverse the flow of more and more rivers, beginning with those in or near arid areas. By 2100 little if any water will flow into the ocean from the Nile, Niger, Indus, Columbia, Sacramento, Colorado, and similar rivers. All fresh river water will then be diverted into irrigation and urban water-supply canals in the upper reaches of such rivers.

The ever-growing use of river water for agricultural, industrial, and domestic uses in inland areas will soon begin to curtail the construction of hydroelectric power plants in advanced countries and will later cause the closing down of nearly all such plants in lowland or valley rivers. For instance, the Grand Coulee Dam power plant will cease operating before 2100, because all Columbia River water originating above that dam will by then be consumed. For similar reasons the immense new Siberian hydroelectric power plants will also stop generating power, sometime during the twenty-first century. The same fate awaits the Boulder Dam power plant, on the lower Colorado River. The long canals now used to transport Colorado River water to the California seacoast will be abandoned or reconstructed to carry desalted sea water inland. All the water in the Colorado River, and a much greater quantity of imported river water, will be used in the upper parts of the Colorado River Basin.

The reversal of water flow in most large rivers will eliminate many famous waterfalls, as well as most hydroelectric power plants. Niagara Falls will stop flowing before 2200. The dams and channels built to stop and reverse the flow of water in rivers will also gradually reduce the number and severity of floods. The proportion of flood damage to national income will fall over 80 percent in advanced countries before 2200.

The farther water can be economically transported, the larger is the geographical area which should be served by a single water agency. The American Southwest has long needed such an agency. Disputes among communities in this immense region have seriously delayed and increased the costs of its major water facilities. When it becomes economical to transport water from Alaska and the Yukon to Illinois and Texas, a single continental water agency will be needed. Some cultural lag is inevitable, but by 2200 the entire North American continent will have a single water-supply agency which will plan the continent's water supply at least 100 years in advance so as to minimize the total cost of all the fresh water used. By 2300 every continent will have such a continental water agency, and all will be supervised by a single world water agency.

The growth of population and industry during the past 200 years has caused a steady increase in water pollution. Most rivers and coastal waters near urban areas are now heavily polluted with sewage and industrial wastes. Efforts to check such pollution have been growing in recent decades. They will continue to grow until they end all uneconomic dumping of sewage and industrial pollutants in river, lake, or coastal waters. By 2100 nearly all urban sewage in advanced countries will be processed near its source and converted into chemical products and purified water. Every industrial plant or area will then be required to bury, burn, or transform and utilize nearly all its waste products.

The rapidly growing costs of water purification will be increasingly allocated to the industries and people responsible for them by imposing special taxes varying with the volume of pollutants dumped. Such taxes will turn the social costs of water pollution into money costs of production. They have already proved highly effective in limiting water pollution in the crowded Ruhr River valley.

Price discrimination by water suppliers has long been customary. Prices have been based more upon estimates of ability to pay than upon costs. For instance, in 1960, Los Angeles paid $20 per acre-foot for Boulder Dam water, while nearby farmers paid only $2.25. Such discrimination is highly uneconomic. It makes money costs less-accurate measures of real marginal costs and economic calculation less useful. Growing numbers of economists have condemned it. Hence the practice will be gradually eliminated. By 2100 all water in advanced countries will be priced at marginal cost, and all users of each water supply will pay the same prices.

THE WORLD WEATHER SATELLITE SYSTEM

by S. FRED SINGER

FLORIDA, 1984.—Only thirty years ago the concept of an artificial earth satellite which would carry instruments and perform

Reprinted from *The World in 1984,* vol. II, ed. by Nigel Calder. By permission of Penguin Books. First published in 1964.

some useful function was looked upon with great amusement and disbelief, even by the scientific community. But six years later, on 1 April 1960, a small beginning was made when the first weather satellite, *Tiros,* was launched from Florida and demonstrated the immense value of satellites for the spotting of dangerous storms and for general weather prediction.

Just twenty years ago, a plan for an operational weather satellite system was made firm, and shortly thereafter the first such system came into being; it was based on a modification of the *Tiros* satellite which, in the meantime, had proven itself to be very successful and reliable. By 1970, a second generation satellite took its place with vastly augmented functions; and about five years ago our present system, a third-generation satellite, came into being. It would be difficult to imagine the world today without this satellite system. It is saving lives and property by predicting severe weather conditions; it is advancing economic operations everywhere; and it is generally contributing to the well-being of the citizens of the world.

It is important to realize how the functions of the weather satellite system have grown to encompass the monitoring of all kinds of data about our environment, not only the atmosphere, but also the earth, the oceans, and space. It is important to realize, too, how economically useful the many ancillary functions have become, such as navigational services, geodesy, and data relay.

Our World Weather Satellite System uses three satellites in polar orbits at an altitude of about 2,000 miles. Their orbital planes are spaced 120° apart so that they cover different regions of the world at different times and provide more or less continuous observations. The satellites themselves are large and heavy, and nuclear-powered, in order to run the sensors, on-board computers, recorders, transmitters, and so forth; their operating life, safeguarded by stand-by circuitry, is about ten years.

The instruments carried by the satellites for detecting radiation emanating from below include advanced television cameras which can "see" the clouds day or night, infrared sensors to measure heat radiations, and microwave sensors to measure emitted radio waves. All of these radiations come either from the surface of the earth, from its atmosphere, or from material in the atmosphere such as clouds. Through specialized sensors and computers, the satellite is able to measure the vertical pattern of temperatures of the atmosphere; it can deduce the winds and other important meteorological quantities such as humidity; and it measures the content of important atmospheric constituents such as ozone and water vapor. In short, the satellite gathers all the data which are important for making accurate weather prediction possible.

The quantities which cannot be directly measured by the satellite sensors are measured by ground stations and ocean buoys; thousands of these are distributed all over the earth; they operate automatically, radioing their readings to the satellite as it passes overhead. The satellite stores these additional data on magnetic tape and its computer integrates them with the data which are observed by the satellite's sensors.

All of the data are then spewed out, once per orbit, to central receiving stations located near the North Pole. One of these giant stations was constructed in 1963 near Fairbanks, Alaska (serving America and East Asia), one was built in Scandinavia, and a third one in northern Siberia. From these receiving stations data links go back to the four complex data-processing and analysis facilities, in Washington, Tokyo, Geneva, and Moscow, where high-speed electronic computers dissect and reassemble the nearly 10,000 million bits of data which pour in every day, and put them into a format from which skilled meteorologists produce forecasts of global weather.

In addition to data collection, the satellite is also used for data relaying. After the forecast charts are produced at the data-processing station, the analysis is sent back to the receiving station and from there transmitted up to the satellite; the satellite in turn carries this global analysis to all of the weather stations throughout the world, to ships at sea, and to anyone who wants to tune in to its message. The satellite also provides a direct readout of meteorological data for the particular area over which it passes. The forecaster then combines this local cloud picture with the global analysis.

A supplementary meteorological satellite system has been developed in connexion with the so-called "synchronous" or "stationary" communication satellite; the combining of functions has been shown to lead to a considerable saving in costs. A satellite in equatorial orbit at an altitude of 22,000 miles moves with the same rotational period as the earth and appears to be stationary above a particular point on the equator. The Syncom system, used extensively for transcontinental communications, has proved extremely valuable also for certain specialized meteorological applications: short-lived weather phenomena, small severe storms, tornadoes, and the like can be missed by the polar-orbiting World Weather Satellite System, but synchronous satellites can, on demand, keep any specific area of the globe under continuous surveillance.

In addition to observing the clouds and the atmosphere, the satellite system has proved itself outstandingly useful for monitoring other phenomena on the earth's surface. It can observe the distribution of ice, and this information has been used to make ice forecasts and to direct icebreakers and ice reconnaissance aircraft. It measures the distribution of snowfall and precipitation; from these data the amount of snow which will melt is calculated and hydrological forecasts are prepared for managers of flood-control projects, irrigation reservoirs, and for agricultural planners.

The satellite can observe drought conditions and flood conditions, the areas of the world under cultivation, and even the state of the crops; it thus produces all of the basic data which are important in economic forecasting, and thereby has made possible more efficient planning and more efficient use of the world's food supply.

The infrared sensors of the satellite monitor the world's oceans and the meandering of ocean currents; a technique for computing the distribution of fish has been deduced and has made possible the more effective utilization of the ocean's resources. Scientific "farming" of the oceans is now becoming a practical enterprise.

Disaster warning services based on satellites are now quite well developed. The satellite is able to spot forest fires and other conflagrations in their incipient stages and produce early warnings which prevent the great economic losses from fires that get out of control. The same sensors monitor the activity of volcanoes and give warning of impending eruptions. Satellite cameras can track clouds of desert locusts swarming across Africa and Asia and alert the locust fighters to get their planes ready. At high altitudes the satellite monitors the motions of icebergs and warns shipping.

With radio sensors the satellite monitors the earth's ionosphere and uses this information to predict the propagation conditions for long-distance radio communications; with instruments turned upward the satellite monitors the sun and obtains data which are necessary for the forecasting of solar eruptions, which in turn affect communications services on the earth.

The satellite records changes in the earth's magnetic field, in the intensity of high-energy particles, and in other space phenomena, which together comprise the inputs for an extraterrestrial "weather" forecasting system. The satellite also picks up astronomical and geophysical data from observatories around the world and adds these to the data measured directly by the satellite. Extra-terrestrial "weather" forecasts can then be prepared to aid in planning manned voyages to the moon and to other planets.

The satellite carries a flashing light, not only to aid in its tracking, but also to provide a convenient means for geodesists and cartographers to measure distances between points on the earth with extreme accuracy. For less accurate use, the satellite carries a simple radio transmitter whose "doppler shift," when measured on the ground, can be used to infer the position of the ground receiving station. In other words, the satellite supplies a simple but effective navigational system. All merchant vessels, aircraft, and even many yachts now carry the very simple receiving equipment which makes all-weather day-or-night navigation possible.

These are just some of the more important economic applications of a satellite system which was originally designed for weather reconnaissance but which can also fulfil many other useful functions. The economic impact of the World Weather Satellite System has, in fact, become so great that it has affected the political thinking of many nations. It has proved itself a most valuable tool in protecting citizens of all countries against the destructive influences of the environment. It was therefore recognized in the late 1960's that this immensely useful system must be protected in the event of a conflict between nations. Later, it was placed under the control of the United Nations.

After 1984

I hope I may be forgiven for speculating about the future, up to the end of the century. Some very challenging scientific analyses of world climate have been published recently, using about twenty years' worth of global satellite data. The agreement between independent investigators on different continents is very gratifying; it is quite evident that extra-terrestrial influences on the upper atmosphere do produce important "triggering" effects on weather near the ground. Clearly, it will soon become possible to determine the nature and also the origin of climatic fluctuations and to understand much better why it is that climates vary, both in the short-term and on a longer-term basis. It is exciting to consider the possibility of finding the cause of the ice ages, which constitute extreme fluctuations in the climate. This information will come partly from the weather satellite system, but partly also from a better understanding of the history of the oceans and of the earth, and from refined astronomical observations.

Once a better understanding of the climates has been obtained, the road would be clear for climate control, or "planetary engineering" as it might properly be called. Over the past two decades, various attempts have been made to modify weather on a small scale. Now experiments will be made to trigger changes in the climate.

But in order to check whether these changes are in fact occurring and to determine their exact course we need highly refined observations; many of these will be carried out by a specially constructed orbiting meteorological and geophysical observatory. I would visualize this observatory satellite as manned, since many of the instruments may require continuous adjustment, and since special observations may be called for which cannot be anticipated. Furthermore, the instrumentation will be so complex that an unmanned observatory is simply not feasible from an economic point of view; its reliability would become too low. The observatory satellites may be either continually manned, or perhaps manned only during the special occasions when "planetary engineering" tests are undertaken.

It is clear that these attempts to modify the environment in which man lives on our planet will be fraught with great risks, but it is clear also that they will be among the most exciting and promising ventures of the last part of this century. Very likely, all of these activities will again be carried out under the supervision of a world body, such as the United Nations, in order to avoid any unilateral actions that might be detrimental to specific countries. Today, in 1984, a good beginning has been made in climate modification experiments; we can therefore predict with some degree of confidence that man will soon control his environment on the earth to suit his convenience and to achieve a better life.

HOUSING IS A PROCESS

by *JOHN P. EBERHARD*

Sir Edward Coke said once that "the house of everyone is to him as his castle, a fortress as well for his defense against injury and violence as for his repose." I suggest that a house as we shall want to consider it here is a very personal thing. Each of us has probably lived in several houses. Those of you who have come from approximately my generation, the generation of mobility, have probably lived in many houses. I've been married for 14 years today. My wife and I have lived in no less than ten houses. Therefore, while Sir Edward's words strike a responsive chord in my heart when he speaks of my castle, his concepts when displaced into the second half of the twentieth century in the United States must rely on the images in our hearts. This displaced image is more appropriately called a "home," and the "house" therefore can be no more than an envelope.

The house may be thought of as a kind of space value set at the

Reprinted from *Environment of Change*. Copyright © Time Inc. 1964. Courtesy *Time*.

confluence of our busy lives. It no longer serves, as it did in former times, as the place where we can be born, as the center of wealth-creating activities of the clan, or as a piece of ourselves to be cherished and passed on to succeeding generations. One can still find the Southern mansions of pre-Civil War days in the part of Maryland in which I presently live, but they are occupied now by the "horsey set." While the externals may resemble the house at Tara from *Gone With the Wind,* the internals are modern slaves produced by General Electric and Westinghouse. And this is, I think, where science and technology have not been adequately used as an opportunity for innovation.

Science and technology now offer an opportunity to do something about the house, not as a *product;* the opportunity lies in modifying the *process* that brings the house into being. The product itself may change, presumably will have to be changed, but the emphasis will be on doing something about the process. The process of building a house begins at the time that raw materials are extracted from the ground and is finally completed when the house is removed or destroyed. The process begins at the raw-materials stage; goes through the process of having these raw materials converted into finished materials; these materials are, in turn, fabricated; fabricated materials are put into a distribution network for wholesalers and retailers, etc. The design process which parallels this sometimes uses an architect, but not very often in the case of a house. An engineer may get involved in the structural concept; a landscape architect may help with its setting; the political community imposes upon it restrictions of what can or cannot be done; the financial community provides funds; the contractor hires subcontractors; the subcontractor hires tradesmen to come and work on the house, etc. All of these things are included in the process of bringing together that product which is known as a house. The opportunities that we have are to modify this process in such a way as to give to it what we might call "systems characteristics."

Systems characteristics means that there are feedback loops, that it is possible for the process to benefit by experience. I don't think we really benefit in any direct way by the experience of previous generations or, more importantly, by the experience of people who are in the building business in other parts of the country or in other parts of the world. The young architect makes most of the same mistakes his predecessors did. The contractors, particularly home builders, make the same mistakes that their predecessors did, and as a result the mortality rate of home builders is tremendous. In our time we use science and technology well enough to be able to build rockets capable of sending a man to the moon, but we build these rockets in buildings that still leak after 3,000 years of building technological experience.

Now if we're going to modify the process of building, it seems to me that there are a number of directions which we might identify as both opportunities and responsibilities.

The first opportunity and responsibility that I see is the problem of refurbishing housing units in the inner city. Let me give you some statistics: The 1960 census showed that 7 million non-farm dwelling units in the United States could be classified as deteriorating. This is in addition to 2.6 million dwelling units classified as dilapidated, and another 3.5 million that were in sound condition but lacking in some plumbing facilities. The solution in many cities has been to tear down the dilapidated buildings and replace them with new buildings. Experts could tell you better the kinds of sociological and health problems this has made, because this has uprooted whole communities, whole ways of life. In addition, housing at the economic level which the displaced families can afford has not been replaced.

There are, as I understand it, a whole host of buildings in the inner core of our large cities which are structurally sound, but which are dilapidated and which are lacking in what we now consider to be the necessary amenities of life. There may be many approaches to this problem, but they should include a self-improving feature for the people who live there, rather than by those who come from some other sector of society. As an example: my recommendation to the poverty program has been that if groups of dropouts are going to be recruited for training purposes, that they be given new kinds of skills rather than train them to develop the skills of the carpenters, the bricklayers, and electricians. I suggested that one way to create new kinds of jobs and new sorts of markets was to take a new look at what we might do about dilapidated, deteriorating, inner-city housing units as self-improvement projects. My suggestion was that groups of young people, young men between 18 and 20 years old who have been dropouts, should be brought together with a multi-purpose skilled craftsmen as a team unit leader. The team would be told such things as, "You have $200 to fix up this tenement apartment. What would you do with $200?" I doubt that they're going to put in sparkling kitchens. Let them create new solutions within the restraint of the $200. I'm willing to bet one of the major things they will do will be to clean the apartment up, and make it habitable. The clutter which surrounds such lives begins to be a problem with which people find it difficult to cope. Overcoming such clutter would give many people an opportunity to overcome the problem of inertia.

I think that it might be possible to develop programs for encouraging landlords to spend $200 or $300 to make such places more habitable than they are, rather than press in all cases for remodeling programs which involve several thousand dollars per apartment in a dilapidated condition. What happens under such conditions is that the rental required is raised to the point where people who were living there can no longer afford it. This would create a different kind of market for industries like the plumbing industry, because it might require a different kind of fixture than is presently on the market. Most of the products that are on the market now, such as plumbing fixtures, or electrical fixtures, or the mechanical parts that go into buidlings, are designed for new-housing markets. They are somehow or other adapted for older buildings, but with a great deal of difficulty in many cases. There is a market, I believe, for developing systems through technological research whose use would be primarily in the reconditioning of existing buildings.

Another kind of opportunity will come from changing our goals for research in the housing and building field. The major goal for all research that's been done since World War II has been to reduce the cost of building. I think this is absolutely the wrong goal for research, even though it may be useful for development projects. If we are going to insist on mentioning "R" and "D" in the same breath, then we should change our goals.

Our concept of waste-disposal systems was greatly changed

about seventy years ago when we developed fixtures and systems based on a knowledge of hydraulics. We developed a systems concept within cities of sewers (and sewage-treatment plants) supplied by water run through pipes from reservoirs. When we did this and displaced the outhouse, we made the house cost an awful lot more money, but we made it a better place to live. So much a better place to live that the census figures now report as unfit to live in those places that don't have plumbing.

We changed the concept of environmental control from that demanding an independent, rugged individual who went out and chopped wood for his fireplace, to one which was based on mechanical systems utilizing new sources of energy.

First came coal. Dependent on coal was a whole system of mining, distribution (getting it to the house), burning it in a central place and then distributing the heat from the central place. We gradually modified and improved this system as we developed new fuels and new sources of energy, replacing coal with oil and gas for the most part. This all made the house cost more money, but it made it a better place to live. No one would propose that we go back to the fireplace as the sole source of heat.

When we put electricity into the houses, making possible such things as air conditioning, we added frosting to the cake in terms of making it a better place to live. In Washington, it's pretty difficult to get anybody to work in an office without air conditioning. We've also done some little things, like adding garbage disposals to the sinks. As far as my wife is concerned, these make the house a better place to live.

But we have not exhausted the technological possibilities of the United States. If these possibilities are desirable but make the house cost more, then let's make the house cost more. Who said that the American consumer should spend as much of his disposable income on automobiles as he does on shelter? If he spends more in the lower income brackets right now on buying automobiles than he does on shelter, isn't it a disproportionate way of spending income?

Perhaps, if we had the opportunity, if the technological devices were there, living units, building units, could be better places for living, for self-expression, a challenge for the housewife. This is where I think one of the technological opportunities is. Let's make all the houses an extension of the housewife's interests instead of a cell she wants to leave, because all the labor-saving slaves are there now. I don't know what it's going to take; maybe it's the possibility of changing wall panels for color and material, rearranging the floor plan of rooms. Maybe we could make the house a complicated enough instrument that it requires "learning" to play it, the way you have to learn to play the piano. This would become a challenge to the creativity of the woman, so that this thing called a house begins to complement all parts of the woman's personality. And somehow or other, once she has injected herself into it, it once again becomes a "home."

These are technological opportunities we won't find if we are always trying to make the house cost less. We tend to underplay or overlook the major opportunities when our goal is reduced cost. The plastics industry looks at the building market and they say, "Ah-ha, here's a big market in siding." Now siding's shape originated technologically from the method of sawing wood and the logical use of wood to cover the exterior of buildings. Aluminum companies had copied this same shape. They introduced some characteristics of life expectancy that perhaps would be better than wood when it was painted, so they invaded this market. The plastics people, looking at what the aluminum people had done, say, "Ah-ha, here's a market for us to invade." They go at the market by looking for a way to cut costs. Maybe not by cutting the first costs but to cut the maintenance costs. I do not think this is the real opportunity for plastics, or aluminum. Each has properties that other materials don't possess. Why copy? Let's find things that new materials can do with buildings that may make them cost more, but that *will* make the buildings more capable of being used for living.

There is another area, besides the dilapidated-housing market I mentioned earlier, in which cost-cutting is an important item. This is multiple housing for low-income families. For instance, it's economically impossible in the city of Chicago, if you make $6,000—which is not starvation wages—to buy an adequate house or an apartment, or to rent such an apartment from an entrepreneur who has built it with private capital. It simply cannot be done.

According to the 1960 census, there are 6.7 million households with incomes under $3,000, and about 3 million households with incomes between $3,000 and $5,000. Here is a market opportunity, in addition to the rehabilitation of existing units. Hand-me-down products of existing housing are not going to be able to take care of this market. By the end of this decade, if we continue with the present rate of rehabilitation and removal of existing units, there would still be over 4 million units in unsatisfactory condition.

It is not likely that at this point in our history we will be able to do anything significant about reducing the cost of housing through technological improvements. Technological improvements of sufficient magnitude to reduce the cost of housing by 25 to 35 percent would likely require capital investments on the order of $500,000,000. In order to obtain a reasonable return on such an investment, a firm would have to have a market of 50,000 to 75,000 houses per year. Present housing markets are only about one-tenth this size, even at their largest. If we begin now to invest in research which would improve the *process* of building houses, we might evolve by the end of the next decade the technological capability of producing truly low-cost housing in spite of such market constraints.

Just by industrialization of the building process, we can get at this market and cause a technological revolution. By industrialization of the building process, I don't mean prefabricated houses. Prefabricated houses have simply taken existing technology from the field, taken it out of the mud, and put it in a factory where work can be done under controlled weather conditions. But it hasn't modified the existing technology of how houses are built. Buckminster Fuller has tried in his career, I think twice, to produce the industrial house in terms of the total house.

One of the things that is probably going to be necessary to market industrially produced houses, to market buildings, is to get away from the idea of standardization. The presumption is that if we are going to mass-produce, we need to mass-produce ten thousand items identically. I think you know we now have the capability of producing large industrial complexes, what Bernard Muller-Thym calls a productive array, that do not depend on volume and standardization. A machine that makes tail pipes has been developed which can make every one of them different because its set-up instructions are computer-programmed.

The machine that wires the back panels in IBM 1401's can make every one of them different. An industrial capability that is computer-programmed (which therefore is capable of readapting itself from minute to minute, from product to product; which is based in the beginning on a raw-materials technology; which has its design perimeters reorganized by designers who work with things like the special-purpose computer system sketch pad) could begin to offer opportunities which architects have not had within the last five hundred years. This is the opportunity to deal with design as a total design problem from materials to maintenance, but with each individual problem as a new opportunity. We don't as architects now design buildings as though each were really a new opportunity. We put together the pieces that we buy out of manufacturers' catalogues, and we design the building around it. With computer control of a productive capability which begins with the raw materials, the designers who deal with this kind of a complex will have a truly creative opportunity. I don't see computers as anything which we need to fear, either as architects or as individuals. I think that this kind of opportunity, the opportunity science and technology can give us in the building industry, is indicative of the things that can be done in other industries. I see the next couple of decades as something that I look forward to with a great deal of excitement.

DROP CITY: A TOTAL LIVING ENVIRONMENT

by ALBIN WAGNER

It is impossible to define Drop City. It fell out a window in Kansas three years ago with a mattress and a balloon full of water and landed in a goat pasture near Trinidad, Colorado. At first Droppers lived in tents and tarpaper shacks. And then others began to see the same vision and began making things. Geodesic domes. Now there are sixteen to twenty Droppers living in ten domes and as many different ideas of what Drop City is as there are Droppers.

We have attempted to create in Drop City a total living environment, outside the structure of society, where the artist can remain in touch with himself, with other creative human beings.

We live in geodesic domes and domes of other crystalline forms because the dome shape is easier to construct. We live on a subsistence level and almost entirely scrounge the materials for our own buildings. All materials are used. Car tops, cement, wood, plastic. The cheapest and least structural of building materials are structurally sound when used in a true tension system.

We can buy car-tops in Albuquerque, N.M., for 20¢ each. We jump on top of a car with an ax and chop them out, stomp out the back glass, strip off the mirrors, and pull out the insulation. All of it can be used to cover a large dome for the small cost of about $30.

We have discovered a new art form: creative scrounging. We dismantle abandoned bridges by moonlight. We are sort of advanced junkmen taking advantage of advanced obsolescence.

Reprinted by permission of *Avatar*, an underground newspaper. First published in 1967.

Drop City was begun without money, built on practically nothing. None of us is employed or has a steady income. Somehow we have not gone hungry, or done without materials. Things come to us.

America, the affluent waste society. There is enough waste here to feed and house ten thousand artists. Enough junk to work into a thousand thousand works of art. To the townspeople in Trinidad, five miles away, we are scroungers, bums, garbage pickers. They are right. Perhaps the most beautiful creation in all Drop City is our junk pile. The garbage of the garbage pickers.

Drop City is a tribal unit. It has no formal structure, no written laws, yet the intuitive structure is amazingly complex and functional. Not a single schedule has been made, and less than three things have come to a vote. Even though Droppers rarely, if ever, agree on anything, everything works itself out with the help of the cosmic forces. We are conscious of ourselves and others as human beings.

Each Dropper is free. Each does what he wants. No rules, no duties, no obligations. Anarchy. But as anarchistic as the growth of an organism which has its own internal needs and fulfills them in a natural, simple way, without compulsion.

Droppers are not asked to do anything. They work out of the need to work. Out of guilt or emptiness the desire to work, hopefully, arises. It is no longer work, but pleasure. Doing nothing is real work. We play at working. It is as gratifying as eating or loving. We are based on the pleasure principle. Our main concern is to be alive.

Droppers come in all sizes, shapes, colors: painters, writers, architects, panhandlers, film-makers, unclassifiables. Each has his own individual endeavors and achievements. These perhaps tell what we are doing more than anything else. But they cannot be enumerated. They have to be seen, read, touched, heard. They speak for themselves. But we do all have this in common—whatever art we produce is not separated from our lives.

Droppers have painted the Ultimate Painting. A rotating infinite sphere, a circular geodesic structure loaded with spatial paradox, complete with strobotac. A painting to walk up the stairs into and lose your mind by. The Ultimate Painting was done by five Droppers, to make it five times better. The Ultimate Painting is for sale for $60,000.

The Droppers have printed a comic book called The Being Bag. We welcome the feds and postal inspectors who come to harangue us about its content. Our poet looks forward to the inspectors and their reading of his work.

Droppers make movies, black-and-white wind poems, flickering TV beauties with all the subliminal delights of pulsating Coke ads, the crystal-molecular good sense of a dome going into time-lapse, and the grunting goodness of sex. We have two movies on Drop City for distribution.

The second weekend in June we held a Joy Festival. The First Annual Drop City Festival and Bacchanal Post-Walpurgis and Pre-Equinox Overflow and Dropping. Over 300 people attended. It was a freakout in all media, 96 hours of continuous mind-blow.

We want to use everything, new, junk, good, bad, we want to be able to make limitless things. We want TV videotape recorders and cameras. We want computers and miles of color film and elaborate cine cameras and tape decks and amps and echo-chambers and everywhere. We want millionaire patrons. We need the most up-to-date equipment in the world to make our things. We want an atomic reactor.

Drop City is the first attempt to use domes for housing a community. Buckminster Fuller gave us his 1966 Dymaxion Award for "poetically economic structural achievements." We hope to buy more land, build more Drop Cities all over the world, the universe. Free and open way stations for every and anyone. Living space and heat can be made available to all at a fraction of the present cost through application of advanced building techniques such as solar-heated domes. Already Drop South is firmly established near Albuquerque, N.M.

Drop City is Home. It is a strange place. An incredible webbing of circumstance and chance, planning and accidents, smashed thumbs and car-tops. We are not responsible for what and where we are, we have only taken our place in space and light and time. We are only people who want love, food, warmth. We have no integrity. We borrow, copy, steal any and all ideas and things. We use everything. We take things, we make things, we give things.

Drop City pivots on a sublime paradox, opposing forces exist side by side in joy and harmony. A psychedelic community? Chemically, no. We consider drugs unnecessary. But etymologically, perhaps. We are alive. We dance the Joy-dance. We listen to the eternal rhythm. Our feet move to unity, a balanced step of beauty and strength. Creation is joy. Joy is love. Life, love, joy, energy are one. We are all one. Can you hear the music? Come dance with us.

THE UNIVERSITY COLLEGE SYSTEM

by DON BENSON

IT IS important for a person to specialize, but if he does not want to be merely a more or less useful tool of some establishment then he must also become a general manager of the world. Those who do not insist on managing for themselves—on participating in the fundamental decisions that structure their lives—are available to be managed by others. When many people allow others to make the basic decisions about what work they shall do, how they shall live and how their environment shall be modified, human society becomes inexorably corrupt. I mean you get a society in which the many are managed by the few, the few are busy managing the many, and nobody manages the world.

They let God do it, forgetting that God only helps those who help themselves. The many feel that managing the world is not their responsibility, that it is ridiculous even to try, considering all the world's problems. And the few cannot even manage their own lives, they are so busy managing the lives of the many.

Slaves and masters alike, we discard our trash for God to take care of. We play political games and leave the world's problems—the problems of human beings in relation to their environment—for God to solve. I don't doubt that God can manage. The universe can compensate itself for our stupidities. But let us not go blindly into that good dump.

Let us grow new institutions which will enable us to respond intelligently as whole human beings to our whole environments. Let us call these institutions "universities."

We need to get organized. But how? How can we have a university which works but does not oppress us? I feel that we can have such a university by starting with small, family groups and generating a network of councils according to our needs.

There is hardly any real social organization in the Western world today. We have been divided and conquered by civilization. Our vitality is shunted and channeled by a vast array of special organizations. We have financial, religious, governmental, recreational, bureaucratic, professional, political, military, educational, industrial, and charitable organizations galore, and yet our society is not well organized. We search in vain for community, for some general social organism in which we can really belong as whole persons.

Survival, belonging and growth. These are the fundamental human priorities. But specialist organizations inevitably forget about human priorities, unless some generalist organization exists to remind them. Therefore, it is time now to create a generalist organization—to conserve and organize our human vitality while we still can.

All the evidence available to me seems to indicate that human beings can integrate their lives most readily in small groups of about a dozen persons, plus or minus five. I would propose, therefore, that we attempt to construct a university system entirely of small groups.

People have been segregated by age, sex, income, skin color, occupation, education, religion, and innumerable other criteria. We have urban ghettos for the blacks, adolescent ghettos for the young, old folks' homes for the elderly, suburbs for the middle class, and so on. What we need now is a means of bringing people together in balanced social units. I am tired of experiencing society in bits and parts. I want to participate in a whole society, not merely in some fragment of a society.

If we are to have a whole society, we shall have to organize into whole families. At present, there are hardly any whole families in the United States. Instead we have detached individuals (who tend to be thoroughly exploited and regimented as students, soldiers, certain types of workers, patients or clients, etc.) and "nuclear" families (which reliably provide adjusted, portable personnel for the great specialist empires). What little we have in the way of family organization seems designed simply to supply and maintain parts for the corporate business structure. Nothing freaks out a civilized person quite so much as the idea of an "extended family"—twelve or so persons living together cooperatively with a sense of love and responsibility for one another. But this is the kind of family we need for the purpose of reintegrating human society.

I evaluate cultures in terms of how well they provide for the full synergetic development of all. Since it seems to me that people have a much better opportunity to achieve full development of their constructive capabilities in a social milieu characterized by well-developed small groups than they do in a milieu characterized by mass organization, I would assume that the optimal way to grow a viable world culture is to generate a global network of small groups.

I would start by organizing intentional families. A normal family might consist of a dozen persons—two in each of the following age categories: older than 60, 45–60, 30–45, 20–30, 10–20, and younger than 10. Families of this kind would keep individuals in touch with the different phases of life. The generations would not be estranged from one another. We could organize families intentionally according to complementarity and compatibility of the individuals and not merely according to genetic relatedness.

Each family might meet in council perhaps once a week. Following a simple meal or period of meditation, each person would speak briefly about his or her current spiritual condition, pleasant and unpleasant experiences, problems, projects, interests, and concerns. The council members would engage in dialogue about these issues so as to increase comprehension and decide what should be done. Individuals could then decide who they would need to work with and what resources they would need in order to continue their development as fully human beings.

Every family council might appoint a person to serve on a neighborhood council to deal with issues that are beyond their scope. The neighborhood councils would each be responsible for coordinating the efforts of anywhere from seven to seventeen families to increase their well-being. The neighborhood councils in turn could appoint people to serve on community councils, which would coordinate the formation of policy at the community scale.

Human beings are genetically programmed to maintain intimate, loving relationships in groups of about twelve. This is also the scale at which it becomes possible to have social units which are balanced in terms of age and sex. We are programmed to function as friends and neighbors, clansmen or fellow tribesmen in groups of approximately twelve squared or one hundred and forty-four. We can be aware of one another as unique individuals, not just types or categories, in groups on the order of twelve to the third power or seventeen hundred persons. (Don't take my word for this. Do your own research.)

The structure of the university council system which I envision has nine degrees of scale or generality: families, neighborhoods, communities, towns, cities, metropolises, regions, nations and the world. In Africa and India, as well as in many other areas of the world, imposed national boundaries and top-down governmental structures are doing great violence to non-civilized human beings. The university structure I am advocating could serve as a means whereby increases in social synergy could evolve from the pre-existent patterns of cooperation which have been refined over hundreds and thousands of years.

Perhaps the greatest need in the world today is for a *generalist* system such as this which would enable people to integrate their lives and participate in formulating the basic policy decisions affecting their lives. At the present time we have only a hodgepodge of overlapping and conflicting specialized empires. We don't have coherent social units, on any scale, to which we can relate and within which we can achieve our human identities. But the time has come to develop these social units and learn what it can mean to be fully human.

Within family units, we can learn to be loving and healthful in the primary activities of living. Within neighborhoods, we might have well-equipped seminar facilities, an information center, a transportation pool, a health consultant, a number of interesting adults who like children, and so on. At the community scale, we could support a co-operative store, a good medical team, a liberal arts faculty of about ten persons, a hundred visiting students from other parts of the world, a small research and development team concerned with housing, food production, waste management, and communications, and recreational facilities suitable for seventeen hundred self-actualizing people. A range of small businesses could be developed at the town scale. Cities might develop major productive enterprises and participate in metropolitan and regional planning for intelligent environmental management, the generation and use of power, etc.

But the function of this university at each degree of generality would be to co-ordinate general learning activities and formulate policy, to decide *what* needs to be done. The business of deciding *how* to do things and of working out detailed programs is best handled by specialist organizations. Therefore, the university council system would be complemented by a system of colleges. The colleges would consist of associations of colleagues who share an interest in particular problems, possibilities or subsystems. The colleges would be specialist systems for co-ordinating professional activities both within and among the various social units.

The university councils would work to insure that we do not lose sight of whole human beings and communities as we move to develop and apply our knowledge and technologies. Concurrently, the colleges would work to insure that our concern for the well-being of all human beings everywhere will not bog down in mere good intentions but will be supported by a surge of creative activity, each person being enabled to make his or her own special contributions.

I have been advocating vast structural changes in human society. How would these changes affect the organization of individual lives? What might constitute a normal pattern of "learning a living" in a world organized by a university college system?

In the early years of living, children would have a much richer and more encouraging environment. Parents could reasonably expect their neighborhoods to become safe areas for young children to explore. There could be sufficient educational opportunities within every community or town to enable young people to acquire all the fundamental conceptual skills practiced in their own culture and become familiar with the origins of their culture as well as the current state of the arts and sciences—prior to puberty. Following puberty, it might be most appropriate for young people to travel around the world, live in many different communities, experience a wide variety of cultures and life styles, and learn about the primary problems and possibilities of life on this planet.

At the age of eighteen or nineteen perhaps a person ought to have a chance to settle into some community for several years and try to integrate all his experience into a coherent and personal philosophy of living or guide to the universe. This would be a time to develop the close personal relationships which give meaning to adult life. A man or woman might be ready then to enter some college or play an active role in community life. It now seems quite likely that the majority of adult persons may significantly change their pattern of life and work every few years in response to personal and societal needs.

But people are not going to allow themselves to be pushed around, manipulated and exploited as they have in the past. If man has any future at all on this planet, he will have to leave off being a civilized man and become a learning man. Learning man, like primitive man, is a very sensitive person. He cannot survive even the routine abuse civilized men put up with every day, "getting and spending . . ."

THE ULTIMATE HUMAN SOCIETY

by DANDRIDGE M. COLE

THE TERM "ultimate" like the term "impossible" is likely to provoke a negative reader response and neither term should be used without qualification. However, within certain carefully defined and limited areas there are impossibilities such as self-contradictory ideas, for example, and likewise there are ultimates. Within our present knowledge of thermodynamics, the Carnot cycle represents an "ultimate" although something beyond it is not necessarily completely impossible. The velocity of light represents an "ultimate" velocity within our present understanding of physics but it is not necessarily impossible to exceed it, at least in some sense.

The term "ultimate human society" is a little frightening to us since it implies an end to social evolution—an end to social progress. We are used to thinking in terms of continuous improvement and the implication that we will reach a stable and permanent social form is abhorrent to Americans in general and liberal Americans in particular. The concept of the ultimate human society as described here is not intended to represent anything which will necessarily come about, at least in any particular form. Obviously, no one knows what the ultimate society will be like or even if the evolution of society will come to an end.

What is to be described here is a very general picture of an ultimate society which appears to be the most likely end result of a number of trends which can be observed in present social changes and which have been in operation for centuries or even millennia. Some of these well-established trends are as old as society, some are as old as life, and some are as old as the universe itself. The disturbing aspect of many of these trends is that they

Reprinted and abridged from *Social and Political Implications of the Ultimate Human Society* (General Electric Company, Space Division, privately published). By permission of General Electric Company. First published in 1961.

seem to lead to catastrophe. When put in graphic form and extrapolated only a few percent they lead directly to disaster in a disturbingly short time. Some of these trends can be expressed quantitatively and can be accurately plotted. Others can be expressed only qualitatively. However, when put together they give a rather clear picture of a major cosmic event within the next hundred years.

A long-term trend which can be handled quantitatively and presented graphically is population growth. Another long term trend is that of energy control and release. A few years ago this could be measured in tons of TNT in the form of high explosives. Then we were rudely jolted by the emergence of the kiloton bomb. Soon it was the megaton bomb. There is now talk in military circles of gigaton bombs which can destroy entire countries. Each one of these steps in a decade or less represents a thousand-fold increase in destructive potential. It does not take much extrapolation of this curve to turn our sun into a nova.

There is an age-old trend in nature toward development of forms of matter which can transform energy in ever more efficient ways. There is the correlated trend toward more intricate and complex organizations of matter. There is a long term political trend toward larger political groupings which seems to lead inevitably toward a world government. There is a contrary and highly disturbing tendency toward increased nationalism and the proliferation of new small "independent" political units. But the independence of these new countries is partly illusory, as is demonstrated by the use of the "world army" to enforce order in the Congo.

Our fund of scientific knowledge is expanding like the population at an ever-increasing rate which is accelerating faster than the population itself. Higher productivity permits larger fractions of the population to take up science, and we are rapidly improving our techniques for learning from nature. We are now making scientific studies of the process of creative thought and giving courses in creativity. Also we are just beginning to appreciate the practical value of basic research and even beginning to see some urgency in the discovery of new fundamental principles. We are heading for an explosion of knowledge comparable in magnitude and significance to the population explosion.

Other significant and well known trends include the increase in the life span and the trend toward machine labor. We are right on the verge of the final conquest of disease and the ability to replace worn-out body parts. The time is not too far off when accidents and suicides will be the only major causes of death and the average life span will be at least doubled. Besides taking over the functions of the heart, the lungs, and the kidneys as machines are about to do, technologies are replacing man in all types of labor. It has often been stated that automation may have consequences exceeding those of the industrial revolution. The use of computing machines to aid or even replace man's mental functions, aside from other effects, will cause even greater increase in the rate at which we accumulate new knowledge.

While we might expect trends which have continued for centuries to go right on for centuries more, this may not be possible. The natural pattern is not for indefinite increase but increase to a limit. An explosive mixture of oxidizer and fuel may warm up gradually over a period of hours and days until the ignition point is reached. Then a chain reaction takes hold and there is an explosion which results in a stable chemical compound. An unloaded electric motor does not accelerate indefinitely—it flies apart. Prenatal discomforts and labor pains increase only to a point and then end in birth. And it is an absolute impossibility that the population growth trend will continue for a hundred years since it leads to an infinite number of people in only sixty-six. Of course, population growth could continue for an indefinite period, but not following the trend of the last two thousand years.

Social evolution will not continue forever or even for another century. Society will crystalize into a stable, permanent form. The cold war and the epic struggle for the minds and the souls of men will come to an end.

The extraterrestrial colony of the near future will provide an early and extreme example of the ultimate human social organization toward which evolutionary trends have been pointing for millennia. Such a colony must have an enormously high energy-to-volume ratio and all matter within the sealed enclosure must be recycled with maximum efficiency. As the population of the earth grows we will find that the same efficiency is needed here.

This need for greater efficiency will lead to more and more curtailment of our individual freedoms.

Conservation and restoration of natural resources, including tree farming, irrigation projects, etc., are indications that we are approaching the need for the carefully balanced ecology of the extraterrestrial colony. Waste products of factory, automobile, and home can no longer be dumped indiscriminately but must be processed and to some extent recycled. Thus, we have laws to control production of smog, anti-litter laws, anti-pollution laws, etc. and we find that the sewage of a modern community must be processed before dumping into a stream so that their downstream neighbors can use this "recycled drinking water."

Even without the external threat to our society of the Communist bloc countries, the United States will experience an increasing need for highly trained specialists of all types. It will be necessary to insure the training of the numbers of skilled workers required to carry on essential functions. And as pressures increase, it will become necessary to regulate in some way the motion of these specialists within the country. Already we may note as a warning to ourselves Cuba's need to forbid emigration of many categories of specialists.

Population pressure, the desire for higher living standards and greater material wealth, and the effects of new technological developments such as automobiles, aircraft, atomic power, etc., are forcing society toward such a highly coordinated and regulated interrelationship of components that the components can no longer live as independent entities and must continuously act in the prescribed manner which most greatly benefits the whole of society.

The oft-noted stresses of modern life are increasing rapidly toward some unknown climax and we tolerate them only by learning the most complex and intricate behavior patterns. In fact, this accelerating frenzy is reaching such proportions that we may well wonder what cosmic orgasm is about to take place. And if we are indeed witnessing the preliminaries to a new birth, we may well ask what sort of new creature is our society about to spawn? In a sense society can be said to be pregnant with a mutant creature which will be at the same time an extraterrestrial colony of human beings and a new large-scale life form.

This concept of a new life form which I call Macro Life and Isaac Asimov calls "multi-organismic life" serves as a convenient shorthand whereby the whole collection of social, political, and biological problems facing the future space colonist may be represented with two-word symbols. It also communicates quickly an appreciation for the similar problems which are rapidly descending on the whole human race. Macro Life can be defined as "life squared per cell" or more particularly as "multicellular life squared per cell." Taking man as representative of multicelled life we can say that man is the mean proportional between Macro Life and the cell, or Macro Life is to man as man is to the cell. Macro Life is a new life form of gigantic size which has for its cells, individual human beings, plants, animals, and machines.

It is not too difficult to see that the members of an extraterrestrial colony will have to function as a closely knit team in order to survive. This cooperation and interdependence will not be just a haphazard marriage of convenience but a carefully planned, optimized integration which can be at least suggested by the harmonious mutual efforts of the members of a symphony orchestra. It should therefore be apparent that the colony will take on many of the aspects of a true independent life form.

Imagine for example, a colony of some 10,000 people living on a 50,000 to 100,000-ton space ship (a space Queen Mary). This vehicle or Macro Life creature can move (with rocket propulsion), it can grow (given a food supply in the form of natural resources from the asteroids and elsewhere), it can respond to stimuli received through its optical and electronic sensing devices, it can think with the brain cells of its human colony and its electronic computers, and finally, it can reproduce. The asexual reproduction or mitosis of Macro Life would be the result of construction by human-directed machines of a complete new vehicle structure—or exoskeleton, if you wish—and duplication of the human, animal, and plant cells by normal biological reproduction. If we assume a period of, say, fifty years for the doubling of the human population, then it would be necessary to construct a complete new vehicle during that period.

In every respect except possibly that of size, this synthetic product of our civilization fits our current picture of what constitutes a life form. And a size limit has never been a part of a definition of life. Thus the ultimate human society is, in a sense, not a society at all but the next major step in evolution—a new level in the organization of living matter for more efficient transformation of energy, a new form of life as far advanced over human life as man is advanced beyond the single cell. . . .

Students of evolution may be led to speculate concerning the next step beyond the present highest form of life which is generally agreed to be man. It has usually been concluded that the next step would be in the same line of development which led to man and perhaps as much above man in mental ability as the chimpanzee is below him. Thus we might imagine a superman who has a mental ability at only two or three years of age comparable to that of the most brilliant human beings in their prime. As the superman matured he would presumably develop powers far above anything of which we are capable—powers that we could no more comprehend than could a chimpanzee understand our ability to develop higher mathematics.

While no one can prove that the emergence of such a superman is impossible, there are a number of reasons for believing that the next step in evolution will be a major organizational advance rather than a mere refinement in a type already at peak development. If a new mutant life form is about to appear it will be Macro Life rather than superman. Our great problems are social and political, not individual. We need an improved society, not a new form of man.

The population explosion, or biodetonation, and the nuclear bomb present life on earth with the greatest challenge it has faced in the last few million years. The rapid increase in numbers of the highest life form, one of the most direct and obvious expressions of racial purpose, will necessarily come to a halt because of vanishing living space, and may end in complete futility in a war of extermination, unless man can achieve sufficient understanding of himself and society to take his peaceful and useful place as a component of Macro Life. The rising curve of destructive capability when extrapolated only a short time into the future shows a serious threat to the continued supremacy of man and even to the existence of life on earth. A further refinement of the humanoid line of development would seem inadequate response to a challenge of this magnitude.

Before arguing for the replacement of social man or Macro Life by superman we should examine man's limitations and the possible advantages of a superior humanoid. What are the limitations of man, not as an individual but as part of the Macro Life team? It is difficult to conceive of anything which is physically possible which could not eventually be accomplished by the Macro Being.

One example of a possible superior power or class of powers often ascribed to superman is the psychic or paramental ability. With these magical powers superman will be able to communicate with his kind (telepathy), control the motion of material objects (psychokinesis), and move himself through space at will (teleportation). It is argued that these powers would help superman meet the challenges of nuclear energy, space travel, etc., and that they would represent a major advance over the feeble powers of homo sapiens. And yet the proof offered for the possible existence of such powers is that certain members of the species homo sapiens have exhibited them!

If psychic powers are part of the real world, then I think that homo sapiens, individually or collectively, will learn to master them. But whether real or imaginary the Macro Being could get along quite well without them. How much better is mental telepathy than radio? If any supposed advantages can be demonstrated then we will eventually learn to duplicate synthetically what nature has done through evolution. If one brain can receive messages from another, we will eventually learn to build receivers and transmitters with the same capabilities. If teleportation is possible, homo sapiens will learn to do it, probably with the aid of mechanical devices. If it is not possible, we may still approach these intriguing capabilities by developing the slightly more plausible matter transmitter.

In short, there appears to be no theoretical basis for distinguishing between the future limitations on man and his technology on the one hand, and evolution on the other. Both may accomplish anything of which we can conceive and may accomplish much of which we cannot now conceive. The only possible difference in limitations which appear are those which may be introduced by man himself. A superman may not appear for the simple reason that homo sapiens will not permit it!

Asimov has pointed out that no new phylum of organisms has been established in perhaps 600,000,000 years. Within the last phylum established—the chordata—there has been no new class established in at least 250,000,000 years. And within the most advanced class—the Mammalia—nothing higher than the placental mammal has appeared in 100,000,000 years. It may be that multicelled life has run out of possibilities for improvement, and that it is time for a new major organizational advance.

It is difficult to define life except in a very loose way by listing properties generally exhibited by what we agree are living things. However, life seems to be associated with exceedingly complex combinations of matter. Extreme complexity is a necessary condition of life although it is not a sufficient condition. The complexity of a dead human body may be very much higher than that of a living snail. Organic chemicals in general are more complex forms than the inorganic molecules. And among organic forms the most complex is the protein molecule. And the protein molecule is generally assumed to be a necessary ingredient of life.

While inorganic crystals growing in a solution of the proper concentration show most of the properties of life, we do not ordinarily class them as living creatures. The main difference between them and organic life is in their level of complexity. This general advance in the complexity of organization of matter has continued since the beginning of the universe. It has pursued its inexorable course through the elaboration of the chemical elements, to the giant organic molecules, to single-celled and multicelled life, to man and finally to Macro Life.

The first recognizable step in the organization of energy and matter was that from pure energy to the subatomic particles. The second step in organization and in time was the combination of subatomic particles into atoms. After all possible stable atomic forms had been produced and the temperature of the primordial gas had dropped sufficiently, the next level of organization—atoms to molecules—began. This third step covered an enormous range of complexity from the simplest diatomic molecules to the giant protein molecules that form the basis for life.

The fourth step, from molecule to single-celled life includes the grey area of the uni-molecular viruses. Are they cells or molecules? Are they living creatures or lifeless chemicals? It is of consequence here only that they are a further step in the organization of matter into more complex structure permitting more versatile behavior. Step five is that from single-celled life to multi-celled life. And this took place only after countless varieties of single-celled life had been developed and many experiments in loosely organized cell colonies had been tried.

In every previous step the highest developments at a given level are used as the units upon which the next organizational level is erected. For example, the molecule reaches its highest organizational state when it uses as its basic unit the most versatile combining form, the carbon atom. Likewise, some cells exhibited the versatility and adaptability to give up some of their individuality and specialize. The specialized cells could become part of a permanent colony or multicellular organism, but in doing so lost the freedom to live as hermits or isolated individuals.

The next step is fairly obvious. Multicelled organisms which have already demonstrated the ability to live in colonies will form permanent associations, specialize, and give up their ability to live as independent individuals. Some, like the ants and the bees, have already done this to some extent, but man has gone even further along this road.

Silicon can form many compounds but it cannot compete in versatility with carbon. Likewise the insects cannot specialize to the almost unlimited extent displayed by homo sapiens. In forming complex organization the insect cannot hope to compete with man. We are already far along in this transition from individual multicellular organisms to the Macro Being. It will take only the new challenge from biological and nuclear detonations to bring about the final crystallization into a stable and permanent form.

IV

Cities

Architecture will be brought to its fullest realization when the deepest knowledge of human life as
a total event in the biological whole is available.
One of its important components is the ordering
of man in space, making space comprehensible by
its articulation. . . . The root of architecture lies
in the mastery of the problems of space; its practical development lies in technological advance.
—L. MOHOLY-NAGY,
The New Vision (1930)

MULTIPLE CHOICES

by MARTIN and MARGY MEYERSON

THE CITIES of 1984 can be built now. Indeed, in large measure, they are being built and have already been built, for most of what exists will survive another twenty years, barring a catastrophic war. We mean, of course, that there is enough unutilized technology and enough prototype technology to revolutionize the size, the function, the arrangement, and the appearance of cities, if enough resources were devoted to such purposes. It is even possible for the first time to by-pass the historic city and to achieve (or sustain) industrialization through patterns of development so different from the present ones that they may be regarded as "non-urban."

The gap between technological possibilities and technological achievement is not, of course, unique to city development. On the one hand there is a great deal of resistance to large-scale innovation, and on the other hand, there is a great deal of participation in creeping change. The failure of planned decentralization and the overwhelming spread of metropolitanization are illustrations. Nowhere in the world has government been able to carry out major programs of redistribution of the population and of economic enterprises despite the use of stringent sanctions. Nor has any government of a developed country been able to halt the postwar suburbanization or "scatteration" of industry, retail trade, and residences. The present urban pattern is the result of the interplay of many forces, including the mechanization of agriculture (which permitted many more people to live in cities), the shift from rail to motorized transport (which made many parcels of land in a metropolitan area equally accessible), the change in the structure of industry (which required larger land allotments and

Reprinted from *The World in 1984*, vol. II, edited by Nigel Calder. By permission of Penguin Books. First published in 1964.

fewer workers per unit of production), the rationalization of retail trade (which produced scale economies in supermarkets and regional shopping centers and not just in central business districts). These forces, together with the baby boom, higher incomes, and changed consumer tastes have markedly altered during the past twenty years the circulation, the density, and the land use of the urban community.

These changes did not come about because of the mere knowledge of better or cheaper ways of building or of controlling the environment. The city is a dependent variable; its future physical form, like its past form, will be a response to the particular mix of human desires and economic pressures which operate nationally and locally. Thus, we foresee multiple choices rather than a single direction for the cities of 1984: for example, between centralization or decentralization of urban units and between collective or individual facilities for leisure time.

Transportation, as an illustration, can reinforce centralization or decentralization. Moving sidewalks, the monorail, the hovercraft—all are feasible means of transportation. The hovercraft potentially might have the greatest impact on urban areas. Since it moves on air cushions instead of rubber wheels, it could free people from the paved road just as they were liberated at an earlier time from the fixed rail. By traversing all kinds of terrain it could open up to development vast areas now inaccessible. Will it be used for mass transportation or for individual transportation? Will it be used to spread people more loosely through miles of urbanized development or will it be used instead to maintain the density of existing cities by making escape from the cities into the rural retreat more possible? Will those who wish to preserve a highly concentrated downtown district on a small land base park the hovercraft on the outskirts of the central business district, or will those who wish a dispersed downtown group buildings with surrounding hovercraft-parking compounds?

How attractive will the centers of cities be, and to whom? Now that much of industry and wholesale and retail trade (in the United States and increasingly in Britain) has removed itself from the very center, and now that some office functions are leaving, will closed-circuit television and the walkie-talkie and other forms of communication be used so extensively that the need for face-to-face contact is further reduced? Will airports be the locus of new centers for entertainment, restaurants, clubs, recreation, wholesaling, and professional services as more and more meetings and other activities of executives are held there? They have already become such centers in several American cities.

What will happen to the centers of cities when more and more unskilled and semi-skilled jobs are taken over by machines? The possibilities of further automation of continuous-flow processes, of further computerizing of billing and record-keeping, and of other kinds of mechanization raise questions not only about the location of these activities—on the outskirts of metropolitan communities or even in rural areas—but also about the work force. Will the population be freed for more education, more skilled service and professional activity, more leisure, more creative enjoyment? Or will people be so freed from the discipline and dignity of earning a livelihood that they become alienated from the world of increasing technology and turn to antisocial behavior? The former reaction would call for using the city increasingly as an educational, cultural, and entertainment apparatus. We are not sure about the implications of the latter—might there be a city specially adapted to the teenage gangs, for example?

What happens when prefabricated (even portable) buildings and utility systems are so economical to erect that the buildings of the past and present are anachronistic? Will this mean that the heritage of existing structures will be destroyed or revered? Will our cities be of such unstable form that there will be neighborhood rotation similar to crop rotation?

What happens when more and more environmental control is possible—when snow can be melted before it sticks to the ground, when an air-conditioning shed can be erected over the entire community, when irrigation can temper the landscape and bulldozers can make hills and even mountains on a former flat plain? Will this stop the migration of people to the areas of most natural amenity and of pleasantest climate, and help to equalize population distribution throughout a country or the world?

These are questions which would seem, at first glance, to be more appropriate to the developed nations than the developing nations. And yet, in a sense, they are not. Technology has always permitted the developing nations to leap-frog some urban history. However, whether the cities of 1984 are to be a delight in either the developed or the developing countries will depend more on political, economic, and social than on technological changes.

A COMPREHENSIVE PLAN FOR STABILIZATION

by KENNETH B. CLARK

An ANALYSIS makes clear that piecemeal approaches to the problem of our cities and to the problems of the relationship of whites and Negroes will no longer work. What is now required is the development of a comprehensive plan that takes into account the inextricability of all components of this problem. Such a plan requires large decisions; the mobilization of adequate economic resources; the organization of city planning oriented to the needs of the people; a working relationship between cities and suburban areas; the solution of the problems of public school financing and of the organization and reorganization of public education in cities and surrounding metropolitan areas; and the solution of the problems of population redistribution and freedom of choice in mobility for all.

The logical first phase of such a comprehensive plan should seek to control the volatility and turmoil of the ghetto through a campaign of rehabilitation of housing to increase housing opportunities within and outside of the ghetto, and to clean up ghetto streets.

An increase in the efficiency of sanitation services seems capable of almost immediate solution. Crash techniques similar to those

Reprinted from *Agenda for the Nation,* edited by Kermit Gordon. Copyright © 1968 by The Brookings Institution. By permission of the publisher.

used to clean up after downtown parades, and techniques employed after natural disasters, could be models for an immediate program in all ghetto areas and for a long-range program to sustain the cleanliness of the streets. Such a mass cleanup would improve the health of the ghetto, but it would have an even more immediate psychological effect. It would demonstrate to the residents of the ghetto that someone cares.

If the streets are cleaned and if the areas of ghetto ugliness are transformed, there would be a strengthening of the self-image of the ghetto resident and a building of renewed confidence in the possibility of other solutions. It would be a mistake to believe, however, that this alone would be an acceptable substitute for dealing with the unsolved problems of housing, schools, and jobs. It must be seen as a first step, followed immediately by more rigorous code enforcement, and rehabilitation of ghetto housing for all economic levels.

The next stage in the opening up of the ghettos would involve massive reorganization of education, social welfare, and health services, and significant expansion of job and economic opportunities.

A dramatic improvement in the quality of schools which children are now required to attend is an essential immediate step. Attempts to decentralize these schools and to ensure the accountability of the schools to the parents are prerequisite. Strengthened ghetto schools should, in the long run, lead not to reinforced segregation but to growing desegregation as the gap between educational facilities and academic achievement in ghetto and other schools closes.

Parallel to a strategy of decentralization and community control is the provision of alternative forms of education for the ghetto resident. These alternative schools may be quasi-public, quasi-private educational models organized by business and industrial firms or by social agencies, schools run by state or federal governments. Such programs, like the parochial school system, enlarge educational opportunities for the ghetto child.

Further, the Defense Department, rather than reject adolescent males who now are below the minimum requirements for Army service, could continue and strengthen its compensatory educational programs to raise the level of academic competence. The success of the Defense Department's project to train each year 100,000 men rejected by the Selective Service system is a clear rebuke to the inefficiency of the public-school systems. These first steps to upgrade the quality of education must be followed by massive reorganization to remove the last vestiges of segregation. True quality education for both Negroes and whites requires desegregation.

The nonrational demands of black nationalists for racist curricular controls in the schools, and the persistent resistance to racial desegregation on the part of white segregationists, may be viewed as disturbing evidence of the negative consequences of past and present racially segregated schools. This pattern of black and white racism, a serious threat to the stability of the nation, can be resolved only by serious desegregation of American schools. Although clear upgrading of the quality of education available to Negro youngsters is a necessary part of the overall planning for desegregation, these problems cannot be resolved by better education alone. Even with the best intentions and the highest degree of emotional involvement of the Negro population in community-controlled schools, segregated schools can never be adequate to meet the needs of American society, which include increased educational quality and racial inclusiveness.

The psychological problems inherent in the history and dynamics of segregated education will not be ameliorated for either white or Negro children by even the best of segregated schools. The fact that race is irrelevant to the process of education must be reflected in the schools. The burden of the racial myth is that it is socially divisive and deflects energy from human effectiveness. Separatism, which is a form of ignorance and debilitating superstition, is inimical to the broadening perspectives that should be the goals of education.

Programs of social welfare and health services must be detached from the tradition of the charitable poor laws. The plans designed to achieve a guaranteed annual income and family subsidies represent a shift away from a public welfare approach toward the establishment of an economic base below which no American family will be required to attempt to exist. But the economic problem of welfare would seem to be less difficult of solution than the psychological problem. The chief psychological problems posed by all attempts to redefine welfare emphasize the need to provide support in ways consistent with human dignity and self-esteem; this need is not satisfied by hypocritical semantic changes which perpetuate the self-doubt, stigma, and feelings of inferiority now associated with the condition of being a welfare recipient.

It is possible to develop programs for economic support of families geared to training, child care, and other services essential to the improvement of the living conditions of the poor, and at the same time safeguard the self-image and self-esteem of the individual involved in such programs.

For example, the Head Start preschool program could involve parents of these children far more extensively than at present, in paraprofessional roles that provide services for these children and at the same time provide for parental training in child care, nutrition, health, and the education of children; service, training, and supplemental income could be combined in a single program. Such a program would go a long way toward removing the stigma of welfare and at the same time enable the individual to make some contribution in return.

It would be important, in addition, for paraprofessional and service roles not only to guarantee a minimum family income but also to ensure that the jobs are not dead-end or patently makework jobs, but provide an opportunity for upward mobility and differential achievement. Such achievement should be stimulated by incentives and reinforced by evaluation of the individual's contribution.

Paraprofessional roles will, of course, not cover the large number of welfare recipients who are old or handicapped or infirm. For these persons, who form a high percentage of those on welfare rolls, it is necessary as a minimum to abolish the term "welfare," and to substitute a designation associated with human dignity, like "insurance" or "family security." No American citizen should be deprived of a minimum economic base for living or of necessary health services because he cannot endure the taint embodied in the acceptance of needed aid. He must be assured of the psychological security enjoyed by others who seek and receive government support without stigma—farmers, veterans, small business firms, aviation interests, and others. Business and government must cooperate to provide jobs and job training for all who need and want them.

The psychological problems inherent in the relationship between the poor and the rest of society pervade not only the area of health and welfare but of essential municipal services. One crucial area of risk is the relationship between the community and the police and others responsible for the administration of justice. Improvement of the quality of human relations and acceptance between police and the residents of low-income areas is essential to any serious program for the restructuring of American cities. The problems of the police in low-income areas are complex. Police are themselves, for the most part, products of lower middle-class families. Their status, like that of minority group members, is marginal. They are generally poorly educated and subject to the frustrations of the upwardly mobile; they tend to seek scapegoats and to interpret complex social problems in oversimplified terms. In addition, their task is more hazardous than that of most government employees. They tend to see the inhabitants of the ghetto as adversaries and inferiors. They do not behave toward these persons as they behave toward those they consider their equals or superiors. They act not with the courtesy they show to those they regard as worthy, but often with suspicion, arrogance, bellicosity, or indifference.

The residents of the ghetto, in turn, react to the police as adversaries; they tend to see them as occupation troops and either do not cooperate with them or often reveal overt hostility. As a result of this mutual suspicion and hostility, ghetto residents report a high degree of police brutality, verbal and physical. More pervasive than the claims of physical brutality—which at times can be directly substantiated—and the verbal abuses is the ghetto resentment that results from the fact that police services and protection provided to the ghetto are markedly inferior to those provided to more privileged areas. The chief victims of urban crimes—personal assaults, robberies, and homicide—are the residents of the ghetto. The non-criminal majority of the ghetto frequently claim that they are powerless to obtain from the police adequate protection from criminal elements. The crime statistics, particularly the unsolved homicides and burglaries, tend to substantiate these claims.

Furthermore, it has been stated with some justification that crime in the ghetto such as prostitution and narcotics traffic could not be so prevalent without collusion and involvement of the police. The problem of the ghetto community-police relationship, therefore, cannot be understood or dealt with in the simplistic terms of police brutality. It must be understood in the more complex terms of inadequate police protection and the more insidious and disturbing problems of corruption which seem to characterize police operations in ghetto communities.

Closely associated with these issues is the fundamental problem of the administration of justice. The evidence supports the contention that minority group members are subjected to bail when others would not be, and to higher bail than others, and are more likely to be convicted for similar offenses and to be given longer prison terms for minor and serious offenses, particularly if these offenses involve whites as adversaries.

Such racially biased administration of justice—prevalent in northern cities as well as the South—offends the sense of justice of the community, increases the incidence of racial disturbance, and thereby threatens the stability of the society as a whole. It would follow, therefore, that a comprehensive plan for stabilizing and increasing the viability of our cities would have to include a realistic program to eliminate all racial considerations in the operations of our courts and penal institutions.

The challenges inherent in the effort to make our cities more viable are awesome. But one must assume that they are not beyond the capacity of human intelligence, commitment, and resources. In the process of freeing America from its slums and ghettos and the associated pathology of human cruelties, the problems of environmental control, population control, sanitation, water and air pollution may also be solved. But these are far less difficult than the problems of educating human beings to accept and master the challenges of human conflict. Predictions of success in solving these are more difficult to sustain.

THE EXPERIMENTAL CITY

by ATHELSTAN SPILHAUS

Most cities grow unplanned; they just spread haphazardly, like a thicket of thorns or a colony of mold on a piece of cheese. The result is the present urban mess—too many students for the schools, too much sludge for the sewers, too many cars for the highways, too many sick for the hospitals, too much crime for the police, too many commuters for the transport system, too many fumes for the atmosphere to bear, too many chemicals for the water to carry.

Half of the people in the United States live on one percent of the land, and there is a continual drift to the big cities. Urban renewal encourages the increase in the size of the cities. Two- or three-story slum buildings are torn down, and sterile, high-rise, so-called low-cost housing brings more people into the center of the city than ever before, compounding the problem.

I have proposed, as a corrective, the development of a system of dispersed cities of controlled size differing in many respects from conventional cities, and surrounded by ample areas of open land. If the present 200 million people in the United States were living in 800 cities with a population of a quarter of a million each, and if these cities were scattered evenly across the United States, we would not have the pollution, the traffic congestion, the riots, and many of the other ills that develop where cities become too large.

No engineer or industry would proceed to build anything so costly and complicated as a city without having an experimental prototype. The experience of many industries tells us that it is often cheaper to build a new modern plant than to patch an old one. Similarly, it may be cheaper and more beneficial to create a

Reprinted from *Dialogue*, II/1 (1969). By permission of the USIA and the author.

new city than to try to rehabilitate an old one. This is the concept behind the Minnesota plan for an Experimental City.

The project simply could not be accomplished through any attempt to rebuild a present city, regardless of its size or location, for, without exception, our cities are bound by tradition, outmoded building codes, restrictive legislation, and the consequences of unplanned, unhealthy growth. We must be prepared to discard old codes and conventions and to experiment with new and radical ideas. We must utilize the most advanced methods of construction, transportation, communications, waste removal, and city management.

For these reasons the Experimental City Steering Committee has begun to work on the organization and financing of a scheme to build an experimental city from scratch, to house a quarter of a million people and the industry and commerce needed to support them.

The Experimental City will be unlike other cities that similarly started from scratch. It will not be a bedroom satellite of an existing city, like some of the New Towns in England. It will not be a single-occupation town, devoted to atomic research like Oak Ridge and Los Alamos or to government like Islamabad, Brasilia, and Washington. Nor should it be confused with "demonstration" or "model" cities that try to show what can be done temporarily to renew old cities, although it will conduct experiments based on the experiences of such "model" cities.

The Experimental City will try to represent a true cross-section of urban America—in terms of people, income levels, business and industry, recreation, education, health care, and cultural opportunities. It will be designed for an optimum population size, and its growth will be stopped when it reaches this number. It will provide a laboratory for experimentation and a prototype for future cities of high concentration and controlled size.

Funds have been allocated by the federal government and private industry for studies to define more precisely the character of the Experimental City. In the first stage, surveys were made of existing literature and past experience, and exploratory conferences and workshops were held, under the auspices of the University of Minnesota. The next phases will include laboratory evaluations of new concepts and systems, experimentation with small-scale models, and construction of a pilot model. Then the city will be designed, constructed, and occupied. Finally, after it has been in operation for some time, the Experimental City will be studied further, changed, and developed.

The final stages—building the city and supervising its operations—will be the responsibility of a quasi-governmental, quasi-private corporation, following the example of the Communications Satellite Corporation, which owns and operates various satellites for telephone, teletype, television, and data-transmission purposes.

Early in planning the Minnesota Experimental City we set some guidelines. (1) The ultimate maximum population would be a quarter of a million. The community would be (2) economically viable as a unit of the U.S. economy, (3) truly experimental, (4) at least 100 miles from any major existing urban center, and (5) a densely populated center surrounded by open land. This surrounding land, which would have an area perhaps 100 times that of the densely populated center, would be used for forests, outdoor museums, recreation, or agriculture, or just left as a rural area.

Plans for building the Experimental City differ in many respects from plans for building other kinds of cities. Conventional cities grow above the ground, and as they grow, and as people demand transportation, power, water, gas, and sewers, the ground and rock underneath the city are tunneled for subways or the streets are dug up and the utility lines are buried.

In the Experimental City the whole substructure will be planned and built either by excavation or by building on the natural surface and then raising the "ground level" on which the city dwellers tread. Power lines and utility lines will be installed before the city is built. Knowledge that the city is to be of a certain size will make this possible.

Much of the equipment for servicing the city will be invisible and inaudible underground. Water and building materials can be stored there. Heating plants and cold-storage facilities can be located there. Underground pipelines can carry out solid wastes conventionally carried by trucks. Snow and rainwater from the streets can be channeled to underground reservoirs.

Pollution-producing vehicles can come in underground, and fume sewers can take the gases out to scrubbing and processing plants in the surrounding open-land area. Air-burning vehicles that connect the city with the rest of the nation can be parked underground. Police, ambulance, and emergency vehicles will all have underground throughways. By eliminating the need for some service vehicles, restricting those that are needed to the substructure, and providing a free above-the-ground transportation system (discussed below), we hope to eliminate all vehicles from ground-level streets.

A lawyer at one of our planning sessions asked whether the Experimental City might not eventually disintegrate and become merely a more modern, but no more effective, city complex. "If Chicago, Minneapolis, and New York are willing to allow smoke to billow from new factories," he said, "if they permit automobiles to crowd their streets, and if they do not restrict building construction from occurring in illogical patterns, why should we expect anything different in the Experimental City?"

The answer is simple. Industries, before they are selected or approved for participation in the Experimental City, must agree to abide by the city's building programs. They will be required to conform to certain waste-disposal methods. Presumably they will be willing to do so because they will benefit from the City's central waste-processing facilities, smoke sewers, and other underground disposal facilities.

All the buildings in the Experimental City will be constructed of the newest light-weight materials, and modular techniques of assembly will be used. Thus buildings can be easily erected and quickly disassembled as we learn what is needed, and as needs change.

The average useful life of a building has been estimated to be between twenty and thirty years. All buildings in the Experimental City will be designed with this in mind, and methods of construction that leave permanent outmoded monuments, or later require the services of the wrecking crew, will be abandoned. We will get away from the idea of building forever and, instead, will build for living, recognizing that people have continually changing desires.

With new building materials and freedom from obsolete codes and practices, both public buildings and commercial structures can be made extremely flexible, with adjustable floors, curtain-walls, and ceiling heights. It may even be possible to use inflatable buildings, which can be instantly deflated. Housing units may be precast, even prefurnished, in the manner of Expo's Habitat, with units put together like building blocks and arranged and rearranged as desired. Practical application of this idea is no dream. Precast rooms were used recently in building San Antonio's Hilton Hotel.

The disassembly of a building will resemble the disassembly of an erector set. Reusable components of the building will be swallowed by the city's substructure. There will be no cluttering of streets with cranes and other moving equipment. An obsolete building will disappear like ice cream that melts and drains out through the truncated bottom of the cone. In building new structures, the process will be the reverse. Materials will be lifted from the substructure into the middle of the site, and adjacent activities will not be disturbed.

Certain parts of the Experimental City probably will be domed, so that the advantages and disadvantages of totally enclosed cities can be determined. It is our current view that not all of the city should be domed. Doming only a part of it will enable us to determine the extremes of climate under which total enclosure is economical and acceptable. In this domed portion, which may enclose a medical complex, we can undertake experiments on allergy control, and studies of acoustics, ventilation, and maintenance of a clean atmosphere.

Buckminster Fuller, the designer of the geodesic dome, estimates that a dome two miles in diameter, made of glass, would cost approximately $80 million, but it would eliminate the need for snow removal and would make heating more efficient and less costly. Savings equivalent to the cost of its construction could be achieved in a 10-year period.

With a controlled city, savings can be realized, too, through new methods of waste collection and through use, reuse, and recycling of wastes. It may not be possible to achieve complete recycling immediately, although that objective would always be borne in mind in our planning. Total recycling is the ultimate answer to the waste problem for a closed-system earth.

Imaginative things are being done to control waste at its source. Fly ash from smokestacks is collected for use in making cement and bricks, but so far only one sixteenth of the total has a market; a plant in Florida uses a city's garbage to make fertilizer; dust from grain elevators is made into pellets for cattle feed; iron-ore dust from steel plants is fed back to make steel; sulfur dioxide from factory chimneys and sulfur from old refineries are made into sulfuric acid. There are examples of industrial symbiosis where one industry feeds off, or at least neutralizes, the wastes of another—inorganic wastes from a chemical plant may neutralize the overabundance of organic nutrients from sewage and prevent uncontrollable growth of algae.

In many of these cases, the cost of recovery far exceeds the value of the recovered material. But if a clean environment is our aim, it costs the nation less to recover wastes where they are generated, even if they have no value, than to clean them up after they have been dispersed. Costs resulting from control at the source must be passed on in the cost of the product, but the total increase in manufacturing costs would not compare to the amount the nation would have to spend for cleaning up after the filth is dispersed in rivers, in the air, or on the land.

In the pollution-free Experimental City the utility tunnels would carry away the liquid and gaseous wastes, and many of the solid wastes, to the processing plants. New systems for moving wastes may be used—pneumatic, hydraulic conveyors or unitized trains. If we can reduce the bulk of solid wastes and package them suitably, special trains and trucks can take them away from the city to the open-land area, where they can be processed and then stored or reused, perhaps to build ski slopes, arenas, or other recreation facilities. Wastes that are not immediately reused can be sorted and stored in "mountains," to be mined when reuse becomes economically desirable.

In water-rich areas, water can be used first for drinking and then reused at least twice, for cooling and then for purposes of recreation. But if the Experimental City is to show the way for cities in arid areas, complete recycling of part of the water should be attempted.

One of the most pressing problems of our urban living is transportation and the use, care, parking, and garaging of the private automobile. Constantinos Doxiadis, the noted Greek city planner, recognizes that it is a tragedy when our city buildings are primarily designed to accommodate cars, both stationary and moving, and thus destroy the "human scale." Lewis Mumford points out that the private car no longer performs the role of "facilitating meeting and sociability" and that its "assumed right" is a "license to destroy a city."

How can we provide people with a transportation system that facilitates the desirable social relationships which constitute the joy of city living yet does not have undesirable side effects?

We must remember not to force people into what is technologically easy, but to find a technological solution which is practical and closely meets their desires. What people basically like about the private automobile is the fact that it is a small pod and gives them a sense of privacy in a world where any kind of privacy is becoming a scarce luxury. They also like the automobile because it takes them from where they are to where they want to go without stopping where everybody else wants to stop. But when so many automobiles crowd the streets that we cannot move because of traffic jams, and when our average speed in a pollution-producing vehicle is eight miles an hour, it is time to look at the alternatives.

Now in the process of design are many systems that can move people in motorless, driverless, noiseless, semi-private pods—computer-controlled so that passengers travel from where they are to where they want to go without stopping. If you want to go to the store you don't go to the station and then walk to the store; your pod is sidetracked right into the store. The various systems have a common denominator: they are driven by a propulsion system built into the track. The pods are inexpensive, thus many of them can be used at the same time.

Moving sidewalks, moving platforms, and other wheel-less systems are all technically feasible. One important concept that has emerged in our discussions is this: if we are to use mass transportation in the Experimental City it should be free, like elevator service. You don't pay a fare to ride vertically in an elevator. Why should you pay a fare to ride horizontally? The cost can be embodied in the service costs of the city.

Eliminating the automobile by means of a modern transport system of this kind does away with the need for freeways and traffic control, eliminates smog, saves lives, lessens stress, and saves valuable space. Making the transit system free saves the costs otherwise associated with ticket-selling and ticket-taking. Because free transportation would reduce or eliminate the sale of automobiles, the parking-lot business, and other businesses basic to the economy of older cities, it can be introduced readily only in a newly planned, centrally governed city such as the Experimental City.

Among the greatest innovations that can be tried in the Experimental City are the new technologies in communications that have been developed but not yet put to practical use. The current view is that radio frequencies should be reserved for purposes, such as communication to or from a vehicle in motion, where wires are not feasible. The substructure of the Experimental City would be wired, and coaxial cable would reach to every point where, conventionally, there would be a telephone. These wires and cables can be planned and located in the substructure even before we have a clear-cut idea of what terminals, picture-phones, computers, facsimile machines, and the like may ultimately be needed.

Such a communication system can provide access from any point to large highspeed digital computers, for purposes of city management (on the basis of real information), crime prevention through the use of video monitors, and maintenance of up-to-the-minute data banks for the social experiment that the city constitutes. The same lines, in conjunction with smaller computers and other video terminals, can provide a means of decentralizing schools and hospitals and of bringing together electronically the now separated functions of shopping, charging, banking, credit, and business. Video terminals can even provide "tele-babysitting." The advanced system will provide an ideal laboratory for determining how to insure privacy of computer use yet insure that computers are used to the maximum benefit of society.

The Experimental City would also provide opportunities for test-marketing new products, building materials, and postal systems. New materials would give architects a tremendous scope in developing new forms. No traffic at ground level and no land owned by individuals or individual corporations would offer a degree of freedom not possible in cities where ownership of property delimits plots. Even the materials used in the buildings themselves would be such that they could be taken down and reused if found to be obsolete or inferior. Architecture, with its emphasis on form and the visual environment, is fundamental to the success of the Experimental City. Architects would be freer to exploit the mutuality of function and form in producing a visual environment with other improved qualities. In Philadelphia, for example, the planners have done a magnificent job of improving the visual environment, but their work is mitigated by the stench of oil refineries.

In the Experimental City, we will seek a total optimum environment without hampering diversity of architectural forms and combinations. We will experiment with enclosing portions of the city within domes that will be conditioned as to temperature, humidity, fumes, and light. It is, of course, not at all certain that people want a perfectly controlled climate. The sense of beauty and well-being involves exposure to some degree of variation. Artists know this in their play with light and shade and with colors that clash. Slight breezes and variations of temperature might be necessary to transform even clean air into the fresh air that stimulates our sense of health.

Many artists feel that art centers, now so much in fashion, are already outmoded, and that the newest forms of music, art, theater, and dance have very little to do with exhibit galleries, proscenium stages, and conventional auditoriums. Increased leisure should lead to active participation in all the arts instead of passive exposure. For this we need an arts-recreation space completely flexible in lighting, sound, television, film, electronic devices, and physical dimensions.

Buckminster Fuller, architect and imaginative member of our Experimental City Steering Committee, feels that industry of the future, largely automated, will be located outside the cities, and that the many functions of the city which in the past were directed toward facilitating the exchange of physical goods will in the future be directed toward the exchange of what he calls metaphysical values—ideas, learning, and culture.

How will the Experimental City be populated? Once we have decided on a city's optimum size, how do we prevent the uncontrolled growth that leads to many of today's urban problems? Politicians say you can't move people. Many sociologists, who are more interested in studying what is happening and predicting doom than in taking the steps necessary to avert it, agree. But the fact is that, with our existing legal and governmental structure, we do move people. We push people around everywhere, always with the excuse that it is for their good. We move them in wars; we displace them when we build highways; and we move them when we clear slums and build much larger buildings than were there before. We move them, but often in the wrong direction, into the already overgrown cities.

Urban renewal in its worst manifestations is the construction of the slums of the future. Many people in the present overgrown cities might like to move out into new complexes which provided the advantages of city life without the physical and social distress. Many others whom the authorities say they cannot move have never contemplated moving because they have been trapped, lacking the opportunity to go anywhere else. The fact is that most of those who can afford to do so have already fled the cities, to suburbs that will become the slums of tomorrow.

We must build a city for today's city-dwellers and suburb-dwellers to go to. We must provide people with a different choice, not just that between life in a dirty overgrown city with suburbs or a completely rural existence. We can provide a middle choice— clean cities of controlled size, with plenty of space and an exciting new environment. The answer is *not* to control individuals, but to design a mix of industrial, commercial, and other employment opportunities that keeps the population in a healthy equilibrium.

Who will manage the Experimental City? It would seem that the idea of running a city as a public utility by a quasi-public, quasi-private corporation should be tried. Present-day hotel complexes, with their associated shops, restaurants, transportation facilities, and so on, are growing larger and larger. Many of them are run very well. It is not much of a jump to think of experimental cities of controlled size as huge hotels. It seems to me that management of the city-hotel-corporation type should be tried.

Daniel Moynihan, director of the Harvard-M.I.T. Joint Center for Urban Studies, says realistically that the government cannot do everything well, and that many public services are best contracted to private enterprises. In the Experimental City, contracts for many such services would be let on a performance basis. The federal government, too, is beginning to move in this direction. Agencies have let contracts to private enterprise for carrying out social-work programs. Why not go the whole way and have responsible corporations provide all the services needed in the Experimental City?

It is realistic to recognize that a large sum of money is needed for planning and building the services substructure, which will utilize new technologies involving costly experimentation and research. Part of the construction costs could legitimately be funded by a Federal Housing Authority mortgage. Part of the costs of experimentation and research would be met by the private sector. Imaginative American industry needs a place, a city laboratory, in which to try out new technologies of waste management, communication, transportation, and construction. Industries are at present investing large sums in elements of these areas. Our plan for the Experimental City shows that it is the best and most economical place to do this research.

Other approaches to the problems of today's cities are being tried. The government's Model City program, an urban renewal program administered by the Department of Housing and Urban Development, is an attempt to alleviate the overwhelming problems of the overgrown cities. The objective is a most important one, but, in general, the means are the tearing out of slums and their replacement with new construction. The government is becoming the new slum landlord.

Worthwhile experiments in the building of new cities are being made by private enterprise. Examples are Columbia (Maryland); Disneyworld's experimental prototype city in Florida; and Westinghouse's community proving ground in Florida. More than two hundred "new cities" are either in the design stage or under construction in the United States. These government-financed and privately financed "new cities" are similar to the Minnesota Experimental City in one respect: they are built from scratch. On the other hand they are, in the best meaning of the term, real-estate developments, and consequently they tend to be satellites of existing urban complexes—communities where people live and from which they commute to work.

That this is the case may be seen from the fact that almost all of the "new cities" are growing along the coastlines—East, West, and Gulf of Mexico—where the overgrown cities already are. Generally their size is not controlled, and one can anticipate that even the best of them, such as Reston (Virginia) and Columbia, will be swallowed up as nearby urban complexes—in this case Washington and Baltimore—expand. Because they do not have sufficient reserved open land around them, even the best of the "new cities" will become engulfed; moreover, since they are close to existing huge cities, they cannot develop with enough independence to try novel technologies.

It is obvious to me that we must use all of our land for living, not just tiny fractions of it. To do this we must look at solutions that envisage urban dispersal, and if we are to disperse into new planned cities, a national experimental-cities program is an urgent must.

Suppose we built an experimental city in every one of our 50 states. If each such city were populated by a quarter of a million people, we could care for only 12½ million people, barely the predicted increase of population in the United States in three years. Yet, according to our most optimistic estimates, just the building of an experimental city will take longer than three years, and if we merely keep up with the increase in population we will do nothing to alleviate the problems of over-growth in our existing cities.

The problems of our large cities indicate an urgent need to move toward the dispersal concept immediately. If the need is urgent in the United States, it is even more urgent in the world as a whole, especially in those countries where the birthrate is much higher than ours.

Let us look ahead and suppose that the world population, if we do nothing about population control, reaches 15 billion by A.D. 2068. And let us assume that our technology permits us to build cities on any solid land, from Antarctica to the tropics, from desert to rain forest. The area of all the continents is about 2.3 billion acres. If we built cities of controlled size, dispersed throughout the world, there would be 60,000 cities of a quarter of a million people each, and each such city would be surrounded by 40,000 acres, or 62 square miles, of open land. The alternative of allowing the present big cities to grow unplanned, or to accelerate their growth through so-called urban renewal, would mean that vast tracts of the earth's surface would be uninhabited and the urban complexes would be intolerable.

(There is no magic in the figure of a quarter of a million. It may be that a city of half a million would better provide the choices that people want, or it may be that cities of different sizes would be needed. The important thing is that the size be controlled and that the cities be kept within a small area, with bounds, so that they would remain surrounded by open land.)

The advent of atomic power opens up the possibility of building verdant cities even in desert areas, if these areas are near the sea. An atomic plant which would generate a million kilowatts of electricity could distill half a billion gallons of fresh water from seawater and, from the residue, make enough fertilizer to grow the food to feed the entire populations of ten cities the size of the proposed experimental city.

We must try these schemes and others that will emerge. Clearly, we cannot continue to experiment in bits: each new technology affects others; better communications change patterns of travel, medical care, and education; new methods of cleaning and noise-proofing make zoning unnecessary. The city is a completely interacting system, and, thus, the experiment must be a total system. Nobody knows the answers to city living in the future, and when answers are unknown, experiment is essential.

WHY NOT ROOFS OVER OUR CITIES?

by R. BUCKMINSTER FULLER

T HOSE WHO have had the pleasure of walking through the great skylighted arcades, such as the one in Milan, Italy, are familiar with the delights of covered city streets, in which outdoor restaurants and exhibits are practical. They can envision the effect of a domed-over city, where windows may be open the year round and gardens bloom in the dust-free atmosphere. From below, the dome would appear as a translucent film through which the sky, clouds and stars would be visible. It would not create a shut-in feeling any more than carrying a parasol above one's head on a sunny summer day.

There are other persuasive arguments in favor of domed-over cities. (It is no aesthetic accident that nature gave us no cubical heads, eggs, nuts or planets, but encased the contents in curvilinear structures.) There is, for example, no method more effective in wasting heating and cooling energy than the system employed by New York and other skyscraper cities of the world. A dome over mid-Manhattan would reduce its energy losses approximately fiftyfold. Such a dome would reach from the East River to the Hudson at 42nd Street on its east-west axis, from 64th to 22nd Street on its north-south axis, and would consist of a hemisphere two miles in diameter and one mile high at its center. The cost of snow removal in the city would pay for the dome in 10 years.

Studies made at the Snow Institute of Japan and by Japan's Mitsubishi company indicate the cost of heating the surface of the dome with electric resistance wires imbedded in the skin. To maintain a temperature sufficient to melt snow and ice (with the heat turned on only during the time of snow and ice formation, for cities in the snowfall magnitude of New York) would cost far less than amortizing the expense of the additional structure necessary to support the cumulative snow loads throughout the winter months.

When rain falls on New York City and its counterparts around the world, it runs down the buildings into the streets, then into the gutters and on to the sewers to be polluted with all the other waters. Year after year, New York and other cities have suffered water shortages, though they are deluged with summer thunder-showers, when enough water falls to take care of the city for days. With a domed-over city, both the melted snow water and the rain would run neatly to a guttering, clear of the pollution of the streets, down into a canal around the dome's lower rim from whence it would flow to great collecting reservoirs. The dome would be high enough to cause the water to flow gravitationally back to the storage reservoirs in Westchester County.

Because the energy losses would be so greatly reduced for the covered portion of the city, its heating and cooling could be handled most economically by electrical energy wired in from generators, far from the domed-over city. A new ultra-high-voltage electrical conducting system will soon bring New York electrical energy, by wire, all the way from the Pennsylvania hills, where the coal is to be mined and burned in steam-driven electric generators at the mine mouths. This will eliminate all fumes from the dome-covered atmosphere. The dome would also be able to umbrella away the fumes occurring outside the dome.

Calculations on the two-mile dome for mid-Manhattan indicate that the individual structural elements would be invisible, as invisible as the wires of a screened porch when viewed from a 100-foot distance. For this reason the appearance of the dome would be seen as a glistening translucent form. One would get the same effect if he photographed an ordinary kitchen wire strainer turned upside down and placed 100 feet away.

Such a shielding dome would also exclude the sound of passing jet planes. The lower edge of the dome would be at such a height as to make it appear an oversized umbrella above the city, with plenty of blue sky visible under its rim.

The dome's skins, consisting of wire-reinforced, one-way-vision, shatterproof glass, mist-plated with aluminum, would have the exterior appearance of a mirrored dome, while the viewer inside would see out without conscious impairment. This will cut down the interior sunlight to nonglare level. Such domes would also provide a prime shielding against atomic radiation fallout.

When such large domes are made, the captive atmosphere in itself is enough to support the structural shell, as in a large pneumatic tire. Double the diameter of a tractor tire and it takes eight times as long to let the air out through the same sized valve. The larger the dome, the lower the pressure necessary to carry a given load. With such very large domes, the air introduced with the air-conditioning would keep up the shell-sustaining pressure.

As three-quarters of planet Earth is water, and man is now trending swiftly to occupy the world's waters, as well as space, spherically-enclosed floating cities will soon dot the oceans at safely negotiable small-yacht distances apart that will permit world-around cruising. Spherically-enclosed subterranean cities, sky-floating spherical cities and independent spherical spaceship cities probably will be developed by humanity during the next century.

Before we build our spherically-enclosed and domed-over cities, however, we must know how humanity is going to get from one to another. This involves studying every aspect of world transportation, and within that the air transport industry.

The whole industry of the earth could be integrated in such a way as to employ credit cards, computerized ticketing, and automated follow-through of the whole transportation process—with all its economic and technical ramifications. A traveler could thereby "book" by vending machine in the nearest downtown office, or be ticketed in any hotel lobby or corner store, or even over his two-way TV facsimile, cable, or radio-beam closed-circuit system, operating from any spot from which he may wish to initiate his travel. He would insert his credit card into the transmitter and press buttons to indicate the time he would like to leave from one point and arrive at another, anywhere on earth, in the shortest possible time, and in the most economical way, including terminal helicopter flights, automobile rentals, stopover hotel accommodations, et al. Out from the vending machine would come a ticket printed with his routing and booked passage with the amount automatically charged to his credit card for officially automated accounting.

Whenever necessary, the traveler could cancel his ticket by putting his credit card back in any travel-vending machine and pushing the canceling button for the same routing, plus the transaction number which had been imprinted on the vending ticket when he received the machine's commitment to carry him. The travel vending machine would thus be able to print out bookings in split seconds, or cancel them in another split second. The ticket would be all the individual needed to take with him as his automatic key-of-entry at the most convenient downtown embarkation point.

At his downtown airlines contact point he would enter his private traveling quarters and be transported therein to the point of major flight embarkation. These quarters would be within an angular segment of what I call a "fuselage cartridge." Each cartridge would be a circular section, like a banana slice or a Lifesaver mint, as one of many such units packed in parallel as a section of a cylinder cut perpendicularly to the cylinder's axis. The long, tubular assembly of these sections would fit together to form a complete cylindrical cartridge fitting neatly into the tubular-shaped fuselage of the air transport. There could be hundreds or more of these sections. Within any angular segment of one of these, the traveling quarters would provide the maximum sitting space without one human physically touching another; the integrity of each individual's privacy would be physically ensured. The sitting device would convert to a full-length bed that could move within the cartridge section by mechanical means. Luggage would be stored within the passenger's circular cartridge section.

All of these sectioned compartments would be routed by helicopter lift from "downtown" to the dispatching airports. At the airports, the cartridge cross sections would be loaded into the next transport bound for their particular destination, or series of destinations—the cartridges being loaded in proper sequence for detachment on jigs at their respective destinations. The cartridge sections, recombined at each airport, would be loaded through the open tail of the tubular fuselage as cargo loadings are made through the open tail of cargo planes. This marshaling or separating out and recombining of cartridge sections could be accomplished at each airport with computerized switches.

At destination airport, the passenger cartridge sections would be helicopter-lifted or vacuum-tube-sucked to the nearest downtown disembarkation points. The same world travel and freight traffic computerization would also take care of all hotelling and dwelling accommodations.

The design of future cities will therefore be inexorably linked with transportation design. Some experimental cities will be undertaken scientifically by advanced industry as a general systems problem in the same way design scientists organize the comprehensive and detailed planning of great steamships and the soon-to-be giant ships of the air which later, as veritable sky cities, will become air-deliverable at supersonic speeds. Next will come cities on the oceans, in space, on the moon and, last, scientifically organic cities rocket-delivered around the earth.

The first officially undertaken experimental city in the USA is now going through its initial phase of official consideration. It is prescribed by its backers—the Federal and Minnesota State Governments acting with private industry, banks and press—that it be located somewhere in Minnesota at least a hundred miles away from any present city. This is to guarantee its not becoming a dormitory extension of an already existing city. Logistical engineering considerations show that the research, development, and government-financed prototyping, fabrication, and installation of such a city will take a minimum of ten years, even employing today's most advanced science and technology.

This means that the city cannot be realized before 1977. By then, major world traffic between the Americas' 12 percent of the human family and the 72 percent of all humanity living in Asia and Europe will be carried on over the northern polar routes, which are the shortest distances between these people. Since Minnesota occupies precisely the center of North America, it is the most inclusively effective marshaling point of the continent's part of the world air traffic pattern as it interconnects North America with both the Eurasian continent and South America.

If we assume that the present rate of acceleration of man's

technoeconomic evolution is to persist, we also will have to assume that the world's present political divisioning into separate, sovereign states will have become as obsolete as the days of history when men belonged to city-states because they were inherently immobilized by lack of transport or were even identified only as lifelong members of a single tribe, or township, or even a single borough or ward within a township—or with a single room in a single building as a numbered prisoner. The degrees of freedom to be attained are physical as well as metaphysical.

THE LOST PAGEANTRY OF NATURE

---

by GYORGY KEPES

WE LIVE in a time of crisis—deep, pervasive, expanding. But it is also a time of enormous promise and vitality. The most creative members of the artistic community are responding to the scientific revolution with power and imagination, and are exploring it intensely for its latent poetry.

In order to take on new tasks of unprecedented magnitude, some artists have given up a portion of their traditional isolation and are working in collaborative groups. There are few master spirits projecting their egos as far as possible. Instead, there are emerging cross-disciplinary teams of artists, scientists and engineers. The notion that has been most insistent in shaping the aims of one team—the MIT Center for Advanced Visual Studies—and controlling its formulation of tasks and methods in a highly ambitious group project is a strongly felt awareness of the interdependence of individual and civic scale.

Reprinted from *arts canada* (December 1968, Volume XXV No. 5 Issue No. 124/127). By permission of the publisher.

Immensely expanded scale, both in magnitude and in complexity, is the prime characteristic of our contemporary world. One aspect of this exploding spectrum has become so prominent as to present strong symbolic significance: the interdependence of the very small and the very large on every level of existence.

Two examples epitomize this significant interdependence. The immense nuclear accelerator in Geneva, a circular structure, a third of a mile in diameter yet precise to $\frac{1}{10}$ of an inch, probes into fantastically minute particles of matter by accelerating protons until they approach the speed of light. The interaction of men and machines in a complex system, whose terminal point is the astronaut on his orbital mission, is based upon exquisite knowledge and control over the smallest ranges of known matter. We face serious difficulties when the concatenation of the large and the small eludes our grasp. A few years ago the failure in Canada of one tiny bit of a huge interlocking international electric system brought power failure and total blackout to most of the northeastern United States.

Knowledge of the interdependence of polar opposites—the small and the large, the part and the whole, the simple and the complex, the individual and society—is by no means new. In our time it has gained amplified meaning because of its potent new contexts.

The harmonious balance of opposing human drives was seen by the ancient Greeks as the source of the good life, not only for the citizen but also for the *polis*. As individuals we seek self-realization, personal happiness, and rich personal experiences. Sensing our part in the ecology of the social community we seek dynamic balance within our milieu in interaction with our physical environment and with other persons. Our poles of orientation are like points with ever-changing contexts; they demand a constant reevaluation of meaning because of their ever-changing frames of reference.

The need to rebuild, clean and enrich the chaotic, polluted, and impoverished environment so that it will evoke a constructive response from all citizens has become a publicly acknowledged social goal. The need to straighten, clean, and replenish twisted, fake, and hollow personal lives is the driving force behind our young persons' passionate search for love, honesty, and intensity.

The nature of the conflicts we face may be understood better by taking an analogy from a physical phenomenon. A physical law tells us that every structure has a limit beyond which it cannot grow without endangering its cohesion and functioning unity. Galileo observed some 300 years ago that if we tried constructing bridges or houses of abnormal size, while retaining the proportions and employing materials which suffice on a smaller scale, the form will collapse. A physical form will fall to pieces of its own weight unless we either change its relative proportions (its structure) or find new, stronger materials.

City traffic cannot increase beyond a certain number of cars or traffic jams will replace traffic. Airports cannot exceed a certain limit of landings and takeoffs without defeating the purposes of safe and speedy transportation. And social growth, too, is limited by its channels of communication, by the lack of awareness of common purposes and aspirations.

As yet, we have not found the political and social system that makes adequate use of our enlarged knowledge and tremendous powers of communication, production, and transportation. We have failed bitterly in our attempts to find a new strength and grace that derive from shared purposes and common loyalties.

The latter is an area in which the artist's contribution can be absolutely vital. The acceptance of technology as a source of rich and exciting forms in scale with the new physical environment is only one side of the story. There is still another important key task to be faced and dealt with if we are to set aright our dangerously eroding social cohesion and our impoverished inner world of thought and feeling. We need to develop equipment that will enable us to sense new connections and thereby revive and strengthen our individual lives. As the urban world grows, so must the increasingly complex task of communication to keep it vital. The interconnection of man and his environment in an embracing dynamic system is the path to a level of existence that makes effective use of new potentialities.

Have artists begun to envisage this new sense of unity? Some have. Art, without loss of personal vision—in point of fact through the expansion of such vision—is fast approaching the

environmental scale and by its own inner dynamics as a craft
becoming a collaborative enterprise involving science and engineering.

The fellows of the MIT Center for Advanced Visual Studies,
now engaged in preliminiary exploration of a major project,
recognize objectives similar to those of other collaborative
groups: absorption of the new technology as an artistic medium;
interaction of artists, scientists, engineers, and industry; the
raising of the scale of work to the scale of the urban setting;
media geared to all sensory modalities; incorporation of natural
processes, such as cloud play, water flow, and the cyclical variations of light and weather; acceptance of the participation of
"spectators" in such a way that art becomes a confluence rather
than a dialogue. But the work in the Center aims at more than
exploitation of new technical potentials. It seeks, above all, to
develop new objectives. These are envisioned as complementaries
of both the private and the civic sector of art: intensifying the
infra-individual world and at the same time developing networks
of communication between individuals, and between the individual
and the environment.

As the Director who organized the Center, I submitted to the
Center's Fellows the following as the first collaborative project:
to explore, individually and as a group, the possibilities of a large-
scale animated, luminous, environmental structure for Boston
Harbor. There are a number of reasons for the choice of this
particular location. The Harbor in itself is an almost ideal setting
for such a work. As the gateway to the city and to the entire
New England region, it is a fabulously beautiful body of water
with many uninhabited islands. Its waterfront forms a gigantic
amphitheatre facing 500 square miles of land carrying populations
of urban density. The Greater Boston region is one of the world's
foremost centers of advanced technological thinking, and an op-
portune source for engaging the collaboration of sophisticated
industry. There is a good chance, moreover, that Boston will
become the center of the Bicentennial celebration of American
independence in 1976; so there are genuine possibilities that the
project may be realized.

At this point, the Boston Harbor project is conceived as an
open-ended form/subject furthering development, growth, and

chance effects of nature, and embodying the following design options.

1. To bring back the lost "Sundays" in the sensory experience of urban surroundings by offering new festive qualities as common property of all citizens; to compensate for the lost pageantry of nature, the new moon and the falling star. These qualities are to be achieved through coupling new technical competence and the artistic imagination.

2. To instill among the citizens of Boston and surrounding cities and towns a sense of group identity, as well as a sense of belonging. Seen from air, sea, and land, the Harbor form is to be not only a strongly molded gateway to an important region but also a focal, symbolic form embodying feelings of loyalty and civic pride. It is to be comparable to the hearth in the home, and to such structures as the Great Circle of Stonehenge in Bronze Age England, the Acropolises of the Greek city-states, and the cathedrals of medieval communes.

3. To introduce a new aesthetic dimension of urban landscape through the controlled exploitation of the luminous accidental richness of the urban nightscape.

4. To develop with an extended range of media an environmental-scale configuration with the same metaphoric strength of dynamic patterns that Piero della Francesca, Poussin and Seurat achieved in subtle geometry within the static limits of a flat canvas.

5. To present not a repeated, unchanging light drama but sequences corresponding to events in time. The performance is to be coordinated with civic life and varied to accord with weekdays, holidays, and Sundays.

6. To create a man-machine system so inspired as to nourish and give symbolic focus to a new self-esteem and dignity for man.

7. To involve the "play" instinct of individual human beings. We speak of playing music but cannot speak of "playing painting." We now have the opportunity to play with light with almost the complete sense of freedom as a child playing on the seashore. The technical possibilities are such that the individual can now participate freely, inventing and re-inventing the changing rules of the game.

In addition to such a practical imperative as avoiding interference with air traffic, one of the considerations taken into account in visualizing the Harbor form has been economy of physical structure, which is the essence of elegance in design and craftsmanlike performance. The "parsimony of nature," the epitome of such elegance, is to be amplified, with special emphasis placed on micro-instrumentation. As a minimal form, the Harbor form should approach the natural form of raindrops and crystals. The theoretical goal of likeness to nature is emphasized once again in the structure's involvement with wind, weather, and change of season.

In the response of today's generation of artists to the challenges of today's world we may well be seeing the emergence of a new sensibility, the successor to that Renaissance sensibility which dominated our responses to the natural world until the dawn of the present era, and even beyond. The harbinger of the Renaissance sensibility was Saint Francis of Assisi, who was enthralled by the beauty of the physical world and its creatures. Saint Francis delivered sermons to birds and flowers, drawing them into the world of man. The small world of Saint Francis is still with us, but we need men who can speak to today's extended world of nature, with its far-off galaxies, ultra-microscopic forms, split-second milkdrops, turbulence patterns, and invisible radiation. Unimaginable beauty is locked within these obscured vistas, as stirring as sunsets, flowers, and the white mantle of winter snow.

It is our duty then to give thought to the manner in which these new forms may be coupled with and based upon utilitarian functions. Such thinking is long overdue; our polluted megalopolis has to be purified of its inhuman elements to rid us of toxic fallout, both physical and emotional. There is a need for homeostasis on a large-scale environmental level. This is a great challenge for the artistic imagination—to be involved in symbolizing and inspiring a new metabolism for our cities by expressing richly sensed events through significant forms.

BUCKMINSTER FULLER'S
FLOATING CITY

by SHOJI SADAO

IT ALL BEGAN early in 1966 with the very unusual request by a Japanese businessman asking Bucky to investigate the technical and economic feasibility of building a tower taller than Mount Fuji. We—Fuller and Sadao, Inc., and Geometrics, Inc. [two Cambridge, Massachusetts, architectural firms that work on Fuller's concepts]—commenced work on the project in the summer of 1966 with what we understood to be a fairly clear and definite scope of work. A month or so later, however, our client asked if the scope could be enlarged to include a study of a super vertical city for a million inhabitants.

We could not accommodate the request at that time and proposed instead that we look into the matter after completion of the tower study. However, Bucky was in Japan at this time discussing the tower study and responded to the request by proposing the idea of a floating tetrahedron city for Tokyo Bay. (A tetrahedron is a pyramid with four faces including the base.) This was accepted by the client. Bucky then began to develop the general case study of an autonomous, sea-going tetrahedron city for a million inhabitants, while we (Fuller-Sadao and Geometrics) continued work on the tower study, completing it in December, 1966.

There followed several months of correspondence with Japan attempting to clarify the scope of the project; finally a meeting in Tokyo in May 1967, which I attended, made evident the fact that there were several grave misunderstandings which proved fatal to the whole study. Several months later, our Japanese client informed us of his intention to abandon the project. However,

Reprinted from *The Futurist*, III/1 (February 1969). By permission of the publisher.

articles by Bucky describing the floating tetrahedron city appeared in *Saturday Review, The New York Times Magazine,* and *Playboy,* and during the summer of 1967 officials of the U.S. Department of Housing and Urban Development discussed the possibility of Bucky continuing his work on the floating city under a HUD grant. A grant was issued to the Triton Foundation, Inc., of which Bucky is president and I am treasurer, in October, 1967, and the study was submitted in 1968.

The study was a broad investigation of the technical and economic feasibility of developing water areas immediately adjacent to the cores of major cities by floating entirely new communities. The study was directed by Peter Floyd of Geometrics and myself. Consultants in city planning, transportation, and economics contributed to the study as well as consulting structural, mechanical, electrical, and marine engineers.

Over 80 percent of U.S. metropolitan areas with a population of 1,000,000 or more are near bodies of water sufficiently deep to accommodate such floating communities. Most have a depth adequate for shipping (twenty-five to thirty feet) and relatively sheltered harbors. At these depths, a maximum average height of twenty stories can be floated. This means that if some sections of the floating structures were lower than twenty stories, others could be still higher.

The technology necessary to build floating cities is already in existence. We have been building superliners for many years that carry populations the size of entire towns. (The S.S. *United States,* for example, holds 3,000 persons, including crew and passengers.) Supertankers now are being constructed which weigh 30,000 tons dead weight. (The 5,000-person neighborhoods we studied would weigh 150,000 tons.) Floating platforms for oil derricks and oceanographic experiments have long been in successful operation, some in conditions of unprotected water—a condition that would not trouble city sites.

The basic unit of the "Triton City" plan is a neighborhood-sized floating community that would accommodate 3,500 to 6,500 people. This unit, averaging 5,000 residents, is the size required to support an elementary school, a small supermarket, and local convenience stores and services. There are two kinds of neighborhood modules designed for the city. One is composed of a string of four to six small platforms, each holding about 1,000 people; the other is a larger, triangular platform which would be of high density and have capacity for as many as 6,500. Three to six of these neighborhoods, with a total population of 15,000 to 30,000, would form a town. At this point, a new town platform including a high school, more commercial, recreational, and civic facilities, and possibly some light industry, could be added. When the community has reached the level of three to seven towns (90,000 to 125,000 population), it would become a full-scale city and would then add a city-center module containing governmental offices, medical facilities, a shopping center, and possibly some form of special city-based activity like a community college or specialized industry.

Because the system of development is based on aggregation of separate modules, flexible arrangements of total communities up to 100,000 persons could either grow gradually, starting with a cluster of two or three neighborhoods, or be built up very rapidly. If needs should change after the city has been established, units can be added or subtracted in keeping with community growth, and not cause disruption of the entire fabric. Cities can develop their facilities incrementally, without having to make a greater expenditure than is actually justified at any given point in time.

Siting of the city on water is an opportunity to overcome some of the expense and delay of ordinary "on ground" construction by taking advantage of more modern production technology. With the sea as highway, an entire neighborhood, town, or city-center unit can be built in another location—such as a shipyard or dry dock—and then towed to its site in one piece. By using a large existing construction facility of this kind, the economy and efficiency of shop fabrication can be applied to construction problems which have traditionally been solvable only at the final site location.

In terms of both structure and organization, it is most sensible to provide relatively small (in terms of city sizes), individual neighborhood platforms—roughly the size, though not necessarily the same proportions, of large liners and tankers. The platforms would be up to four acres in area and house as many as 5,000 people. In this way, the structural elements are kept to sizes which can be reasonably handled by existing shipyard facilities, and movement of the platforms into place is easily accomplished. Larger town and city complexes could then be made by linking these platforms at the final location.

For maximum structural efficiency, the platform (which would be of steel or concrete) and the portions of the buildings rising above the platform are considered as a "megastructure," that is, a single complete framework. This also allows the most flexible distribution of spaces: requirements for large, open spaces are met, and needs for smaller spaces can be readily satisfied by lightweight structural components filling in the larger ones. The infilling components (apartments, classrooms, stores, offices, etc.) are factory-produced as complete, finished units before they are fitted within the frame. This prefabrication of elements is a way of approaching the efficiency of the automobile industry in assembly-line production and of achieving similar economics. Additionally, it would be possible to make subsequent changes by removing outmoded units and replacing them with new ones without disturbing the overall disposition of the city.

Functionally, a whole neighborhood can be treated as a single building and all mechanical services (including water, sewage and waste, power, and heating and air conditioning) centrally provided. This has two advantages: (1) no duplication of costly central plant equipment is required for individual dwellings; (2) distribution of services on a large scale is much more efficient.

The prototype density used for the Triton City communities is 300 dwelling units per acre. This high density of population would economically support some form of transportation between the community and the city core. While there would be automobile access to and from the floating platforms and parking for residents' cars, it is anticipated that movement from platform to platform (that is, from one neighborhood to another) would be a walkable distance or accomplished by public transit. To discourage automobile congestion in the floating city, there is little provision for transient parking. All wheeled vehicles are restricted to a single level in the city complex, which is segregated from pedestrian areas. At this level are truck loading and unloading facilities, transit stations, and ramp access to parking garages. It is probable that the transit system would be rubber-tired and would circulate on the same roadbed as automobiles, buses, and trucks. However, possible use of a system such as the Westinghouse sky bus is being considered.

Because the megastructure is a whole neighborhood, some new departures in aesthetics and safety are possible. All parking is within the flotation, removing from view one major contemporary eyesore, the parking lot. Since wheeled vehicles are not permitted above the entrance level, the streets would be safe for pedestrians. Every neighborhood child could walk to school—and in no danger of being run over. As another precaution, the elevators and stairs, which are housed in vertical towers, would have glazed sides; everyone inside would be visible at all times. The installation of vertical circulation facilities in three centrally located towers also means that they could be surveyed from one vantage point and that they would be intensively used, thus dually insuring the safety of residents. Moreover, there are no dangerous alleyways and no hidden access to any dwelling, as all doors are directly on the streets, which are wide, straight and easily patrolled.

All dwelling units face directly on the water, and the exterior of the megastructure slopes slightly backward. Apartments on higher levels look on the garden terraces of those below, rather than, clifflike, straight down to the water. Apartments on the upper levels give magnificent views while those on the lower levels offer closeness to the water.

The front doors of the dwelling units open onto broad (about eighteen-foot-wide) "streets in the air" that are solely for pedestrian use and very much resemble the promenade decks of ocean liners. These streets are connected by bridges to the schools, shops and other community facilities, which are in the interior portion of the megastructure. At the higher levels, the apartment units surround and enclose the village square, a public space open to the sky. The many roof levels of the structure are terraced and landscaped for various kinds of recreation.

By designing a megastructure (that is, an entire framework of structure and services) for high density residence, great economies in transportation, services, and utilities can be realized. The economy is not only financial, but also in conservation of open space for recreation and in easy access to the core city by high-ways and rapid transit. Preliminary cost estimates indicate that the whole fabric (including housing, schools, and other community facilities, all services, roads and utilities) can be provided at an expense of $8,000 per person, at a density of 300 dwelling units per acre.

The project is preliminary and exploratory in character and it is not expected that HUD will take any immediate action. However, the response of those who have looked at the project has been good. For instance, Charles M. Haar, HUD's Assistant Secretary for Metropolitan Development, has described the floating city as "one of the most unusual new concepts we have seen."

"A community on water, with highway and mass rapid transit to the central city, offers an interesting possibility for relocating people, facilities and services when core area renewal is in progress," Haar said.

I myself am convinced that the floating city offers one of the best means of achieving economically feasible and attractive communities. I believe that such cities will be built within the next few years.

SEA CITY—A MAN-MADE OFFSHORE ISLAND FOR 30,000 INHABITANTS

---

by GEOFFREY A. JELLICOE,
EDWARD D. MILLS and OVE N. ARUP

Within the foreseeable future the great oceans of the world, together covering three-quarters of the earth's surface, must inevitably be harnessed to provide food, to carry

Reprinted by permission of Pilkington Glass Ltd. First published in 1969.

industrial centers and to afford a permanent home to some of the world's increasing population. Sea City, an offshore island in glass and concrete proposed by the Pilkington Glass Age Development Committee, will be a first practical step in this direction. The building of such island cities would mean that industry and housing need no longer encroach on the rapidly shrinking open spaces in industrialized countries. New industries, such as fish farming, would be developed, and a newly discovered source of power—undersea natural gas—could be put to work where it is found, instead of being carried through miles of pipeline to already overcrowded industrial complexes on the mainland. Although such a project may not be realized for fifty years, the structural and engineering techniques required exist today. This has been established by the Committee's architects and engineers, who have produced a blueprint for the design and construction of just such an island city, which would be economically viable and provide all the facilities of a mainland town in a warmer, healthier environment than would be possible on land.

Shoal water covers nearly ten percent of the sea-bed, providing many suitable sites across the world for developments of this kind—for example, Martha's Vineyard off the east coast of North America; stretches of the Yellow Sea and the East China Sea; in the Middle East, off the coast of Israel and in the oil-rich Persian Gulf; off the South American coast from Rio de Janeiro southwards to the River Plate; in the Gulf of Mexico; and large expanses from the Java Sea northwards to the Gulf of Siam. In Europe, large shallow areas are to be found in the Baltic, in the northern half of the Adriatic and off the north coast of the Black Sea, as well as in the North Sea and the Irish Sea. The site selected for the Sea City project is on the Haisborough Tail, a shoal area some fifteen miles off the east coast of England where the water is as shallow as thirty feet and the tidal range low at four to seven feet.

The main structure of Sea City is a sixteen-story amphitheater supported by piles and protected on the seaward side by an encircling breakwater. This outer structure encloses a lagoon with clusters of floating man-made islands; it is broken only at one point, in the southeast corner, to provide a narrow harbor entrance. The city extends 4,700 feet from north to south and is

3,300 feet across at its widest point. To construct Sea City, piles brought from the mainland by barge are driven into the seabed in rows, twenty to thirty feet apart, to form the base for the superstructure. Reinforced deck sections, precast in concrete ashore and towed to the site, are jacked up on guide rails between the rows of piles. The sections are then locked in position at the top of the piles to form a continuous cellular slab. In situ, concrete is used to fill the gaps around the pile structure.

Resting on the completed base and starting thirty feet above sea level at its highest point, the superstructure is made up of concrete cells joined together at the corners. Each cell, prefabricated on the mainland and brought to the site in a bottomless barge, forms either a small flat or part of a large one. The cells, which are winched into position up temporary ramps, are mounted one above the other on spacer units. These spacers form gaps above, below, and on both sides of each cell, which are used as ducts for gas, water, electricity, and sewage. Each concrete cell unit is stressed down to the one below to form a completely monolithic structure.

The islands in the inner lagoon are made up from triangular concrete pontoons sixty feet wide and held in position by anchor chains. Linked by flexible couplings to allow for water movement, these rigid sections can be easily separated and recoupled to form islands of different shapes and sizes up to 10,000 square feet. The top platforms of the islands, carrying lightweight fiberglass-reinforced plastic buildings up to three stories high, overlap the pontoons which contain buoyancy compartments and storage areas. Ballast tanks at the base of each pontoon can be flooded or pumped out to keep the rigid sections level with one another, regardless of the building load they carry.

Designing Sea City involved the need to control winds and rough seas, while creating an artificially warm and equable climate. A wide "moat" of calm water, created by a protective breakwater, surrounds the city. The breakwater consists of cylindrical coated-fabric bags 90 percent full of fresh water and lying side by side. Ideally 100-foot-long bags with a diameter of 6 feet will be used and allowed to float awash, anchored fore and aft in groups of three by flexible cables. The breakwater damps the waves because when struck by an oncoming roller a secondary wave is generated inside each bag. This secondary wave rebounds against the end of the bag to meet the following sea. In bad weather, a curtain of compressed-air bubbles from an undersea pipeline rises to the surface across the lagoon entrance to break up the waves still further and maintain the calm of the inner lagoon.

The 180-foot-high curved wall of the amphitheater protects residents of Sea City from the wind by deflecting air currents over the top of the city. Preliminary wind tunnel tests carried out at Leicester University show that by shaping the outer surface of the wall in the form of an outward-leaning "S," wind is deflected upwards to a height sufficient to allow relatively calm areas below. The result is a very large, slow-moving vortex to leeward, so that air passing over the terraces on the inner surface of the wall moves slowly upwards. Tests also confirmed that this slow-moving air mass extends for a considerable distance across the lagoon and will tend to be maintained there by thermal currents induced by the warmer land mass of the city.

Power for Sea City is supplied by natural gas from the nearby Hewett Field. A power complex, situated inside the city wall at the northern end, processes the gas and passes it to high-speed turbines coupled to generators which produce electricity for the city. Waste heat from the turbine exhaust gases is used to power the desalination plant, as well as for domestic and industrial heating and refrigeration. Finally, the hot cooling water is emptied into the lagoon to raise the temperature of the water an anticipated 5° to 7° F above that of the outer sea water. Beneath the supporting-base platform, sluice gates (raised in good weather to allow tidal currents to cleanse the lagoon) keep the heated water within the city and help to maintain the warm climate. Future expansion of the city will pose no severe technical problems since new terraced walls can be built, outside the existing wall and concentric with it, to enclose more lagoons filled with calm heated water.

The terraced city wall holds sixteen stories of centrally heated or air-conditioned flats to accommodate some 21,000 residents. Other residents have individually designed houses on islands at the southern end of the lagoon. The layout of the flats is varied; they may have up to seven rooms and most have a terraced garden. The width and angle of the windows facing the lagoon ensure that residents can enjoy at least 2½ hours of winter sunshine a day. Flats in the supper eight stories also have fixed windows facing seaward, while the seaward side of the lower eight stories is used as office and industrial accommodation.

Much of the glass in Sea City will have special heat and light transmission and insulation properties to reduce glare and solar overheating, thereby providing a more congenial environment for residents. In various colors and tints, such glass will also enhance the aesthetic appearance of Sea City buildings. The flats and local amenities within the city wall—such as gardens, shops, restaurants and clubs—are served by escalators, travelators and covered walkways. Goods are distributed by a network of conveyors and pneumatic tubes.

To reduce noise and pollution of the lagoon, all internal transport is provided by electrically-powered boats and water buses, and there are battery-recharging points throughout the city. A five-minute water bus service completes a circuit of the town in twenty-five minutes. At the foot of the terraced wall, where traffic is heaviest, there is a one-way system for boats and water buses; elsewhere movement is unrestricted. All public buildings have their own jetties, and private boats not moored underneath the terraced wall are berthed alongside the floating islands. Three feet above water level there are concrete quays, but waterborne craft can also be boarded via watertight doors in the sides of the pontoons or from outside stairways. Visiting craft are not allowed to enter the inner lagoon, but are moored at berths outside the city wall near the lagoon entrance. Supplies for the city are brought from the mainland by barge or in articulated container ships with three sections: one for fresh milk; one for meat, bacon, eggs, butter, cheese, and vegetables; one for bulk dry goods. Ample storage space is provided at Sea City and it is unlikely to be cut off for long periods in any case, because even now hovercraft like the SR.N4 can travel safely at thirty knots in strong winds and over ten-foot waves.

Commuting between Sea City and the mainland is by hovercraft or helibus. Current operating costs for the SR.N4 are 2d to 2½d per passenger per nautical mile giving a cost of five shillings for the twenty-five mile journey to Yarmouth. As yet, there are no figures for the helibus service since the aircraft envisaged is still under development. However, the plane will take off and land like a helicopter; once in the air, the rotors fold into the top of the fuselage and the plane flies like a conventional fixed-wing aircraft. The trip to Yarmouth would take approximately fifteen minutes from Sea City's heliport; once on the mainland, commuters can collect their cars from the multistory car park.

The local government center is at the southern end where the social hub of Sea City is located. However, many public buildings are on the floating islands including most of Sea City's nursery, primary and secondary schools. A one-mile walk takes residents to any part of the city via a network of footpaths and bridges across the islands, thirteen feet above sea level. The full medical service planned for the 30,000 inhabitants includes a 200-bed hospital, clinics, and dental services; a crematorium lies just ouside the city wall. Sea City residents will also be able to call on fire, police, and local government services in the same way as their land-based counterparts, and the city will become part of the GPO network linked by underwater cable to the mainland lines.

Social and cultural facilities include community centers, open air tea-gardens, youth clubs, two theaters, libraries, cinemas, an art gallery and a museum as well as churches for every religious denomination. There are many public gardens with flowers and shrubs chosen to flourish in Sea City's warm climate. Sportsmen of all ages are catered for. The central basin of the lagoon is reserved for water sports—sailing, water-skiing, swimming, and skin-diving—during a season lengthened by the artificially warm climate. There are tennis courts, bowling greens, netball courts, and croquet lawns, as well as a full-size football field on top of the power complex.

A permanent off-shore center like Sea City would be important to the development of specialist marine industries. The College of Marine Studies, with its submarine laboratories, observation posts at the marine zoo, and on-the-spot research vessels, is seen as a first step towards a University of the Sea and an international center for oceanography and underwater studies.

In the fight against world food shortages, the City's biggest contribution would be a highly efficient fish farming industry, cultivating plaice and other flat fish, trout, salmon, eels, shrimps and prawns; possibly also oysters, clams, scallops and lobsters. Rapid harvesting of fish to meet sudden demand is practical; stocks can be quickly replenished because growth is artifically accelerated in controlled-temperature tanks. Artificial nursery and hatchery methods are used and added economic advantages include the use of hot cooling water for tank heating and the availability of fish food made from processed sewage. The yield from a Sea City fish farm should at least equal that of any outdoor warm-water farm operating in America or Europe where an acre normally produces five tons of fish per year. Sea City tanks will also cultivate costly ornamental fish.

Other important factors in the City's commercial life will be the fish-canning industry and revenue obtained from the manufacture of fertilizers out of seaweed and sewage. The large desalination plant will produce enough cheap fresh water to enable Sea City to export large quantities by pipeline to the mainland—important not only in arid regions of the world where water is needed to exploit the countryside, but also in densely populated regions where water shortage is a growing problem.

A SELECTION OF FURTHER READINGS

In the course of reading for this book, I compiled a list of books and essays relevant to the topics of this volume. Needless to say, titles listed under one heading could with almost equal appropriateness be classified under another, and these inclusions are by no pretense either complete or definitive. They are also intended to supplement, rather than duplicate or overlap, the bibliography appended to *Beyond Left and Right* (Morrow, 1968); and here too are more fully documented the sources of the epigraphs distributed through the preceding text. As I noted of the earlier bibliography, "I hope that a perusal of these works would show, contrary to fashionable belief, that the most profound social thinking of our times still manages to slip into print."

I. HISTORY

Earth Photographs from Gemini: III, IV, V, Washington, D.C.: NASA, 1967.

Aron, Raymond. *The Industrial Society.* N.Y.: Praeger, 1967.

Asimov, Isaac. *Is Anyone There?* Garden City: Doubleday, 1967.

Baier, Kurt, and Rescher, Nicholas, eds. *Values and the Future.* N.Y.: Free Press, 1969.

Beckwith, Burnham Putnam. *The Next 500 Years.* N.Y.: Exposition, 1967.

Bernal, J. D. *The World, the Flesh, & the Devil.* Bloomington: Indiana University, 1969.

Bloy, Myron B. Jr., ed. *Technology and Culture in Perspective.* Cambridge, Mass.: The Church Society for College Work, 1967.

Braden, William. *The Age of Aquarius.* Chicago: Quadrangle, 1970.

Brown, Harrison, et al. *The Next Ninety Years.* Pasadena, Calif.: California Institute of Technology, 1967.

Cooper, John Charles. *The New Mentality.* Philadelphia: Westminster, 1969.

Doxiadis, Constantinos. *Between Dystopia and Utopia.* Hartford, Conn.: Trinity College, 1968.

Drucker, Peter F. *The Age of Discontinuity*. N.Y.: Harper & Row, 1969.

Ewald, William, ed. *Environment and Change*. Bloomington: Indiana Univ., 1968.

——, ed. *Environment and Policy*. Bloomington: Indiana Univ., 1968.

Ferkiss, Victor C. *Technological Man*. N.Y.: Braziller, 1969.

Forbes, R. J. *The Conquest of Nature*. N.Y.: Praeger, 1968.

Foreign Policy Assoc., ed. *The World in 2018*. N.Y.: Cowles, 1968.

Jungk, Robert, and Galtung, Johan, eds. *Mankind 2000*. Oslo: Universitetsforlaget, 1969.

Kolakowski, Leszak. *Toward a Marxist Humanism*. N.Y.: Grove, 1968.

Kostelanetz, Richard. *Metamorphosis in the Arts*. N.Y.: Abrams, 1971.

McHale, John. "Toward the Future," *Design Quarterly*, 72 (1968).

——. *The Future of the Future*. N.Y.: Braziller, 1969.

Nuttall, Jeff. *Bomb Culture*. N.Y.: Delacorte, 1968.

Pauwels, Louis, and Jacques Bergier. *The Morning of the Magicians*. N.Y.: Stein & Day, 1964.

Puccetti, Roland. *Persons*. N.Y.: Herder & Herder, 1969.

Reincourt, Amaury de. *The American Empire*. N.Y.: Dial, 1968.

Richta, Radovan, et al. *Civilisace na rozcesti Společenské a lidské souvislosti vědochkotechnické revoluce*. Prague: Svoboda, 1966.

Rudhyar, Dane. *Modern Man's Conflicts*. N.Y.: Philosophical Library, 1948.

Russell, Bertrand. *Roads to Freedom*. London: Allen & Unwin, 1918.

Seidenberg, Roderick. *Anatomy of the Future*. Chapel Hill: Univ. of North Carolina, 1961.

Wager, W. Warren. *The City of Man*. Boston: Houghton Mifflin, 1963.

Warner, Aaron, et al., eds. *The Environment of Change*. N.Y.: Columbia, 1969.

White, Lynn, Jr. "Christian Myth and Christian History," *Machina Ex Deo*. Cambridge, Mass.: M.I.T., 1969.

Winthrop, Henry. *Ventures in Social Interpretation*. N.Y.: Appleton, 1968.

II. TECHNOLOGIES

Asimov, Isaac. "The Perfect Machine," *Science Journal*, IV/10 (Oct., 1968).

————. *The Solar System and Back*. Garden City: Doubleday, 1970.

Block, Henry D. "Simulation of Statistically Composite Machines," in George Shapiro and Milton Rogers, eds. *Prospects for Simulation and Simulators of Dynamic Systems*. N.Y.: Spartan, 1967.

————, and Ginsberg, Herbert. "The Psychology of Robots," *Psychology Today*, I/11 (April, 1968).

Bouladon, Gabriel. "Future Transportation in Cities as Reconsidered Around Man," *High Speed Ground Transportation Journal*, III/1 (Jan., 1969).

Brown, Lester R. "The Optimistic Outlook for World Food Production," *The Futurist*, III/4 (Aug., 1969).

Brown, Ronald. *Telecommunications*. Garden City: Doubleday, 1970.

Diebold, John. *Man and the Computer*. N.Y.: Praeger, 1969.

Fenner, Terrence W., and Everett, James L. *Inventor's Handbook*. New Orleans: Chemical Publishing, 1969.

Landers, Richard. *Man's Place in the Dybosphere*. Englewood Cliffs: Prentice-Hall, 1966.

Mero, John L. *The Mineral Resources of the Sea*. Amsterdam: Elsevier, 1965.

————. "Oceanic Mineral Resources," *Futures*, I/2 (Dec., 1968).

Olson, Walter, et al. *Conference on New Technology*. Washington, D.C.: NASA, 1964.

Parkhill, Douglas F. *The Challenge of the Computer Utility*. Reading, Mass.: Addison-Wesley, 1966.

Parsons & Williams, Inc. *Forecast 1968–2000 of Computer Developments and Applications*. Copenhagen, Denmark: Parsons & Williams, 1969.

Stephens, William M. *Science Beneath the Sea*. N.Y.: Putnams, 1966.

Theobald, Robert, ed. *Dialogue on Technology*. Indianapolis: Bobbs-Merrill, 1967.

Thompson, Gordon B. "Moloch or Aquarius?," *the*, 4 (Feb., 1970).

Wirtz, W. Willard. "The Challenge of Automation," in Howard D. Samuel, ed. *Toward a Better America*. N.Y.: Macmillan, 1968.

III. ENVIRONMENTS

Banham, Reyner. *Architecture in the Well-Tempered Environment*. Chicago: Univ. of Chicago, 1969.

Borrego, John. *Space Grid Structures*. Cambridge: M.I.T., 1968.

Boyko, Hugo. "Sand Deserts—The Granaries of the Future," *Futures*, I/3 (March, 1969).

Brown, Lester R. *Seeds of Change*. N.Y.: Praeger, 1970.

Commoner, Barry. *Science and Survival.* N.Y.: Viking, 1966.

Cook, Peter, ed. *Archigram (1961–68).* Cambridge: M.I.T., 1970.

Finch, Christopher. "Process and Imagination," *Design Quarterly,* 74–5 (1969).

Higbee, Edward. *A Question of Priorities.* Introduction by R. Buckminster Fuller. N.Y.: William Morrow, 1970.

Kormondy, Edward J. *Concepts of Ecology.* Englewood Cliffs: Prentice-Hall, 1969.

McHarg, Ian. "Ecology, for the Revolution of Planning and Design," *VIA,* 1 (1968).

Otto, Frei. *Tensile Structures.* Two Vols. Cambridge: M.I.T., 1967–9.

Rodda, Michael. *Noise and Society.* Edinburgh: Oliver & Boyd, 1967.

Tukey, John. "Research Needs in Environmental Health," NAS-NRC Publication 1419 (1967).

Wagner, Philip. *The Human Use of the Earth.* N.Y.: Free Press, 1960.

White, Lynn, Jr. "The Historic Roots of Our Ecologic Crisis," *Machina Ex Deo.* Cambridge: M.I.T., 1969.

IV. CITIES

Doxiadis, Constantinos A. *Ekistics.* N.Y.: Oxford, 1968.

———. "Ecumenopolis," *Britannica Book of the Year* (1968).

Forrester, Jay. *Urban Dynamics.* Cambridge: M.I.T., 1969.

Fuller, R. Buckminster. "Why Not Roofs Over Our Cities?" *Think* (Jan.–Feb., 1968).

———, et al. *Triton City: A Prototype Floating Community.* Springfield, Va.: Clearinghouse for Federal Information, 1968.

Halprin, Lawrence. *Cities.* N.Y.: Reinhold, 1964.

———. *Freeways.* N.Y.: Reinhold, 1966.

Hilberseimer, L. *The Nature of Cities.* Chicago: Theobald, 1955.

Jellicoe, Geoffrey A. *Motopia.* N.Y.: Praeger, 1961.

———, et al. *Sea City.* St. Helens, Lancs.: Pilkington Glass, 1969.

McHale, John. "Future Cities: Notes on a Typology," *Futurist,* III/5 (Oct., 1969).

Pell, Claiborne. *Megalopolis Unbound: The Supercity and the Transportation of Tomorrow.* N.Y.: Praeger, 1966.

Perloff, Harvey S. *Planning and the Urban Community.* Pittsburgh: Univ. of Pittsburgh, 1961.

———, ed. *The Quality of the Urban Environment.* Baltimore: Johns Hopkins, 1969.

Richards, Brian. *New Movement in Cities.* N.Y.: Reinhold, 1967.

Saarinen, Eliel. *The City: Its Growth, Its Decay, Its Future.* Cambridge: M.I.T., 1965.

Soleri, Paolo. *Arcology: The City in the Image of Man.* Cambridge: M.I.T., 1970.

Stulman, Julius. *Fields within Fields . . . within Fields.* N.Y.: World Institute, 1968.

CONTRIBUTORS

ISAAC ASIMOV, born in Petrovichi, Russia, in 1920, is nominally Associate Professor of Biochemistry at Boston University. He has also written over one hundred books of fiction and non-fiction, many of them dealing with the future.

FRITZ BAADE is head of the Research Institute for the Economic Problems of the Developing Countries, in Bonn and Kiel, Germany, and the author of several major books, including *The Race to the Year 2000* (1962), which has since been translated into many languages.

BURNHAM PUTNAM BECKWITH, born in Carthage, Missouri, in 1904, spent two years at the Harvard Business School and then took his doctorate in economics from the University of Southern California in 1932. After a brief teaching career, he worked for the government, and has since devoted his life to private pursuits. His books include *Religion, Philosophy and Science* (1957) and *The Next Five Hundred Years* (1967).

J. BLOCK is director of Planning and Development for the Paris Airport Authority. His essays have appeared in *Futures,* published in England, and other magazines.

DON BENSON worked with the Vermont Department of Education and the Friends World College before performing alternative service as a conscientious objector. He edited *Dialogue on Poverty* (1967) and contributed to Robert Theobald's *Committed Spending* (1968).

GABRIEL BOULADON, born in 1927 in St. Etienne, France, is head of the Engineering Department of the Battelle Institute's offices in Geneva, Switzerland. His speciality is transportation and mechanical handling. The holder of more than twenty patents, he has written influential essays in several languages for magazines around the world.

NIGEL CALDER, who lives in London, has been successively a research physicist, science correspondent for *The New Statesman,* and editor of *The New Scientist.* His books include *Eden Was No Garden* (1967), published in England as *The Environment Game;* and he edited the two-volume *The World in 1984* (1965).

KENNETH B. CLARK, born in the Canal Zone in 1914, is president of the Metropolitan Applied Research Center, Inc., in New York City, and Professor of Psychology at City College of the City University of New York. His books include *Dark Ghetto* (1965) and *Prejudices and Your Child* (1963).

DANDRIDGE M. COLE, born in 1921 in Sandusky, Ohio, was at his death in 1965 a space programs analyst with the General Electric Missile and Space Division. After earning his A.B. in Chemistry from Princeton and his M.A. in Physics from the University of Pennsylvania, he taught science at the Academy of New Church and Phillips-Exeter. His books include *Exploring the Secrets of Space* (1963, with I. M. Leavitt) and *Beyond Tomorrow* (1965).

KARL W. DEUTSCH, born in Prague, Czechoslovakia, in 1912, is Professor of Political Science at Harvard University, where he took his doctorate. Among his many books are *Nationalism and Social Communication* (1953; revised, 1964), *The Nerves of Government* (1963), and *Arms Control and the Atlantic Alliance* (1967).

JOHN P. EBERHARD, formerly director of the Institute of Applied Technology at the National Bureau of Standards, is currently dean of the School of Environmental Science at the State University of New York at Buffalo. Born in Chicago in 1927, he was trained in architectural design and industrial management and previously served as president of Creative Buildings, Inc., designers and manufacturers of prefabricated structures.

R. BUCKMINSTER FULLER, born in 1895 in Milford, Massachusetts, attended Harvard and the U.S. Naval Academy, taking no degrees. Since then, he has designed a radically original automobile in the 1930's, invented both a system of mapping and the geodesic principles of building construction, envisioned whole cities, and lectured around the world. Currently Professor of Comprehensive Anticipatory Design Science at Southern Illinois University, he has written a long poem, *Unfinished Epic of Industrialization* (1963), and five major books: *No More Second-hand God* (1962), *Education Auto-*

mation (1962), *Ideas and Integrities* (1963), *Nine Chains to the Moon* (1938; reprinted, 1963), and *Operating Manual to the Spaceship Earth* (1969).

THEODORE J. GORDON, formerly chief engineer for the upper stage of the Saturn rocket, is now director of large launch systems at Douglas Aircraft, Inc. Born in New York City in 1930, he took his B.S. from Louisiana State University and his M.S. from the Georgia Institute of Technology, and has since written two books for lay readers—*The Future* (1965) and *Ideas in Conflict* (1966).

J. L. HULT is Associate Head of the Engineering Sciences Department of The RAND Corporation in Santa Monica, California. His essays have appeared in *The Futurist* and other magazines.

GEOFFREY A. JELLICOE, EDWARD D. MILLS, and OVE NYQUIST ARUP collaborated in the Sea City Proposal sponsored by Pilkington Glass. Each holds a C.B.E. decoration from the British government. Jellicoe, born in London in 1900, is currently a senior partner of Jellicoe and Coleridge, chartered architects in London. Mills, born in London in 1915, heads Edward D. Mills and Partners, Architects. Arup, born in Newcastle-upon-Tyne in 1895, is the senior partner of an engineering firm bearing his name.

HERMAN KAHN, director of the Hudson Institute of Harmon, New York, was born in Bayonne, New Jersey, in 1922, and was educated at U.C.L.A. and California Institute of Technology. Among his writings are innumerable essays and reports, mostly privately published, and four controversial books: *On Thermonuclear War* (1960), *Thinking About the Unthinkable* (1962), *On Escalation* (1965) and, with Anthony J. Wiener, *The Year 2000* (1967). He was also the primary contributor to *Can We Win in Vietnam?* (1968).

GYORGY KEPES, born in Hungary in 1906, came to Chicago in the late thirties to teach at L. Moholy-Nagy's New Bauhaus. Also known as a painter, photographer, light artist, and writer on art, he is currently director of the Center for Advanced Visual Studies at M.I.T., where he has been since 1946 Professor of Visual Design. His books include *The Language of Vision* (1944), and he edited a multi-volumed series entitled *Vision and Value* (1965–6).

304   CONTRIBUTORS

J. C. R. LICKLIDER is currently consultant to the Director of Research at IBM, having previously been Director for Behavioral Sciences and Information Processing Research of the Advance Research Projects Agency and vice-president of Bolt, Beranek and Newman, Inc. Principally known for his inventive work in "time-sharing," he also wrote *Libraries of the Future* (1965) and contributed the most speculative essay to *Public Television: A Program for Action* (1967).

ROGER MacGOWAN has been Chief of the Scientific Digital Branch of the Army Missile Command Computation Center in Huntsville, Alabama. He wrote *On the Possibilities of the Existence of Extraterrestrial Intelligence* (1962), and received in 1965 the first prize in the Data Processing Futures Essay Contest with a speculation on future computation developments.

MARTIN MEYERSON, born in 1922 in New York City, is President of the University of Pennsylvania. Previously Dean of the College of Environmental Design and then Acting Chancellor at the Berkeley campus of the University of California, he has co-authored books on *Politics, Planning and the Public Interest* (1955), *Housing, People and Cities* (1962), *Face of the Metropolis* (1963), and *Boston: The Job Ahead* (1966). His wife, Margy Meyerson, was Research Director of the American Society of Planning Officials.

FREDERICK I. ORDWAY, III, currently President of the General Astronautics Research Corporation in London, England, was a major scientific adviser to Stanley Kubrick in filming *2001*. He has also authored and edited many books on space technology, and contributed essays to many magazines around the world.

HASAN OZBEKHAN, born in Turkey, studied law and political science at the University of Paris and then received his B.Sc. (Economics) degree from the London School of Economics. He recently left the System Development Corporation to become General Manager and Director of International Development and Planning, Computer Systems Division, King Resources Company, in Los Angeles. Also a former Professor of International Management at the Graduate School of Business Administration, New York University, he has written many essays for professional and general magazines.

JOHN R. PIERCE, born in Des Moines, Iowa, in 1910, is now Executive Director, Research-Communications Sciences Division at the Bell Telephone Laboratories, where he has worked since receiving his Ph.D. from California Institute of Technology. The holder of innumerable patents, he has also written many books for both scientists and laymen, including among the latter *Signals, Symbols and Noise* (1960) and *Science, Art and Communication* (1968). His science fiction appears under the pseudonym "J. J. Coupling."

OLIVER L. REISER, born in 1895 in Columbia, Ohio, is Professor Emeritus at the University of Pittsburgh, where he has taught philosophy for over forty years. He has published over a dozen major books, most of them unfortunately out of print, including *The Alchemy of Light and Color* (1935), *Philosophy and the Concepts of Modern Science* (1935), *The Promise of Scientific Humanism* (1940), *The World Sensorium* (1946), *The Integration of Human Knowledge* (1958) and *Cosmic Humanism* (1965). His current project is entitled *Magnetic Moments in Human History*.

DANE RUDHYAR, born in 1895, became known in the twenties as an experimental composer and in the forties as a philospher-lecturer, the author of *Modern Man's Conflicts* (1948). His most recent major interest has been astrology.

SHOJI SADAO, born in 1927, is a licensed architect who has collaborated with Buckminster Fuller since 1954, the year he received his B.A. in Architecture from Cornell University. Formerly a job captain on numerous architectural projects, he is currently a principal partner of Fuller and Sadao, Inc., and director and treasurer of the Triton Foundation, Inc., both in Cambridge, Massachusetts.

ARTHUR L. SAMUEL, born in Emporia, Kansas, in 1901, studied at the College of Emporia and M.I.T. He has worked as a research scientist at both Bell Telephone Laboratories and IBM, and taught at M.I.T., the University of Illinois and Stanford. The author of many technical papers and the holder of several patents on electronic devices, he is principally known for programming an early computer to play checkers.

I. S. SHKLOVSKII is a staff member of the Sternberg Astronomical Institute of the Soviet Academy of Sciences, Moscow. CARL SAGAN is an astronomer teaching at Harvard. Originally commissioned to revise a book Shklovskii published in Russian, Sagan wrote an extension, published jointly as *Intelligent Life in the Universe* (1965).

S. FRED SINGER, born in Vienna, Austria, in 1926, got his Ph.D. in physics from Princeton in 1948. Formerly Director of the National Weather Satellite Center of the U.S. Weather Bureau and professor of physics at the University of Maryland, he is currently Dean of the School of Environmental and Planetary Sciences at the University of Miami, Florida.

ROBERT ALLEN SMITH, educated at Edinburgh and Cambridge, was until 1961 head of the Physics Department at the Royal Radar Establishment, Malvern, England. Since then he has been Professor of Physics and Director of the Center for Material Sciences at M.I.T. His several books include *Semi-conductors* (1963).

ATHELSTAN SPILHAUS, a meteorologist and oceanographer, has been Dean of the Institute for Technology at the University of Minnesota and head of the Franklin Institute in Philadelphia. He currently lives in Palm Beach, Florida. His books include *Satellite of the Sun* (1964) and *Meteorological Instruments* (1953).

ALBIN WAGNER, who lived in "Drop City," has contributed essays to the underground American press. He has recently been working as a librarian in Colorado.

ANTHONY J. WIENER, born in Newark, New Jersey, in 1930, is currently Chairman of the Research Management Council at the Hudson Institute. Co-author with Herman Kahn of *The Year 2000* (1967), he is completing a study tentatively entitled *Faustian Progress*.

A Note about the Author

RICHARD KOSTELANETZ has written *The Theatre of Mixed Means* (1968), *Master Minds* (1969), and *Metamorphosis in the Arts* (1970) and co-authored *The New American Arts* (1965), as well as editing several anthologies—among them *The Young American Writers* (1967), *Imaged Words & Worded Images* (1970), *Possibilities of Poetry* (1970), *Beyond Left and Right* (1968), and *Social Speculations* (1970). His articles and critical essays have appeared in many magazines here and abroad, and he has also published fiction and pattern poetry.

Born in 1940 in New York City, where he now lives, Kostelanetz studied at Brown, Columbia, and London universities. Recently a Guggenheim Fellow, he is currently completing, among other projects in process, both an extended fiction and a history of recent American thought.